The Moshav in Israel

PRAEGER SPECIAL STUDIES IN
INTERNATIONAL ECONOMICS AND DEVELOPMENT

The Moshav in Israel

A CASE STUDY OF INSTITUTION-BUILDING FOR AGRICULTURAL DEVELOPMENT

Maxwell I. Klayman

PRAEGER PUBLISHERS
New York · Washington · London

The purpose of the Praeger Special Studies is to make specialized research monographs in U.S. and international economics and politics available to the academic, business, and government communities. For further information, write to the Special Projects Division, Praeger Publishers, Inc., 111 Fourth Avenue, New York, N.Y. 10003.

PRAEGER PUBLISHERS
111 Fourth Avenue, New York, N.Y. 10003, U.S.A.
5, Cromwell Place, London S.W.7, England

Published in the United States of America in 1970
by Praeger Publishers, Inc.

Library of Congress Catalog Card Number: 69-19334

Printed in the United States of America

To
Ranaan Weitz
A Pragmatic Pioneer in Planned
Agricultural Settlement and
Regional Development

ACKNOWLEDGMENTS

This study was financed originally by a grant from the Inter-University Research Program in Institution Building, headquartered at the University of Pittsburgh, which made possible the field work in Israel, Iran, and Venezuela. Additional field research was done in Venezuela in connection with my duties as a consultant for the Inter-American Development Bank.

I am particularly grateful to Professor John Kenneth Galbraith of Harvard University, who read and commented on the original manuscript, and to Dr. Ranaan Weitz, Head of the Settlement Department of the Jewish Agency, who was extremely helpful in supplying information and in the arrangements for the field work. Special thanks are due to the many officials in Israel, Venezuela, and Iran for their excellent cooperation and help in obtaining data and insights that were basic to the study.

CONTENTS

LIST OF TABLES

xiv

The Moshav in Israel

CHAPTER **1** INTRODUCTION

There is general consensus on the importance
of the role of the agricultural sector in economic
development: as a source of food, raw materials,
capital, manpower, as an earner of foreign exchange,
and as a base for industrialization. As a matter of
fact, however, the agricultural sector is not fulfilling its basic developmental roles in most countries. In twenty of the thirty-four countries in
Latin America, the Far East, the Near East, and Africa, for which the Food and Agriculture Organization
of the United Nations (FAO) calculates annual indexes of agricultural production (that is, in well over
half of the countries in the economically underdeveloped regions of the world), per capita food production
in recent years has been the same or less than in the
early 1950's.[1] The agricultural sector, rather than
contributing to general economic development, has been
a brake on progress, and many countries have been
forced to spend scarce foreign exchange to import the
food needed by the rapidly growing urban population.

Many experts on economic development and agriculture believe that cooperatives can play an important role in raising food and fiber production,
increasing farmers' incomes, and improving the social
aspects of rural life. FAO and United States aid
organizations have been active in promoting cooperatives in developing countries. The Peace Corps has
a Cooperative Division for training volunteers to organize and manage rural cooperatives and has an active
program in a number of countries.

The efforts of these agencies have not been, for
the most part, particularly successful. Many cooperatives have been founded, but few have survived for

any length of time. There are many reasons for
their failure. The most important are (1) a faulty
model based on conditions peculiar to economically
developed countries, especially the United States,
and (2) lack of sufficient resources: human, material, and financial.

Yet cooperatives have been and are important
in the development of the agricultural sectors in
many countries throughout the world. One such country is Israel, where cooperative agricultural settlements are responsible for the production of almost
four fifths of the national food supply.[2] The postwar growth of per capita agricultural production in
Israel has been greater than in any other country in
the world,[3] and farm incomes are at a Western European level.[4] This is no small accomplishment, considering that the farmers had little background in
agriculture, and that the land had been fallow for
many centuries. This tremendous expansion in production has, to a great extent, been the result of the
work of the cooperative settlements and their supporting institutions, a development of indigenous
cooperative institutions based on national needs.

The agricultural cooperative settlement in
Israel represents the basic institution that provides
the rural population with its economic and social
needs. The village, which provides producer and consumer cooperative services, is linked to a cluster of
regional and national supporting cooperatives that
provide auxiliary services, and almost all the agricultural cooperatives are, in turn, linked to national organizations serving the larger national economy.

The moshav, the small landowners' cooperative
settlement, is one of the two basic types of settlements in the cooperative agricultural sector (the
other being the kibbutz) where both production and
consumption are organized collectively. Production
and consumption decisions in the moshav are basically
the responsibility of the individual farmer and his
family, whereas purchasing, selling, and other services are generally handled cooperatively. The average
family holding is about 10 acres, a rather small area.

but capable of producing high incomes under the current system of intensive farming.

As of year end 1966, there were 297 moshavim,
with a total population of about 110,000 people. This
is the most important type of agricultural settlement
in the country, representing 42 per cent of all the
settlements and half of the settlements of the cooperative sector. About 85 per cent of the moshavim
has been founded since statehood in 1948, and about
70 per cent of the poststate moshavim was founded in
the three-year period 1948-50, immediately after
statehood, mainly for new immigrant members principally from countries in Asia and Africa.[5] The prestate
moshav, called the moshav ovdim, which means "workers'
settlement," is differentiated from the poststate
moshav, called moshav olim, which means "immigrants'
settlement." The prestate moshavim, founded and settled by pioneer volunteers, differ in organizational
structure and operation from the poststate moshavim,
which were founded by the national authorities for
the mass absorption of the immigrants directed to
them. One of the principal differences is that in
the moshav olim there is considerably more direction
of the village by national authorities.

There are two other types of moshavim in the
cooperative agricultural sector that are less important in the national picture. One is called moshav
shitufi, meaning "collective moshav." It represents
a transitional type between the kibbutz and the
moshav. The production is organized collectively,
as in the kibbutz, but consumption is organized in
private households, as in the moshav. The other is
the middle class or private moshav. This type of
moshav was originally organized for older middle-
class immigrants who came to the country with capital
of their own. These settlements differed from the
moshav ovdim in two major respects: (1) hired labor
was not prohibited; and (2) they did not strictly ad-
here to the principle of nationalized land. These
differences have been pretty much obliterated in actual operation, and the middle-class moshav is very
similar to the moshav ovdim.

PURPOSE OF STUDY

The basic purposes of this study are (1) to
construct a model of the moshav; (2) to analyze the
success of the moshav; (3) to analyze the process by
which the moshav has been built as an institution;
and (4) to examine the applicability of the moshav
or a modification thereof for the development of the
agricultural sectors of underdeveloped countries.

The generalized model of the moshav, both the
moshav ovdim and moshav olim, represents a macrolevel
picture of the institution including its goals,
structure, functions, and interdependencies. It also
includes an analysis of the organization, guiding
principles, and functions of supporting institutions:
particularly the national and regional supporting cooperatives attached to the General Federation of Labor, the Jewish Agency, and the Moshav Movement. This
analysis is based on documents, field observation,
and interviews with officials and members of the organizations concerned.

This analysis yields basic guiding principles
of what constitutes a moshav. These principles are
particularly applicable in building moshav-type institutions in countries other than Israel.

As to the second purpose, the two principal
measures of the success of the settlement in terms of
economic viability are physical output and financial
returns to members. The study, therefore, includes
an analysis based on sample empirical data of the
factors affecting members' net incomes, to determine
how much incomes are affected by the moshav as an institution, and how much by factors external to the
moshav and supporting organizations.

One of the most important variables affecting
economic success is the human factor, particularly
the effectiveness of the moshav member in making decisions in planning the production organization of
his farm and the actual execution of his plans and/
or the plans of his advisors. The study, therefore,
includes an analysis of the extent to which the
development of the member as a successful farmer can

be attributed to the moshav as an institution. Using
empirical data, farmers' production plans and their
implementation are compared to ideal or optimum plans,
assuming perfect rationality, and the role of the
moshav is examined to the extent it helped achieved
the ideal goals or acted as a constraint.

What really is the fundamental measure of the
success of a moshav? In a small country like Israel
with relatively full employment, where the settler
can easily shift from agriculture to the industrial
and service sectors, success implies the willingness
of the settler to make the village his permanent home.
Success, therefore, is not limited to economic outputs alone, but includes the social and cultural benefits of the moshav: schools, housing, and health
services, for example. The study, perforce, includes
some analysis of these noneconomic services.

The analysis of the process by which the moshav
has been built as an institution is conducted at two
levels. One is a macro historical review of agricultural settlement in Israel, with emphasis on the cooperative sector in general and the moshav and its
linkages with other types of settlements in particular. The other represents a micro historical analysis of a small sample of both the moshav ovdim and the
moshav olim. This includes the esamination of the
problems encountered in building a viable internal
structure, and getting both the institution and the
values it represents integrated into the larger environment. It follows the development of the moshav
ovdim from a set of ideological principles of pioneer
organizers to a going institution meeting the current
problems and needs of its members: economic, social,
and political. It follows the development of the
moshav olim from the application of the structure of
the moshav ovdim and its guided evolution to meet the
needs of a new type of immigrant for his development
from a merchant or artisan in a traditional culture
to a commercial farmer in a modern western-type environment.

The application of moshav principles to the
agricultural development of other countries evolves
from the results of the analyses of the factors

contributing to the success of the moshav and the
process by which it developed as an institution. A
number of critical success factors are developed and
analyzed as to their particularity to Israel. The
flexibility of the moshav approach and the degree of
substitutability of critical success factors are examined in the application of moshav principles to
the specific cases of Venezuela and Iran. The moshav
approach is compared with other alternative structural approaches for agricultural development. A
generalized analysis of the transferability of the
moshav model to the differing environments of other
developing countries is made in the framework of
Galbraithian growth models.[6]

APPLICATION OF UNITED STATES COOPERATIVE
PRINCIPLES TO DEVELOPING COUNTRIES

It is claimed that one of the principal reasons
that agricultural cooperatives have failed in developing countries throughout the world is that the
Western model used is not suited to the needs of such
countries. This needs some elaboration, even though
the focus of this study is the moshav and its role in
agricultural development, not the elaboration of principles of cooperative theory or the analysis of the
organization and management of agricultural cooperatives.

American literature on agricultural cooperatives maintains that a true cooperative is one that
(1) limits returns on capital, (2) votes on the basis
of one man, one vote and/or patronage, and (3) allocates all net earnings to member patrons. A quasi
cooperative is one that meets at least one of these
three specifications, but not all three of them.[7]

By such standards all the settlements in the
cooperative sector of Israeli agriculture are at best
only quasi cooperatives. In none are earnings re-
bated to the members; they are reinvested in the village and village enterprises. This is also generally
the case in the national and regional cooperatives
supporting the villages. One man, one vote signifies
democratic control by member patrons. Complete

membership control in the poststate moshavin and other
cooperative settlements may be lacking, and there
may be a considerable amount of outside interference
and control, particularly by the economic planners of
the Jewish Agency and by the external and/or internal
secretaries of the village. These secretaries may,
in the early stages of the village, be appointed members of one of the agencies supporting settlement,
rather than of the cooperative itself.

In the U.S. model, cooperative membership consists of individuals, partnerships, profit-type corporations, or cooperatives themselves who of their
own free will form and operate the cooperative. In
the moshav, the village is the basis of the cooperative. A person wishing to join the settlement has
to become a member of the cooperative. Members are
free to join, and free to leave. But if they wish
to work their farms, they must live in the village
and be members of the cooperative.

The application of the United States model to
developing countries is highly questionable. Complete
democratic control by member patrons is impossible
where the members have little or no education and no
business management experience. Guidance, usually
by public or cooperative authorities, is needed in
the formative years of the organization, at least
until the members are trained to operate the organization themselves. Capital is extremely scarce, and
the money that remains after costs are covered is
needed for reinvestment.

Cooperation in the United States is a way of
business, and savings from cooperative enterprise are
equated with profits. One authority sees little role
for cooperatives under socialism, and in agriculture
where land is nationalized.[8] As a matter of fact,
cooperatives are common in socialist countries, even
in government or publically owned industries. One of
the important reasons for the success of cooperative
settlements in Israel is the nationalization of land.

There is an American cooperationist view that
considers as myths that cooperatives are important
for the poor and weak, that they should strive for

equality, that they have any similarity to labor
unions or should have ties to them.[9] Cooperative settlements in Israel were founded by and for the poor
and weak, strive for equality, and belong to the National Federation of Labor. If cooperatives are to
be an instrument for agricultural development in developing countries, they will have to deal with the
poor, be concerned with some notion of equality for
the members, and may well have some organizational
ties with labor unions.

The most common type of agricultural cooperative in the United States is the cooperative marketing organization.[10] Such organizations are responsive
to the needs of American farmers. The most successful national organizations commonly serve farmers who
raise one or a few closely related products, and are
distant from the principal consumer markets. They
give the members control over their markets and ac-
complish what members individually are unable to do
for themselves.

The moshav, on the other hand, and all the cooperative settlements in Israel are multipurpose in
nature. This multipurpose objective is one of the
basic moshav principles central to the consideration
of its applicability to the agricultural development
of countries other than Israel.

NOTES

1. The State of Food and Agriculture, 1968
(Rome: Food and Agriculture Organization of the
United Nations, 1968), pp. 150-51.

2. Author's estimate.

3. The State of Food and Agriculture, 1968,
supra, 150-51.

4. Based on author's agricultural income estimates for Israel compared with agricultural income
estimates for European countries as tabulated by the
FAO Regional Office for Europe at Geneva.

5. Yair Mundlak, <u>Long-Term Projections for Supply and Demand for Agricultural Products in Israel</u> (Jerusalem: Falk Project for Economic Research in Israel, 1964), p. 23.

6. John Kenneth Galbraith, "Underdevelopment: An Approach to Classification," Paper presented to Rehovoth Conference on Fiscal and Monetary Problems in Developing States, Hebrew University, Jerusalem, August, 1965.

7. Ewell Paul Roy, <u>Cooperatives: Today and Tomorrow</u> (Danville, Ill.: Interstate Printers and Publishers, 1964), p. 111.

8. <u>Ibid</u>., p. 17.

9. <u>Ibid</u>., p. 39.

10. <u>Ibid</u>., p. 112.

CHAPTER **2** HISTORY OF
AGRICULTURAL
SETTLEMENT

This historical review is concerned with the
trends and structure of immigration into the country,
the nature and quality of the people who either voluntarily chose or were directed to agriculture, and
the origins and development of the various types of
settlements, with particular emphasis on the moshav.
The rationale for this historical review is that it
is basic in the analysis of the factors concerning
the success of the moshav and the transferability of
the moshav model to other countries.

IMMIGRATION TO PALESTINE/ISRAEL

The population of Israel was formed by rather
distinct waves of immigration starting in 1882. These
waves are referred to in Zionist history as "aliyot,"
plural of the Hebrew "aliyah," denoting immigration
to the Holy Land.[1]

First Aliyah, 1882-1903

The First Aliyah brought to the country, then
known as Palestine, twenty-five thousand Jews, mainly
from Tsarist Russia.[2] Their arrival not only doubled
the population of Palestine, but completely changed
its character, which had been that of a society of
religiously oriented Oriental Jews who supplemented
their meager earnings from shops and crafts with donations by World Jewry.

The members of the First Aliyah, young and pro-
gressively educated pioneers, fled from Russia because of the pogroms of 1881 and emigrated to Palestin

to make possible the restoration of a Jewish nation.
Their ideology was to leave the traditional Jewish
occupations and to devote themselves to manual work
and farming in their new country. As agricultural
pioneers they founded five colonies in remote areas.

These settlers encountered many difficulties,
mostly because of their inexperience in farming, but
also because of the antagonism of their Arab neighbors, the Turkish officials, and even the native Jewish inhabitants. The ruin of the settlements was
narrowly avoided by the intercession of Baron Edward
de Rothschild, who offered financial support, and
sent them agricultural experts from France. The price
paid for this assistance was high. The settlers
abandoned their original ideas and became gentlemen
farmers, employing Arab labor at low wages.

This wave of immigration would never have
evolved into a politically and economically progressive nation concerned with the ingathering of Jews
from the entire diaspora and their settlement in democratic, cooperative, agricultural communities. But
fundamental changes in the character of the Jewish
community were wrought by the Second and Third Aliyot.

Second Aliyah, 1904-14

The Second Aliyah came predominantly from Russia and brought in nearly forty thousand new immigrants in the 1904-14 decade.[3] The immediate cause
of the migration was the renewal of persecution of
the Jews and the pogroms in 1903.

The people of the Second Aliyah were affiliated
with the World Zionist Organization and with the labor
and socialist movements. Although they were offspring
of middle-class families, they aspired to become workers and farmers. They chose to emigrate to Palestine
to build a national home and to establish a base for
a new Jewish society free of social and racial injus-
tice and economic exploitation. Most of the immigrants
settled in the towns. Those who preferred agricultural life wanted to earn their living by manual work
in the fields. They fought against the colons of the

First Aliyah to substitute Jews for cheap Arab labor.
Their victory was a milestone in the Jewish settlement in Palestine.

The pioneers of the Second Aliyah developed
unions of rural and urban workers and cooperative enterprises that later evolved into the Histadrut, the
General Federation of Jewish Labor. Their return-
to-the-soil movement endowed it with an ideology that
made a cult of manual labor.

Third Aliyah, 1918-22

The Third Aliyah was a continuation of the Second, that had ended with the outbreak of World War I.
The main difference was that the immigrants now came
to a country that had become a British colony. Great
Britain had promised in the Balfour Declaration to
promote a national Jewish homeland. The immigrants,
about twenty-five thousand,[4] again came mainly from
Russia and were of the same character as those of the
Second Aliyah. This aliyah ended when the exit of
Jews from Russia was barred by the new revolutionary
government.

The Third Aliyah continued the work of the Second and was decisive in fixing the cooperative pattern
of Jewish colonization. The kibbutz evolved from an
experiment to a settlement movement and the Histadrut
to an important supporting institution. The early
moshavim were founded. The framework for the national
cooperative buying and selling institutions was established. The pioneers of the Second and Third Aliyot,
who set the pattern of Palestine/Israel's development
even now, constitute the older ruling elite of the
country.

Fourth Aliyah, 1923-26

This aliyah contributed sixty thousand people,[5]
mostly from Poland, who fled the country because of
repressive measures by the government against Jewish
business. Its character was substantially different
from that of the previous two aliyot. Many of the
immigrants were urban bourgeois merchants and artisans

who lacked the intense ideological orientation of
their predecessors and chose to continue their occupations in the larger cities of the country.

Fifth Aliyah, 1932-39

The Fifth Aliyah included nearly 225,000 Jews,
the largest wave of immigration in the period preceding the establishment of the State.[6] About a
third of the immigrants came from Eastern Europe and
another third from Germany and Central Europe as a
result of the Nazi persecution of the Jews. This wave
brought a new class of people to the country, including many professionals from a wide variety of fields
such as medicine, engineering, law, teaching, and
finance. Some had considerable capital.

The immigrants from the Fourth and Fifth Aliyot
became quickly integrated with the national life of
Palestine. Though predominantly city bourgeois, some
chose the role of agricultural pioneers and joined
their predecessors in the cooperative settlements.
The others, even those who had not been Zionists, fitted into the ideological and institutional frame established by the previous settlers. Thus by the time
of World War II the Jewish immigrants had evolved a
viable, well-organized, and politically conscious community. Another 120,000 refugees were absorbed between 1939 and 1948.[7] The Jewish population was about
770,000 when the State of Israel was proclaimed in
1948.[8]

Poststate Immigration

With the establishment of the Jewish State of
Israel, there was a tremendous expansion in immigration and a change in its composition. The country has
received over a million immigrants, a number considerably larger than the Jewish population at statehood.
While only 10 per cent of the prestate immigrants came
from Africa and Asia, these continents accounted for
about 55 per cent of those arriving after 1948.[9]

The cultural and social background of the Oriental immigrants differs widely from that of the European

immigrants. Although outwardly they have been absorbed into the existing society, their integration
into national life still poses a problem, generally
referred to as the problem of the two Israels.

HISTORICAL REVIEW OF DEVELOPMENT OF
AGRICULTURAL SETTLEMENT

The cooperative types of settlement, of which
the moshav and kibbutz are the principal forms, are
indigenous institutions, the outcomes of the problems and difficulties confronting Jewish agricultural settlement in Palestine/Israel at the beginning
of the twentieth century. The kibbutz developed from
the ideological failure of the First Aliyah and as a
reaction to their private farms. The moshav ovdim
developed as an adaption of the particular needs of
a group of settlers from the kibbutz. The middle-
class moshav and the moshav olim developed from the
moshav ovdim.

Formation of Kibbutz

The first Jewish agricultural settlement in
Palestine was begun in the 1870's by a small nucleus
of the twenty thousand people living in the country
at that time.[10] There was additional agricultural
colonization in the last two decades of the century
by the immigrants of the First Aliyah. Most of this
settlement was doomed to failure, except for a small
number of farmers who developed plantations based on
Arab labor.

The pioneers of the Second Aliyah reacted
strongly to the failure of the private settlements.
Dedicated to the idea of Jewish national revival in
the home of their ancestors, they searched intensely
for new social-organizational patterns to promote
land settlement. Their first project was the Conquest
of Labor. Jews could not compete with the poorly paid
Arabs whose standard of living was lower, and who also had their own small farms. Yet the back-to-the-
land movement could be realized only by employing Jewish labor. Although untrained in agriculture and
more expensive than Arab labor, once the new pioneers

learned their trade their services would be economic
because of their greater zeal and superior education.
This was the rationale of the movement.

The Conquest of Labor alone, however, was not
enough. After having gained their point, the new
pioneers still had to endure unaccustomed, harsh
working conditions in a subtropical climate, illness,
long stretches of unemployment, and low wages that
made the attainment of basic amenities impossible.
Within three or four years only the most persevering
remained in agriculture, who then realized that they
had to become settlers themselves and establish their
own villages based on socialist principles.

In 1908, Joseph Vitkin, a Hebrew instructor
with nationalist views, became their advocate. He
pointed out that the Conquest of Labor could only be
realized by the Conquest of the Soil--settlement of
the new pioneers on the land as working farmers. He
proposed that land be given by the Jewish National
Fund, the Zionist land-purchasing agency, on hereditary lease, and that investment funds for the farms
be made available at a low rate of interest by a new
Zionist settlement agency. Vitkin's ideas were to
be fulfilled with the establishment of the Settlement
Department of the Jewish Agency a decade later.

The principal new pattern at the time for the
promotion of land settlement was that of the large
farm in public ownership. Two types were proposed.
One consisted of national farms owned by the Zionist
Organization, or one of its affiliated agencies, and
operated by hired workers. Several farms of this
type were established. The second was a big farm to
be owned and operated by workers' cooperatives. The
workers would receive wages according to their productivity as well as part of the annual profits. This
phase would follow a three-year training period during which the settlement would be administered by an
outside expert. An experiment of this type was tried,
but it failed after a few years.[11]

Although the national farm experiments also resulted in failures, they led to the formation of the
kibbutz. The farm managers, usually foreign, were not

prepared for the environment and problems peculiar
to Palestine and also did not understand the mental-
ity of the socialist worker pioneers, to whom they
were very patronizing. Faulty management, tension
between management and workers, and continued losses
forced the settlement authorities to decide to hand
over the management of farms to the laborers. The
first instance occurred on the training farm of Sejera
in 1908. The workers collectively managed the dry-
farming branch and showed a profit. The group dis-
solved, however, after the yearly experiment.[12] The
second instance was at Kinneret Farm in 1909, where
the workers had gone on strike against the management.
Here the workers managed the whole farm for the year
with considerable success. They left shortly after-
wards and were replaced by another group that established a permanent settlement on the spot called
Degania, the first kibbutz in the country.[13]

The example of Degania was followed by many
other groups and thus became the nucleus for the important kibbutz movement. By the outbreak of World
War I, fourteen kibbutzim had been founded; however,
they did not all survive. The institutional structure
was based on full collectivism.

Emergence of the Moshav

The workers' collective and kibbutz ideas were
not completely acceptable to all pioneers. There
were two main lines of criticism. The first was that
the social organization of the kibbutz made normal
family home life impossible. The second was that all
questions in the kibbutz were decided by majority
vote, and the decisions were binding on all members.
This was felt to interfere with the personal freedom
of the minority to live and work according to their
own wishes.

The first step toward the form of a moshav type
of settlement were experiments made by Zionist agencies between 1907 and 1914 to settle workers near the
plantations that needed farm help. These colonies
were known as moshvei poalim (plural of moshav poal,
meaning settlement of workers). The individual

holdings were small and were planned only as a supplementary source of income. The main income would be
the wages earned in the private farms. These experimental colonies ended in failure. The men did not
have the time to cultivate their holdings adequately.
They either had to employ laborers who would work at
a lower wage than they themselves earned or become
full-time settlers. The first was contrary to their
ideology, and the second was uneconomic because of
the small size of the holdings.[14]

Yitzhak Wilkansky, then chief agricultural advisor to the Zionist settlement agencies and later
Professor of Farm Management at the Hebrew University
and Director of the Agricultural Research Station of
the Jewish Agency, was the first ideologist of the
moshav. He argued that since all the work on the
smallholdings should be done by the settlers and their
families without hired help, the size of the holding
should, therefore, be adjusted to the working capacity
of the family. He suggested the name of moshav ovdim
for such a farm village and that these villages be
established on the land of the Jewish National Fund.[15]

Wilkansky's proposals provoked considerable discussion. Resolutions for founding such a moshav were
adopted at many of the annual meetings of the Hapoel
Hazair (the young worker), one of the early labor
parties. The outbreak of World War I, however, prevented any implementation of this proposal.

Further support came from the work of Eliezer
Joffe, a pioneer of the Second Aliyah who had received agricultural training in the United States.
He delineated the main principles of the moshav in a
pamphlet, "The Foundation of Moshvei Ovdim," published
in 1919. These principles were:

1) Individual farm. Each member of the
village receives his own farm that is the
basis for his livelihood. He cultivates his
own farm on his own responsibility.

2) Self labor. All agricultural work
must be done solely by the owner of the farm

and his family without the use of hired
labor. The size of the individual plot,
therefore, has to be small enough to be
worked without hired labor, but large
enough to support an adequate standard of
living.

3) <u>National land</u>. Like the kibbutz, the
moshav would be on national land. The settler has the right to use the land but not
the right of ownership. Ownership should
be entrusted to the Jewish National Fund,
an affiliated fund of the World Zionist
Federation. The settler holds his lands as
a tenant on favorable terms.

4) <u>Cooperative organization</u>. The settler
should market his products and purchase his
supplies through cooperatives. The economic and municipal services in the village
should also be maintained cooperatively.

5) <u>Mutual aid</u>. This was to consist of
comprehensive arrangements to support any
needy family in the village in case of family misfortune or economic breakdown. This
aid would be in the form of money, food,
free labor, and/or management assistance.
Every farm in the village was to be safe-
guarded against economic deterioration.[16]

Joffe's pamphlet made a deep impression on the
pioneers and Jewish settlement authorities. In 1921
the settlement authorities allocated land for the two
moshvei ovdim in their plans to settle parts of the
Valley of Yizreel. The first moshav, Nahalal, was
founded in September, 1921, and the second, Kfar
Yehezkiel, in December of the same year.[17] The founders of Nahalal were mainly a small group that had left
the first kibbutz, Degania.

There was little difference in the character of
the settlers of the early moshavim and kibbutzim, except that the moshav farmers were, on the average,
somewhat older. The Kibbutzniks and the Moshavniks

were all pioneers, agricultural fundamentalists, and
rabid Zionists, strongly imbued with socialist ideology. As agricultural settlement expanded, however,
substantial differences developed in the character
and ideologies of moshav and kibbutz farmers.

Period of the Twenties

The growth of cooperative settlements was quite
slow in the decade of the twenties. Only thirteen
moshavim were founded in this period.[18] The kibbutz
movement had developed in spite of World War I so
that by 1920 it numbered forty settlements with 650
people.[19] The mushrooming in the number of kibbutzim,
each numbering but ten to twenty family units, left
them in a weak financial and social position. Of the
forty kibbutzim existing in 1920, only five survived
the decade, and the turnover of members in these five
was very high so that but few of the original founders
remained.[20] In 1931, there were only 4,400 members
in the kibbutzim and 3,400 in the moshavim. The total
population of the cooperative village amounted to
merely 4.5 per cent of the total Jewish population
in the country.[21]

There were many difficulties in this decade for
agricultural settlement. Economic conditions were
bad, and there was a deflationary trend in prices.
Jewish agriculture had to compete not only with domestic Arab agriculture but with imports from abroad,
mainly neighboring Arab countries. Costs of production and prices in both instances were lower than in
Palestinean Jewish agriculture. An additional difficulty was insufficient fund allotments by settlement
agencies. In some years plans for the founding of
new settlements had to be suspended, and all the
available finances were utilized for the consolidation of existing villages.

Important changes occurred in the decade of the
twenties in the type of farming and in the structure
of the settlements. Diversified farms became the
normal pattern of agriculture. They provided more
steady employment for the settlers all the year round
with little or no need for hired labor. They also

offered more economic stability and security against particular crop failures.

Fundamental changes also occurred in the structure of both the moshav and the kibbutz. The first decade of the moshavim saw an increase in public initiative and mutual help and responsibility and a definite trend to more intervention by the village in the affairs of the settlers. From the very beginning the moshav had to restrain individualistic tendencies that could harm the cooperative framework of the village. Objectionable features, such as economic inequality among members and trading activities outside the cooperative institutions, soon appeared. Therefore, it became established that the village should guarantee a minimum level of subsistence for every member and that it could exercise controls in the economic activities and plans of its members. Some moshavim, Nahalal, for example, did not allow members to raise private loans. The settlement administration assumed the credit responsibility for the entire village. There was a tendency to provide the economically weak farm with more credit so as to make it economically independent. The principles of mutual responsibility and mutual insurance, even though not completely implemented, were adopted.

The social and demographic structure of the kibbutz underwent fundamental transformation--the development from the small kibbutz called the kyutzah of but fifteen to twenty members to a full-fledged kibbutz of a hundred or more members.

The Zionist leaders in the early twenties favored the moshav over the kibbutz. The fact that the first moshav, Nahalal, was founded by pioneers from the first kibbutz, Degania, encouraged them to believe that the natural development would be the transformation of existing kibbutzim into moshavim. At the Zionist Conference in London in 1920, Chaim Weizmann, then the leader of the Zionist Movement and later the first President of the State of Israel, stated: "If we had the necessary funds, and if the conditions warranted it, we should begin the transformation of the existing kibbutzim into moshavim."[22]

The Zionist movement then reconciled itself to the kibbutz collective form of organization and extended more active support to it. From 1930 to the establishment of statehood in 1948 the kibbutz movement was in the vanguard of agricultural and cooperative settlement. The reasons for acceptance of the kibbutz movement by Zionist leadership were both financial and political. As for the former, the initial investment necessary for a kibbutz was less than for a moshav, and the conversion of the existing kibbutzim into moshavim would have entailed considerable additional investment. On the political side, the pressure of kibbutz groups ready and willing to colonize the country was very strong until the establishment of the State of Israel in 1948.

The groundwork was laid in the 1920's for the national agricultural organizations supporting cooperative agriculture. This included the national settlement organizations, the cooperative marketing organization, and the agency of the Histadrut, which was concerned with administrative and legal matters of the villages. The Moshav Movement, the national organization for the moshavim, was created in 1926.

Period of Expansion, 1931-37

Favorable national economic conditions and a rapid increase in urbanization and immigration were the principal factors causing the expansion of agriculture in the 1930's. The kibbutz movement developed faster than the moshav. It captured the fancy of the Jewish youth throughout the world, who volunteered to join kibbutzim and to undergo the arduous preparation to establish new ones. The Hitler period strengthened Jewish consciousness and the growth of the Zionist movement with its pioneering youth organizations. The number of kibbutzim increased from twenty-four in 1931 to forty-seven in 1936, and their population in these years from 4,000 to 16,400.[23]

Still, there was a significant expansion of moshavim. The number increased from sixteen with a population of 3,400 in 1931 to forty-four with a population of 9,900 in 1936.[24] There was an increase in

profitability in the period and a substantial development in irrigation. Professor Volcani, head of the
Agricultural Research Station, recommended limiting
the size of farm and an expansion of irrigation. He
developed a model version of irrigated farm termed
"the organic diversified farm," twenty-five to thirty
dunams* in area that would increase farm incomes
and not require hired labor. Although the model in
practice did not come up to expectations, the increase in irrigation led to a reduction in the size
of the farms in the new moshavim. Lands were redi-
vided in established moshavim after irrigation was
installed. There was no farmer resistance because of
the rise in income from the smaller plots.

        Two other types of cooperative agriculture were
initiated in this period. One was the middle-class
moshav or private moshav, which represented a type
between the moshav and a private farm. The other was
the moshav shitufi, an intermediate form between the
kibbutz and the moshav.

        The evolution of the cooperative settlements
to commercial farming began in this period, both in
the kibbutzim and the better moshavim. The farms
began using tractors and combines. The spread of irrigation promoted intensive farming. This period saw
the beginnings of a modern poultry industry and the
introduction of native improved crop varieties.

        There was a very large expansion of private
Jewish farming in this period, mainly citrus plantations cultivated by hired seasonal labor. Jewish
citrus plantations increased from 17,079 dunams in
1927 to 148,860 dunams in 1936.[25]

                Period of Struggle for Statehood and
                      World War II, 1937-47

        The period from 1937 to May, 1948, was charac-
terized by the struggle for statehood, seen in the

_____

        *Four dunams to the acre.

bloody conflict between Jews and the Arabs and Eng-
lish and World War II, in which Palestine and the
Jews played an active role. This period saw a very
substantial expansion in agricultural cooperative
settlements, particularly the kibbutzim. The country
was cut off from outside food supplies during World
War II. Domestic demand increased for the quality
production from Jewish settlements by the British
troops stationed in the country and even by the new
immigrants. This was the period in which cooperative
agriculture made further progress from ideological
agricultural communities to commercial farms.

The decade of the 1940's is referred to as the
golden age of the kibbutz movement.[26] Kibbutzim were
secret training centers and supply depots for the
underground forces that were organized by the leadership of the Jewish community. They carried the major
burden of the Zionist, politically motivated campaign
of settlements. Many of the community leaders in the
political, military, and economic sphere emerged from
the kibbutzim, and the kibbutzim have continued to
preserve their strong ties with them. The number of
kibbutzim grew from forty-seven in 1936 to 116 in May,
1948, when the new state was proclaimed. The kibbutz
population increased from 16,400 in 1936 to 47,400 in
1947. The proportion of the total Jewish population
in kibbutzim rose from 4.1 per cent in 1936 to 7.2
per cent by the end of 1947.[27] The kibbutzim also
expanded their industrial production in this period,
mainly in light industry, because of the great increase in wartime demand.

The moshav movement also expanded in this period, but less rapidly than the kibbutz. The number
of moshavim increased from forty-four in 1936, with
a population of 9,900 persons, to sixty-nine in May,
1948, with a population of eighteen thousand.[28] The
moshav lagged behind the kibbutz because it was not
as well adapted to the settlement needs of the period.
Kibbutzim combining military with economic functions
and industrial with agricultural production were more
practicable. They also had greater appeal to the
idealistic youth who wanted to emigrate to Israel to
participate in the establishment of their new homeland.

Statehood, 1948 to Present

The establishment of the State of Israel posed substantial new problems to the agricultural sector. The ingathering of exiles brought the largest wave of immigration in the history of the country and a tremendous increase in the demand for food. Large new areas of the country had to be settled, particularly the South. Agriculture continued to occupy a top priority in national planning. The virtues of rural life and agricultural cooperation had become an established national cult that prompted government authorities to decentralize the population as much as possible. Agricultural settlement on the borders continued as a security and political policy.

Table 1 shows that the number of Jewish agricultural settlements increased from 326 in November, 1948, to 706 at year-end 1967, and their population grew from 110.6 thousand to 270.6 thousand. Actually, the peak of agricultural settlement was reached in 1956 when there were 743 agricultural villages in the country with a population of 379,900 persons.[29] Although the expansion of cooperative villages has slackened since the late 1950's, the relative importance of the cooperative sector as a whole has continued to increase.

After statehood, both the moshavim and kibbutzim of necessity evolved to full-fledged commercial farms, and the output and efficiency of the farm sector increased greatly. The area in agricultural cultivation rose from 1,650,000 dunams in 1949 to 4,190,000 dunams in 1968, an increase of over two and one-half times.[30] The index of agricultural production, with 1949 as the base, increased to 743 in 1967.[31]

The greatest postwar increase in agricultural settlement was in the moshav. The number of moshavim rose from forty-four in 1948 to almost 300 by the end of 1967, an increase of almost seven times.[32] The national authorities favored the expansion of cooperative agriculture, and the moshav was the most natural type of settlement to accommodate the different character of the poststate immigration. The new

TABLE 1

Development of Jewish Settlement and Population, 1945-67[a]

Type of Settlement	1945 No.	1945 Per Cent	1948 No.	1948 Per Cent	1951 No.	1951 Per Cent	1955 No.	1955 Per Cent	1960 No.	1960 Per Cent	1963 No.	1963 Per Cent	1967 No.	1967 Per Cent
A. Moshvei ovdim and														
olim	40	16	44	13	191	31	273	37	295	41	299	42	345	49
Private moshavim	35	13	35	11	42	7	43	6	52	7	47	7	d	d
Moshavei shitufiyim	23	9	25	8	28	5	27	4	19	3	21	3	22	3
Kibbutzim	116	45	177	54	217	36	225	31	229	31	230	33	233	33
Other types[b]	44	17	45	14	128	21	164	22	128	18	102	15	106	15
Total	258	100	326	100	606	100	732	100	723	100	699	100	706	100
B. Rural population[c]														
Moshvei ovdim and olim	18.0	12	30.1	27	60.8	20	92.5	25	85.8	27	106.7	38	121.3	45
Private moshavim	13.2	9	--d	--d	24.9	8	21.2	6	29.3	9	12.3	4	d	d
Moshavei shitufiyim	--d	--d	--d	--d	4.0	1	4.8	1	3.6	1	4.0	1	4.9	1
Kibbutzim	37.4	25	54.2	49	68.2	22	77.8	21	78.0	24	79.8	28	83.1	31
Other types[b]	80.7	54	26.3	24	152.7	49	174.9	47	125.7	39	83.3	29	61.3	23
Total	149.3	100	110.6	100	310.7	100	371.2	100	322.4	100	286.1[e]	100	270.6[e]	100

[a]End of year figures except for 1948 which is for November 1.
[b]Consists mainly of private farms but also includes temporary settlements and agricultural schools of large farms.
[c]In thousands.
[d]Included in moshvei ovdim.
[e]Does not include members of settlements living outside their villages.

Sources: Joseph Ben-David, Agricultural Planning and Village Community in Israel (Paris: UNESCO, 1964), p. 55; Yair Mundlak, Long-Term Projections for Supply and Demand for Agricultural Products in Israel (Jerusalem: Falk Project for Economic Research in Israel, 1964), p. 23; Statistical Abstract of Israel, 1964, pp. 21-22; Statistical Abstract of Israel, 1965, pp. 29-30; Statistical Abstract of Israel, 1968, pp. 26-27.

immigrants, for the most part from traditional cultures of Moslem countries in the Near East and North
Africa and Communist countries in Southeast Europe,
were not likely candidates for a kibbutz. The national authorities decided to direct the new immigrants to
moshavim to develop them into commercial farmers and
to mold the institutional structure of the moshav to
their needs. This created a new type of moshav called
the moshav olim.

The first three years of statehood, from 1948
through 1951, comprised the crash period of moshav
settlement, an emergency period when villages were
founded with little or no economic planning. Forty-
seven moshavim were established in the ten-month
period of December, 1948, through September, 1949,
and thirty-six in abandoned Arab villages. In only
eleven was there any form of preliminary planning.[33]
Some of the older, well-established moshavim received
complements of new immigrants. The period after 1952
has been devoted mainly to the consolidation of established villages. From 1955 on, all new settlements
were established in the context of regional planning
and development. New settlements were established
in clusters near rural centers that, in turn, were
served by regional towns. The first experiment with
the regional approach was in the South in Lakhish. It
has been adopted throughout the country, but it is
particularly prevalent in new areas in the South and
in Galilee.

After statehood, the growth of the kibbutz was
greatly reduced. Its peak year was in 1948 when it
included 7.5 per cent of the total population of the
country.[34] From then on it has declined in relative
importance, and in the late 1950's there was even an
absolute decline in the kibbutz population. This trend
has been reversed in the 1960's. Many of the new
kibbutzim founded since 1955 have been of a paramili-
tary type under army auspices. The kibbutz has been
declining in importance as a type of settlement since
statehood, as it has lost its prestate function of
the absorption of immigrants. It has to compete for
membership not only with the other types of agricultural settlement, but also with the other sectors of
the economy in their demand for labor. There has

even been an emigration of veteran members from the
kibbutz. In the 1948-53 period, it is estimated that
12.7 per cent of the veteran members of the prestate
kibbutzim left their villages.[35] To maintain old
members and attract new ones, the kibbutzim had to
make changes in their institutional structure, particularly in raising levels of consumption, improving the quality and diversity of consumer goods, and
in offering more opportunities for specialized professionals. There has been more stability in membership in recent years because of these changes.
Throughout this period the kibbutzim have raised the
efficiency of their agricultural operations and have
increased their agricultural and industrial output.

The moshav shitufi has been of lesser importance in the cooperative sector. At year end 1947,
there were but twenty-two such villages with 4,900
people (see Table 1). A compromise between the kibbutz and moshav, its growth has been affected by
changes in the institutional structure of both types
of settlements. The kibbutz has improved housing and
has allowed increased differentiation in consumer
goods. The moshav, on the other hand, has increased
the extent of collective agricultural cultivation
where it has proven more efficient than private cultivation, particularly for fruit orchards, unirrigated
grains, and pasture. The moshav shitufi appeals to
the same type of ideologically oriented pioneer as the
kibbutz. It has had difficulty in attracting settlers
for the same reasons as the kibbutz. Most of these
settlements are attached to the national moshav federation that expends the bulk of its efforts on the
moshav ovdim and moshav olim. Many of these moshvei
shitufiyim have developed excellent communal farms.
This particular form of settlement, however, is unlikely to play a major role in cooperative agriculture
in the country.

The middle-class moshav, or private moshav, has
also decreased in relative importance in the poststate
period. The original ideological differences between
this type of moshav and the moshav ovdim in regard to
hired labor, nationally owned land, and obligatory
and all-embracing cooperative institutions have in
actual practice been blurred. The matter of hired

labor is largely academic, since the size of the farm
generally is no larger than can be worked by the
farmer and his family and since the moshav ovdim actually uses a certain amount of hired labor. Many
of these settlements have been founded on nationally
owned land with the assistance of a special unit of
the Jewish Agency organized specifically for this
purpose. These settlements have national cooperative
institutions for buying, selling, audit, etc. that
are as strongly embedded in the life of the village
as in the moshav ovdim. These villages have specialized in very intensive types of agriculture, mostly
poultry, and, to some degree, in vegetables and other
cultures. They were mainly responsible for developing
the modern poultry industry in the country. The villages have shifted in recent years, however, to more
diversified production. The only differences between
this type of settlement and the moshav ovdim are that
the farmers are not necessarily members of the Histadrut and that they have connections with nonlabor
political parties. The middle-class moshav movement
has even adopted a regional approach to settlement
in an area near Rehovot.

     The private agricultural sector has declined in
importance in the poststate period. Private farming
has concentrated on fruit for export, mainly citrus
and grapes for processing to wine. This export market temporarily ceased during the period of World War
II and the war with the Arabs. This accounts for the
out-movement of 54,400 people from 1945 to 1948. The
proportion of the rural population in private agriculture rose sharply by 126,400 persons from 1948 to
1951, its peak year. This was accounted for by both
the postwar return to citrus production and by the
establishment of new large farms, using hired labor,
in response to the high demand and inflationary food
prices. As the national authorities have definitely
favored cooperative over private agriculture, the relative importance of the private sector has decreased
in the 1960's.

     Cooperation is also basic to private farming
in Israel. This sector has strong institutions for
cooperative purchasing, selling, credit, and audit

as well as its own agricultural schools, farmer organizations, and extension services.

SUMMARY AND CONCLUSIONS

All the cooperative types of agricultural settlements in Israel are indigenous and have evolved,
over time, from ideological colonies to full-fledged
commercial market-oriented farms or groups of farms.
While ideology has played an important role in the
founding and formation of all the different types of
cooperative villages, the farm leaders and settlers
were pragmatic idealists who have molded their villages to the practical needs of the country. The
founders and pioneers of the moshav movement were no
less Zionist or Socialist than those of the kibbutz.
They sincerely thought that their moshav pattern of
joint individualism and collectivism better met their
own needs and those of the country.

Before statehood in 1948, agricultural settlement was the outlet of Zionist and Socialist pioneers
who were trained in farming before they founded and
joined their villages. The kibbutz was the principal
instrument for absorbing these politically oriented
immigrants. After statehood, agricultural settlement
changed character and became an outlet for directed
mass immigration. The moshav then became the principal type of settlement for absorbing the new immigrants, who differed sharply in character from the
prestate aliyot. The poststate moshav olim has been
developed to meet the needs of these immigrants and
is quite different in structure and operation from
the prestate moshav ovdim. The problem of transforming the postwar immigrants from traditional oriental
cultures into modern commercial farmers has been but
one part of the national problem of their absorption
into a progressive western-type society.

The quality of the prestate immigrants was basic in the development of the cooperative agricultural
sector. These veteran farmers, both from the kibbutz
and the moshav, were the leaders in the development
and evolution of the moshav structure to meet the needs

of the times and the different character of new settlers. They also developed the national institutions
that promoted and supported the development of cooperative agriculture--the Jewish Agency and constituent
organizations, the General Federation of Labor (Histadrut) and constituent cooperative institutions, and
the national settlement organizations--and were also
responsible for the evolution of these national institutions and regional organizations to the needs of
poststate settlement.

NOTES

1. Much of the material in this section is
based on the work of Professor Nadav Safran, particularly his book The United States and Israel (Cambridge:
Harvard University Press, 1963).

2. Ibid., p. 65.

3. Ibid., p. 67.

4. Ibid., p. 68.

5. Ibid., p. 69.

6. Ibid.

7. Ibid., p. 70.

8. Ibid.

9. Israel, Statistical Abstract of Israel,
1968 (Jerusalem: Government Printing Office, 1968),
p. 91.

10. Haim Darin-Drabkin, Patterns of Cooperative
Agriculture in Israel (Tel-Aviv: Achdud Ltd. Cooperative Press, 1962), p. 19.

11. Ibid., p. 22.

12. Ibid., p. 24.

13. Ibid., p. 25.

14. Shmuel Dayan, Moshav Ovdim: The Small-holders' Settlement in Palestine (Tel-Aviv: Youth Department, World Zionist Organization, Palestine Pioneer Library 6), pp. 10-11.

15. Ibid., p. 15-16.

16. Darin-Drablin, op. cit., pp. 29-30.

17. Ibid., p. 30.

18. Israel, Central Bureau of Statistics, The Settlements of Israel, I, 1961 Population and Housing Census, Publication No. 10, 1963.

19. Eliyahu Kanovsky, "The Economy of the Israeli Kibbutz" (unpublished Ph.D. dissertation, Faculty of Political Science, Columbia University, 1961), p. 17.

20. Yosef Shatil, The Economy of Communal Settlements in Israel: Principles and History (Tel-Aviv: Sifriat Poalim Ltd., 1955, in Hebrew), p. 61.

21. Darin-Drabkin, op. cit., p. 31.

22. Shatil, op. cit., p. 61.

23. Darin-Drabkin, op. cit., p. 37.

24. Ibid., p. 38.

25. Joseph Ben-David, Agricultural Planning and Village Community in Israel (Paris: UNESCO, 1964), p. 21.

26. Kanovsky, op. cit., p. 24.

27. Darin-Drabkin, op. cit., p. 39.

28. Ibid.

29. Yair Mundlak, op. cit., p. 23.

30. Statistical Abstract of Israel, 1968, p. 323.

31. Ibid., p. 365. This index is based on
output data valued at 1949 prices. It includes intermediate products and, therefore, somewhat over-
states the increase in production.

32. Ibid., p. 395.

33. Yitzhak Korn, "Planning of New Moshavim"
(unpublished paper submitted to International Symposium, The Role of Cooperative Organization in Rural
Development, Tel-Aviv, March, 1965), p. 1. (Mimeographed.)

34. Kanovsky, op. cit., p. 26.

35. Benjamin E. Gil, Settlement of New Immigrants in Israel, 1948-1953 (Jerusalem: Joint
Publication of the Central Bureau of Statistics and
The Falk Project for Economic Research in Israel,
1957), p. 110. (Mimeographed.)

CHAPTER **3** STRUCTURE AND DYNAMICS
OF ISRAELI AGRICULTURE

The objective of this chapter is to review the
dynamics of agricultural development in Israel and
to analyze the role of the moshav in this development.

GEOGRAPHY OF ISRAEL

Political and Economic Geography

The area of the State of Israel is 20,700
square kilometers, that is, 7,993 square miles, an
area somewhat smaller (by 226 square miles) than the
State of New Jersey.[1] This area includes a major
part of the former British protectorate of Palestine.
Its borders represented the freezing of the battle
lines of the War of 1948. Ever since its establishment, the boundaries of the State of Israel have
never been accepted by its neighboring countries.
This has resulted in frequent border incidents, wars,
and the constant preoccupation with national security.

Although one of the smaller countries of the
world, Israel is remarkable for the extent of its
topographical, soil, and climatic diversity. This
has complicated national agricultural planning and
the development of products and types of farms suited to the various regions that would yield approximately equal incomes.

There are four basic geographical features in
the country: (1) a range of hills in the center from
Lebanon in the north to the Negev in the south; (2)
a coastal plain of varying width west of that range;
(3) the Jordan depression east of the hills; and (4)
the Negev desert in the south.

These four zones demarcate the climatic conditions in the country. The coastal plain is warm and
humid in the summer and mild in the winter, with prevailing winds from the Mediterranean. The mean annual rainfall varies from 22 to 25 inches.[2] The hill
country is drier and cooler than the coastal plain
in summer and quite cold in winter. The mean annual
rainfall is slightly higher than in the coastal plain.
The Jordan Valley is warm, with rainfall varying from
12 inches in the north to 6 in the south. In winter
the temperature is mild, the humidity medium. The
Negev is a semi-arid zone north of Beersheba and completely arid to the south.

The distribution of rain is not favorable to
agriculture. There are two seasons, a dry summer of
about seven months and a winter of five months, with
uneven rainfall in a few widely distributed periods.

The micro climates, with the extensive variations in soils and topography, give various branches
of agriculture a comparative advantage in different
sections of the country. For example, the moderate
winter climate and ample cheap water resources in the
Tiberias district of the Jordan Valley cause the area
to be the best for banana production. In the western
Negev the combination of high day temperatures, absence of frost at night, and favorable soil make possible a profitable winter vegetable industry.

Transportation Network

Israel inherited a network of roads from the
British mandate. This network has been considerably
expanded since statehood. As of 1968, the system
included almost 5,500 miles of roads, about half of
them hard surfaced.[3] These roads reach every corner
of land actually inhabited or planned for development.

The British also left a small railroad system
that has been maintained and enlarged. The main line,
originally part of the Cairo-Paris system, runs from
Sinai north to Haifa and the Lebanese border. It has
already been extended to Dimona, south of Beersheba,
and will continue to Eilat. The Tel-Aviv-Jaffa to

Jerusalem line is still in operation. As of 1968, there were 477 kilometers of standard gauge line in operation.[4] There is additional mileage of other gauges.

The internal airline is of particular importance in connecting Haifa, Tel-Aviv, and Jerusalem with Eilat. The water and oil pipelines, which extend from the north to the south, are the main arteries of the economic life of the country. A new oil pipeline is now being constructed from Eilat, the port outlet to the Red Sea, to Ashdod on the Mediterranean.

As far as international transportation is concerned, the completion of the new harbor at Ashdod to supplement that at Haifa and the extension of the facilities at Eilat will give the country sufficient port facilities for its needs. The international airport at Lod, near Tel-Aviv, has excellent facilities but is reaching capacity usage. Plans for expansion are now being implemented.

The small size of the country and the facilities inherited from the British have been important factors in the development of the country's transportation network, which has enabled the diffusion of settlements throughout the country.

DEVELOPMENT OF ISRAELI AGRICULTURE

The story of the development of Israeli agriculture is a chronicle of remarkable achievement against tremendous odds. The following sections are specifically concerned with the measurement of this achievement, the analysis of some of the more important variables associated with it, and the importance of the moshav in this development.

Agriculture's Share in the Economy

Four key time series, shown in Table 2, can be used to gauge agriculture's share in Israel's economy. Agriculture's per cent of (1) net national

TABLE 2

Agriculture's Share in the Economy, 1952 and 1957-67

	1952	1957	1958	1959	1960	1961	1962	1963	1964	1965	1966	1967
Percentage of national product[a]	11.5	12.7	13.0	11.9	11.4	10.8	11.1	10.8	9.8	8.6	8.4	9.5
Percentage of annual investment[b]	17.9	17.7	19.5	17.4	16.0	13.5	12.0	11.1	7.8	7.3	8.6	12.1
Percentage of labor force	--	16.3	17.6	16.4	17.3	17.1	16.0	13.9	12.9	13.0	12.3	12.5
Percentage of food consumption value	--	68.8	71.1	71.8	72.2	74.7	(			About 75.0		)

[a]National product at factor cost in current prices.
[b]Gross investment including agriculture's share in water projects.

Source: Central Bureau of Statistics.

product, (2) annual investment, and (3) total labor
force have all fallen from 1952 to 1967, the latter
two much more sharply than the first. The level of
these series in recent years has been at about 9 per
cent for net national product and annual investment
and approximately 12.5 per cent for the labor force.

The percentage of food consumption value represented by national production increased from 63.1 in
1955 to about 75 in recent years. In 1947, the year
before statehood, it was only 45 per cent.[5] It may
not rise much higher, as the aim of the government
is not to achieve complete self-sufficiency in food
but to promote exports of commodities, such as citrus,
in which the country has a comparative advantage, and
to import low-value products that can be produced
more cheaply abroad.

The levels of these four indicators are similar
to those of mature economies in economically developed
countries.

Growth of Output

The performance of Israel agriculture is indicated in Table 3. Output increased over fourfold
from 1952 through 1967. The increase in value added,
the net national product of the agricultural sector,
has also been about fourfold in the same period.

Agricultural production in Israel has increased
faster in this period than in any other country in
the world. This is indicated statistically in Table
4. It compares the development of agricultural production in Israel on a per capita basis with the
world (exclusive of mainland China), its major regions,
and a sample of eleven other countries in these regions from 1952 through 1966.* It is interesting to

---

*The FAO index numbers differ from national
series. They are calculated primarily for the purpose of international comparisons and, therefore, use
constant regional weights based on wheat relative

TABLE 3

Quantity Index of Agricultural Output, Purchased Inputs, and Valued Added,
1952 and 1957/58-1966/67
(1952 = 100)

	'52[a]	'57/58	'58/59	'59/60	'60/61	'61/62	'62/63	'63/64	'64/65	'65/66	'66/67
I. Output	100	206	242	254	275	296	311	343	353	364	413
A. Realized output	100	197	240	260	283	307	326	361	376	392	447
Crops	100	169	205	215	236	254	289	323	348	367	423
Livestock and livestock products	100	240	296	328	357	390	386	423	422	436	489
B. Production for investment[b]	100	290	252	203	195	191	174	178	151	114	119
II. Purchased inputs	100	209	229	261	259	275	298	302	341	374	396
A. Materials	100	240	264	310	299	319	333[c]	335	384	426	451
B. Services	100	189	216	227	246	253	--	--	--	--	--
C. Depreciation	100	138	143	150	159	171	191	207	222	233	243
III. Value added	100	203	250	250	286	310	318	374	357	348	447

[a]1952, calendar year; from 1957/58, agricultural year of October to September.
[b]Value of plantations before bearing, changes in livestock inventory, seed for crops, etc.
[c]From 1962/63 materials and services.

Source: Central Bureau of Statistics.

compare the 1966 per capita index for Israel of 164
(1952-56 = 100) with 109 for the world, 120 for
Western Europe, 141 for Eastern Europe and the USSR,
99 for North America, and 116 for Oceania. The comparison with the developing areas shows even wider
differences: 100 for Latin America, 104 for the Far
East, 109 for the Near East, and 100 for Africa.

    Table 5 presents a comparison of the growth
rates in the agricultural sector in the 1952-67 period with the growth rate of the net national product
of the whole economy. The annual rate of increase of
agriculture's value added averaged 16.2 for the period
under review as compared to 18.0 for the whole economy. From 1953 through 1958, the rate of increase in
the agricultural sector was generally higher than
that for the economy as a whole, while from 1959 on,
except for three years, it lagged behind. The annual
rate of increase for agriculture is also much more
volatile than that for the whole economy. The main
conclusion, however, is that the rate of growth for
the agricultural sector has almost approximated that
for the economy as a whole.

    The growth rate in the agricultural sector was
accomplished during a time of adverse price trends.
A study by the Central Bureau of Statistics indicates
that, in the 1952-62 period, the price of agricultural
outputs increased at an average annual rate of 7.1
per cent, while the price of purchased inputs increased at a rate of 9.5 per cent.[6] More recent data
indicate that the index of prices paid by farmers increased at a rate of 7.25 per cent from 1958/59 to
1966/67 while that of prices received by farmers increased at a rate of only 4.5 per cent.[7] Both sets

---

prices. The concept of production is one of
quasi output not strictly comparable to the national
accounts approach. It is based on total production
less allowances for feeds, seeds, and production
waste. Lack of data on inputs for many countries
prevent the adoption of the national accounts, value
added approach.

TABLE 4

Per Capita Agricultural Production: Regional, Subregional, and Selected Country Indexes
1952 and 1955-56
(1952-66 = 100)

	1952	1955	1956	1957	1958	1959	1960	1961	1962	1963	1964	1965	1966ᵃ
Western Europe	94	102	102	104	106	108	113	112	118	118	118	118	120
Northwestern Europe	95	101	101	102	104	103	114	110	118	117	117	116	116
France	91	102	101	100	101	104	117	112	122	118	118	124	118
Germany, Fed. Rep.	97	100	100	100	107	100	113	100	111	115	112	103	110
Southern Europe	92	104	102	108	110	118	111	116	117	121	121	121	129
Italy	93	104	103	100	113	113	105	114	115	108	115	117	120
Eastern Europe and USSR	93	103	111	113	120	121	120	122	123	117	126	127	141
North America	103	99	100	93	98	98	98	96	98	102	99	99	99
United States	102	100	99	94	99	99	99	98	98	102	100	99	98
Oceania	101	101	101	95	107	106	107	107	111	112	114	106	116
Australia	100	102	102	93	109	106	108	108	113	115	117	106	119
Latin America	100	101	102	103	106	103	102	105	104	104	102	103	100
Central America	100	103	102	112	114	109	110	113	108	105	109	112	108
Mexico	87	110	108	118	124	113	115	117	117	119	124	121	123
South America	100	100	102	101	104	102	101	104	104	104	101	101	98
Argentina	101	94	106	96	103	95	87	95	96	107	103	89	97
Far East	95	102	103	102	104	106	107	109	109	108	109	105	104
India	93	102	103	101	103	104	107	108	106	106	105	98	95
Japan	100	111	107	109	113	112	111	112	119	116	120	119	122
Near East	98	98	105	107	107	109	107	104	111	111	110	110	109
Israel	88	101	116	117	117	140	141	145	152	151	169	169	164
United Arab. Rep.	100	101	102	107	105	107	110	95	111	109	111	112	109
Africa	97	100	102	100	100	102	106	101	105	105	105	104	100
Northwest Africa	95	92	102	89	96	90	94	71	85	90	85	85	66
Algeria	94	94	102	92	83	87	88	67	78	80	69	75	54
South of Sahara	98	101	102	102	101	104	108	105	108	108	108	107	106
South Africa	87	104	104	106	100	104	107	113	113	116	109	104	109
Worldᵇ	98	101	103	102	106	106	107	106	108	108	109	107	109

ᵃPreliminary.

ᵇExcluding mainland China.

Source: The State of Food and Agriculture, 1968 (Rome: Food and Agriculture Organization of the United Nations, 1968), pp. 150-51.

42

of data support the conclusion of a continuing deterioration in the terms of trade of the agriculture
sector.

TABLE 5

Annual Growth Rates of Value Added by
Agriculture and Net National Product,
1952-67

	Value Added by Agriculture	Net National Product of Whole Economy (Value Added)
1952 to 1953	32.0	30.7
1953 to 1954	38.0	30.3
1954 to 1955	13.5	21.5
1955 to 1956	21.9	19.3
1956 to 1957	22.5	16.0
1957 to 1958	23.8	15.8
1958 to 1959	1.1	13.4
1959 to 1960	0.3	12.6
1960 to 1961	21.5	18.4
1961 to 1962	8.7	18.7
1962 to 1963	26.2	24.3
1963 to 1964	8.6	16.8
1964 to 1965	5.0	19.0
1965 to 1966	1.2	10.4
1966 to 1967	19.0	3.4
Average annual rate of increase 1952 to 1967	16.2	18.0

Source: Central Bureau of Statistics.

Capital Investments

Following the mass immigration after the War
of Independence, agriculture was faced with the enor-
mous job of feeding a rapidly burgeoning population.

To carry out this task, very large investments were
channeled into the sector, mainly through the government development budget. The investment in agriculture in 1952 amounted to about 40 per cent of the
agricultural net output, and it remained above 35 per
cent until 1955 (Table 6).

TABLE 6

Gross Investment in Agriculture as a
Percentage of Value of
Agricultural Output,
1952-67

Year	Per Cent	Year	Per Cent
1952	40	1960	21
1953	43	1961	20
1954	35	1962	20
1955	36	1963	25[a]
1956	29	1964	20
1957	29	1965	17
1958	29	1966	16
1959	24	1967	14

[a]Series after 1963 not strictly comparable with previous years but statistical discrepancies estimated
as minor.

Source: Central Bureau of Statistics.

The early years of the State were a period of
scarcity with comprehensive rationing and price controls to encourage farmers to expand production without fear of a precipitous slump in prices. By about
1954, the gap between supply and demand began to
close and surpluses started to appear. This was reflected by a reduction in investment in agriculture
to 29 per cent of net output in 1956. By 1967, it
dropped to about 14 per cent.

The amount of gross investment in the agricultural sector, however, increased steadily after

statehood until 1964.   Investment funds dropped for
the first time in 1965 and remained at about the same
level in 1966.   The figures on gross investment in
current millions of Israeli pounds in recent years
have been as follows:[8]

1961/62	234.7
1962/63	264.1
1963/64	265.5
1964/65	219.9
1965/66	218.4

The principal conclusion is that there has been a
continuation of large investments in agriculture, a
highly developed sector, to maintain continued growth.

Returns to Factors of Production, Labor and Management Incomes

The distribution of factor shares shows a remarkable stability over the years.   Since 1952, wages
and salaries have accounted for about 24 to 30 per
cent of the value added, interest and rent together
5 to 8 per cent, and share of family labor and profit
was 64 to 70 per cent.   There is little indication
of a definitive secular trend in any of these com-
ponents.[9]

The data in Table 7 make possible a comparison
of incomes of farm operators with those gainfully
employed in the entire economy.   It shows that their
incomes are consistently lower.   The difference is
not great, and in 1967 it amounted to but 15 per cent.
Taking into consideration that the agriculture income
figures comprise all types of settlements, both Jewish and Arab, the average income of farm operators in
Israel is indeed quite high: $3,220 in 1967.

These figures are of a macro variety for the
entire agricultural sector.   As far as the moshav is
concerned, the aim of the national authorities has
been to equalize the earnings of the farm operators
with the incomes of trained labor in the industrial
sector.   As of the periods 1964 and 1965, the average net family income of poststate moshav farms from

TABLE 7

Farm Income Compared with Average Income in Entire Economy 1959 and 1962-67

Year	1959	1962	1963	1964	1965	1966	1967
1. National income originating in agriculture[a]	337.8	532.5	643.4	683.5	717.4	763.3	893.5
2. Wages paid to hired labor[a]	98.7	128.0	155.2	179.8	190.7	212.0	215.0
3. Interest and rent paid[a]	27.8	33.1	36.7	41.3	45.8	48.0	52.5
4. Income of farm operators from agriculture[a] $4 = 1 - (2 + 3)$	251.3	371.4	451.5	462.4	478.1	503.3	626.0
5. Gainfully employed in agriculture[b]	119.7	125.9	112.6	109.9	114.4	107.4	104.1
6. Hired labor in agriculture[b]	46.0	46.5	44.1	46.8	45.6	41.7	39.3
7. Non-hired labor in agriculture[b] $7 = 5 - 6$	73.7	79.4	68.5	63.1	68.8	65.7	64.8
8. Average income per non-hired employed[c] $8 = \frac{4}{7}$	3,410	4,680	6,590	7,330	6,950	7,660	9,660
9. National income[a]	3,121	4,793	5,959	6,957	8,281	9,141	9,454
10. Total gainfully employed in the economy[b]	680.0	787.9	873.2	854.1	879.2	873.9	830.7
11. Average income per gainfully employed in the whole economy[c] $11 = \frac{9}{10}$	4,590	6,010	7,330	8,150	9,420	10,460	11,390

[a]Millions of Israeli pounds at current prices; [b]thousands; [c]Israeli pounds.

Source: Central Bureau of Statistics.

farming alone was 5,000 to 6,000 Israeli pounds,
about 85 per cent of that of workers in the industrial sector.[10] Many of the families earned additional income from nonfarm sources, administrative posts
in the village, work with the institutions supporting
the cooperative settlements, public works, etc. The
income of the prestate moshavim in the same period
was 10 to 20 per cent higher than city workers in the
industrial sector. Family income from agriculture
alone was at the 9,000 to 10,000 Israeli-pound level.
Income from outside work is also a substantial factor
in their total earnings. The relative income position of the moshavim can be considered good.

Manpower Requirements and Labor Productivity

The number of persons gainfully employed in
agriculture reached a peak in 1961 and has been falling steadily in recent years.[11] Yet agricultural
production has continued to rise. This obviously indicates an increase in labor productivity.

Actually, there are considerable data indicating
very sizable increases in labor productivity since
statehood. A detailed study made by the Department
of Agricultural Economics of Hebrew University found
that the increase in production in the period of 1950
through 1961, unexplained by the increase in inputs,
was 5.3 per cent per year. Increases in productivity
accounted for 40 to 48 per cent of the annual rise in
production. The rise in productivity is attributed
mainly to the improvement in technical competence of
the farmers in the new settlements and the introduction of new products, such as industrial crops and
beef herds.[12]

The large increases in yields are evidence of
the improvement in technical efficiency. Average
yields for 1948/49 and 1966/67 are presented in Table
8. Both were years of good rainfalls. There were
large increases in yield of both irrigated and unirrigated crops. Data from a national supply and demand study indicate that the average yield for all
vegetables and potatoes in 1960 was 56 per cent higher
than in 1953. The increase in tomatoes was 219 per

cent.[13] The annual rate of increase in milk per cow
for the 1953-60 period was 3.8 per cent for the
branch as a whole.   It was 5.5 per cent for regis-
tered herds and 6.0 per cent for a sample of kibbutzim.   It was 3.4 per cent in the 1953-58 period in a
sample of moshav ovdim.[14]

TABLE 8

Average Yields of Main Field Crops,
1948/49 and 1966/67
(Kilograms per Dunam)

Crop	1948/49	1966/67
Wheat	75	265
Barley	140	240
Maize for grain (unirrigated)	110	240
Maize for grain (irrigated)	290[a]	415
Sorghum for grain (unirrigated)	60	245
Sorghum for grain (irrigated)	270[b]	530
Hay	320	375
Green fodder (unirrigated)	950	1,815
Green fodder (irrigated)	5,500	7,055
Sugar beets (irrigated)	1,205[c]	4,725
Cotton lint (irrigated)	95[b]	110
Cotton seed (irrigated)	175[b]	180

[a]1949/50
[b]1954/55
[c]1952/53

Sources: Statistical Abstract of Israel, 1966,
p. 365; Statistical Abstract of Israel, 1968, p. 320.

Some international yield comparisons are relevant. For the new industrial crops of sugar beets,
groundnuts, and cotton (lint), yields in Israel in
recent years have been the highest of all countries
in the world. Similarly, milk yields per milking
cow have also been the highest.[15]

The decrease in labor requirements in the poststate moshavim is indicated in Table 9, which shows

the norms used by the economic planners of the Jewish
Agency. These norms are derived from actual operational data of average sample farms. It is the opinion of the Settlement Department of the Jewish Agency
and the Department of Agricultural Economics of Hebrew
University that workdays per unit of area and per ton
of product will continue to decrease with the increasing specialization of agriculture.

While yields in Israeli agriculture are high,
there is still need for improvement in labor produc-
tivity--that is, man-hours expended per unit of output, particularly in the moshav. Part of the
difficulty is due to the small size of the individual
farms and the lack of sufficient inputs. The national
planners are working on this problem and expect further increases in labor productivity. The five-year
plan for Israel's agriculture, 1964/65 to 1968/69
calls for a 7.3 per cent annual rate of increase in
output with only a 1.5 per cent annual increase in
labor requirements.[16]

Land and Water Constraints to Development

Agricultural land is probably the most important natural resource in the country. The conquest
of the soil represents the greatest accomplishment in
its economic development. While potentially usable,
agricultural land is plentiful but water resources
are scarce. It is estimated that of the total area
of the state about 3.4 million acres are potentially
available for dry farming, including natural pasture
and afforestation, and 1.3 million acres are potentially available for farming under irrigation.[17]
About 75 per cent of the potential dry farming area
is actually cultivated, while only 40 per cent of the
area available for farming under irrigation is actually used.[18] For the latter, the country has had to
apply about 75 to 80 per cent of its total usable
water supply.*

The possibilities of expansion of the cultivated area depend mainly on an additional supply of

----

*See Table 10.

TABLE 9

Labor Requirements of Poststate Moshavim, 1955, 1960, and 1965

Branch	to 1955 Norm		Workdays According to 1960 Norm		to 1965 Moshav Plan	
	Per Dunam	Per Ton	Per Dunam	Per Ton	Per Dunam	Per Ton
Groundnuts	10	33.3	4.6	13.1	3.5	10.0
Sugar beets	10	2.8	5.5	1.1	7.0	1.4
Irrigated cotton	12	54.5	8.5	28.3	2.5	--
Spring potatoes	13	6.5	9.5	4.2	8.0	3.0
Autumn tomatoes	37	12.3	22.8	6.5	28.0	6.5
Cucumbers	23.5	23.4	17.5	8.7	16.0	8.0
Citrus	14.5	4.8	13.4	3.8	12.0	3.4

Source: Ranaan Weitz, Agriculture and Rural Development in Israel, Projection and Planning (Rehovot: Hebrew University, 1963), p. 39, for 1955 and 1960; letter from Weitz for 1965.

water. The likelihood of a significant increase of
cultivable land through reclamation is small. Certain
cultivable areas in the Negev may even have to be
given up because of the frequency of droughts. There
are some possibilities, however, that may not as yet
be fully exploited, particularly natural and improved
pastures.

Table 10 shows the poststate growth in water
consumption. The amount of water used for agriculture in 1960/61 was four times higher than in 1948/49.
Its consumption has been stabilized since because of
more efficient utilization. The introduction of rationing water to local authorities in 1961 has been
effective in decreasing nonagricultural consumption.

The need for new sources of water for development has been the rationale for the drive behind the
implementation of the national water plan. The principal purposes of the plan are to divert a substantial part of surplus water from the Jordan and other
sources in the north to the Negev, to store excess
supplies from periods of surplus to periods of drought,
and to unify the various regional water-supply systems.
The master plan is scheduled for completion in 1970.
Additional projects are also being carried out for the
detention of storm waters and purification of sewage
water. The additional water destined for agriculture
from these supplementary sources will be comparative-
ly small, as most of it will be used to increase the
supply to industries and cities and to remedy the ex-
cessive pumping of underground waters.

When the master water plan is completed, further resources will depend on desalting sea water.
Research work has been conducted on desalination of
sea water in both Israel and other countries, and
practical possibilities are beginning to be realized.
For the present, such water is too expensive for wide
use by agriculture. It may be economic to use desal-
inated water to dilute brackish waters. It seems
quite possible that in the relatively near future the
costs will be low enough to make desalination of sea
water an economically justifiable venture to increase
the supply of fresh water.[19]

TABLE 10

Water Consumption, 1948/49-1966/67
(Million Cubic Meters)

Type of Disposal	1948/49a	1952/53	1956/57	1960/61	1963/64	1966/67
Total consumption	---	---	1,060	1,275	1,249	1,474
Total agricultural consumption of which:	257	563	830	1,025	1,020	1,115
Field crops	45	114	225	305	290	330
Vegetables, potatoes, and groundnuts	35	137	140	135	110	125
Fruit plantations	108	139	250	365	405	455
Fish ponds	62	146	170	168	160	150
Miscellaneousb	7	27	45	52	55	55
Non-agricultural consumption	---	---	230	250	229	359

aOctober to September.
bAuxiliary farms, nurseries, flowers, etc.

Sources: Statistical Abstract of Israel, 1968, pp. 354-55; P. Zussman, unpublished lecture (Rehovot: Hebrew University). (Mimeographed.)

52

Structure of Outputs

It is of interest to present a summary overview
of the changes in the agricultural structure, both in
outputs and inputs, that have accompanied the spectacular growth in Israeli agriculture.

A statistical summary of the changes in the
relative position of the principal output groups from
1952 to 1967 is presented in Table 11. It shows that
realized output as a proportion of total output increased about 5 per cent in the period because of the
decrease of production for investment. The proportion
of realized output accounted for by crops declined in
the 1950's and rose in the 1960's, while that for
livestock and livestock products showed a contrary
movement.

The group breakdowns in this table show important changes, changes that accompanied the development
of the moshav. The most dramatic change was the
doubling in the relative importance of meat production,
from about 10 per cent of total output in the early
1950's to 20 per cent in the 1960's. At the same time,
the output of vegetables decreased from about 20 per
cent in the early 1950's to about 9 per cent in the
1960's. Another important change was the increase in
fruit from 22 per cent in 1952 to about one third in
recent years. Most of this increase was due to the
expansion of citrus production, to a large degree in
the moshavim. There was also an important increase in
industrial crops, the basis for the expansion of the
moshav in the South from about 4 per cent in the early
1950's to 8 per cent in the 1960's.

Changes in the relative position of the values
of the commodity groups reflect the combined effects
of the changes in output and prices. These changes
can be isolated. The national quantity index of production increased 73 per cent from 1959 to 1967, while
the national index of prices received by farmers increased 36 per cent in the same period.[20] Output has
risen every year from 1948 to 1967. Farm prices have
also risen, but less than the levels of output, and
in some years there have even been sharp drops in the
price averages.

TABLE 11

Group Breakdowns of Agricultural Output Value at Current Prices,
1952 and 1957/58-1966/67

(Per Cent)

	1952[a]	'57/58	'58/59	'59/60	'60/61	'61/62	'62/63[b]	'63/64	'64/65	'65/66	'66/67
Total Output	100.0	100.0	100.0	100.0	100.0	100.0	100.0	100.0	100.0	100.0	100.0
I. Realized output	89.7	86.5	88.9	91.5	92.2	92.5	94.3	93.9	94.8	95.7	95.0
A. Realized crop products	50.6	43.8	43.4	45.0	45.7	47.4	52.3	50.0	53.2	53.7	54.4
Cereals and pulses	1.3	2.3	2.3	1.1	1.3	1.0	1.0	2.4	2.8	1.8	3.8
Industrial and oil crops	4.1	4.6	5.9	7.1	8.0	7.4	5.9	6.3	7.7	7.7	7.5
Melons and pumpkins	2.9	1.1	1.2	1.0	1.1	1.2	1.1	1.3	1.3	1.5	1.2
Vegetables	19.3	10.4	8.8	8.6	8.4	9.1	9.0	9.8	9.5	9.8	8.9
Fruits	22.4	25.1	24.8	26.8	26.5	28.2	34.6	29.5	31.2	32.2	32.1
Miscellaneous crops	0.6	0.3	0.4	0.4	0.4	0.5	0.7	0.7	0.7	0.7	0.9
B. Realized livestock and livestock products	39.1	42.7	45.5	46.5	46.5	45.1	42.0	43.9	41.6	42.0	40.6
Milk	13.4	11.2	11.4	11.5	11.4	11.5	9.7	9.9	9.8	10.5	10.1
Eggs	11.2	11.0	11.5	11.4	11.7	10.3	8.9	9.4	8.8	8.3	8.9
Meat	9.6	17.4	19.5	20.4	20.4	20.3	20.4	21.2	19.8	19.5	18.4
Fishing	4.3	2.8	2.6	2.7	2.5	2.5	2.5	2.8	2.6	3.1	2.6
Miscellaneous livestock products	0.6	0.3	0.5	0.5	0.5	0.5	0.7	0.7	0.7	0.7	0.9
II. Production for investment[c]	10.3	13.5	11.1	8.5	7.8	7.5	5.7	6.1	5.2	4.3	5.0

[a]1952, calendar year; from 1957/58 agricultural year of October to September.
[b]Series from 1962/63 not completely comparable with previous years.
[c]Value of plantations before bearing, changes in livestock inventory, seed for crops, etc.

Source: Central Bureau of Statistics.

54

Structure of Inputs

A major causal factor in the poststate growth
of agricultural output has been the increased use of
purchased inputs. The relative importance of the
principal import groups from 1952 to 1967 is shown
in Table 12. The most important change has been in
feedstuffs, which rose from 17 per cent in the early
1950's to about 35 per cent in the 1960's. This made
possible the large growth in the livestock industry.

The value of agricultural inputs purchased from
other sectors of the economy amounted to 690.1 million Israeli pounds in the 1967 agricultural year.[21]
The import groups in order of importance in 1967, excluding depreciation, were feedstuffs, packing materials, transport, water, and the group including fuel,
libricants, and electricity.

The national quantity index of purchased inputs
shows that there was almost a fourfold increase in
amounts purchased from 1952 to 1967. The amount of
feedstuffs purchased increased almost eight times and
that of plant and animal protection materials, over
six times. There were more than fourfold increases
in miscellaneous services, fertilizers, and packing
materials.[22]

Changes in the value of the inputs purchased
also reflect the combined effect of changes in the
quantities bought and changes in price. The national
quantity index of purchased inputs rose 43 per cent
from the 1959 agricultural year to 1967.[23] The index of prices paid by farmers rose 58 per cent in
the same period.[24] With the unfavorable terms of
trade, average prices paid by farmers were higher
than average prices received. The economic rationale
of the rise in purchased inputs that were accompanied
by increases in net farm incomes is the increase in
productivity achieved through the use of these inputs.
It does not necessarily follow that according to economic criteria the optimal amount of inputs were purchased and used. It does indicate, however, that
intensive use has been made of feeds, water, fertilizers, insecticides, machinery, and other factors

TABLE 12

Group Breakdown of Purchased Agricultural Inputs[a]

1952 and 1957/58-1966/67

(Per Cent)

Purchased Inputs	1952[b]	'57/58	'58/59	'59/60	'60/61	'61/62	'62/63	'63/64	'64/65	'65/66	'66/67
	100.0	100.0	100.0	100.0	100.0	100.0	100.0	100.0	100.0	100.0	100.0
Feedstuffs	17.4	37.1	37.7	41.8	39.5	36.8	35.3	32.3	34.4	35.8	35.5
Water	11.1	10.3	10.1	10.2	9.6	10.3	9.6	8.1	8.2	8.8	7.4
Packing materials	8.4	7.6	8.1	7.3	6.3	7.5	8.9	9.5	9.7	9.6	10.3
Fertilizers	8.3	5.9	5.5	5.0	4.7	4.8	4.8	4.7	4.9	4.7	4.8
Transport	7.3	5.5	5.5	5.0	5.4	5.1	7.1	7.6	7.5	7.3	7.6
Spare parts, repairs, and tools	6.6	5.0	5.1	4.3	5.3	6.0	4.9	6.4	5.9	5.4	5.2
Fuel, lubricants, and electricity	4.3	2.9	3.0	2.7	3.1	2.8	2.7	3.4	3.1	2.9	3.0
Plant and animal protection materials	2.7	3.4	3.2	3.2	3.8	4.1	3.7	3.4	2.9	2.8	3.1
Government	4.3	2.9	3.1	3.2	3.7	3.5	3.4	3.1	2.7	2.6	2.5
Seed and seed cleaning	2.0	1.4	1.4	1.2	1.3	1.3	1.0	0.7	0.6	0.6	0.5
Services, miscellaneous	2.5	1.8	1.8	1.8	1.8	1.8	2.2	2.1	2.2	2.1	2.4
Depreciation	22.4	15.0	14.4	13.5	14.6	15.2	15.1	17.2	16.8	16.1	15.9
Miscellaneous expenses	2.7	1.2	1.1	0.8	0.9	0.8	1.3	1.5	1.1	1.3	1.8

[a]Value at current prices.

[b]1952, calendar year; from 1957/58, agricultural year of October to September.

Source: Statistical Abstract of Israel, 1968, pp. 352-53.

necessary to secure high yields, and of transport for marketing efficiency.

Trends in Food Consumption

The development of food consumption is a function of changes in the supply of food, growth of population, and changes in prices and incomes. Mundlak's study of trends in supply and demand of agricultural products in Israel indicated a 40 per cent increase in the per capita consumption of food from 1952 to 1961.[25] It showed that the real price of food, actual prices deflated by the national consumer price index, was remarkably stable through the entire period. The changes in income, therefore, explained most of the increase in food consumption. The income elasticity of demand for food in this period was estimated at 0.643.[26]

Food consumption has continued to increase in recent years, and Israel can now be considered a rather high food-consumption country. Per capita calorie supplies per day in 1967 were 2,850, higher than any of the countries in the Far East, Near East, Africa, and Latin America, except Argentina and Uruguay, and only slightly below the average for Western Europe.[27] The per capita consumption of fats per day is almost 100 grams, generally below Western Europe, but exceeded in the underdeveloped regions, again, only by Argentina and Uruguay.[28] In terms of per capita grams of total protein per day, the average is slightly under 90, higher than all countries in the developing regions except Uruguay, about the same level as Europe, and only slightly below North America and Oceania.[29] The animal protein, which averages about 40 grams per day, is exceeded in developing regions only by Argentina and Uruguay, but is somewhat lower than the average for Western Europe.[30]

Foreign Trade in Agricultural Products

A review of the outlets for expanding agricultural production and the sources for expanding food consumption requires an examination of foreign trade in the sector. Mundlak's supply and demand study

showed that the excess of imports over exports in agriculture as a percentage of the total national unfavorable balance of trade was reduced from 26 to 7
per cent in the period from 1953 to 1960.[31] There was
an increase in food and agriculture imports in the
period but a much larger increase in exports. This
means that the increased agricultural production has
made it possible to raise food consumption and at the
same time to reduce the excess of imports over exports. The foreign-trade position of the agricultural
sector has continued to be good, relative to the entire economy, until now it is almost self-sufficient,
export earnings approximately balancing import needs.

Food and agricultural products account for substantial portions of total exports and imports. Since
1965, the value of total agricultural exports has
been over $100 million. In 1967, it was about $145
million. The value of citrus exports alone in 1967
was over $85 million. Citrus was the most important
export through 1958. Since then polished diamonds
have assumed first place. Other important agricultural products that have been developed are processed
fruits and vegetables, livestock, poultry products,
groundnuts, fresh vegetables, and fruit other than
citrus. The proportion of total exports accounted for
by the agricultural sector has been decreasing since
1953 because of the diversification of exports and the
greater relative increase of nonagricultural products.[3]

Food and agricultural imports amounted to about
$150 million in 1967. The most important items are
grains, meat, and dairy products, oilseeds, and textile fibers.[33]

The price elasticity of many agricultural products is relatively low. A solution to this problem
is to find outlets that are relatively elastic. Israel
has experimented with the development of two possibilities: import substitutes and exports. Examples of
the former were the introduction and expansion of cotton and sugar beets, but the prices of these and other
agricultural imports are relatively low. Therefore,
the costs of dollars saved in these products are high.
Cotton and sugar beets have fitted in the regional

agricultural development pattern for the South. According to economic criteria, it would be better to develop exports of high-valued export crops, for which Israel has a comparative advantage, processed foods that have a high income elasticity, eggs and poultry meat, and off-season fruits and vegetables, for example. Great effort is being expended in these directions, and new moshavim specialized for export crops are being developed.

POSITION OF THE MOSHAV IN AGRICULTURAL DEVELOPMENT

The importance of the various types of settlements on the basis of contribution to total agricultural output can only be estimated. The following estimates have been made on the basis of data obtained from the Histadrut, the Central Bureau of Statistics, and the Agricultural and Settlement Planning and Development Center of the Ministry of Agriculture:

	Per Cent of Total Agricultural Output
Moshavim	45
Kibbutzim	33
Private sector	20
Other*	2
Total	100

The growth in percentage of total production of the postwar moshavim has been spectacular. Their percentages of total output of all settlements attached to the Histadrut have been as follows: 1951/52, 5; 1956/57, 13; and 1962/63, 24. The actual contributions were higher since the production figures did not include the middle-class moshavim not attached to the Histadrut. The proportion of production of the kibbutzim was above 30 per cent in all three periods.

---

*Agricultural schools, experiment stations, etc.

The proportion of production of the veteran moshavim
has declined with the tremendous expansion of the
postwar moshavim. The moshav olim now supplies more
than half of the total moshav output.

An examination of production data indicates
that with the development of Israel agriculture the
moshav has been able to achieve a specialized role.
Although the origin of the moshav was based on ideological differences with the kibbutz on how to obtain
a better cooperative agriculture, the commercializa-
tion of both types of settlements has produced differences in commodity specialization and operation.
The moshavim have concentrated on labor-intensive
products, such as farmyard livestock and livestock
products, and certain types of tree crops. The kibbutzim have specialized where the big farm has advantages, as in grain growing, field crops that can be
mechanized, beef cattle, and branches that demand
high capital investment and use of water, such as
specialized types of fruit orchards and fish ponds.

There is specialization within branches between
the kibbutz and moshav. In poultry the moshavim specialize in eggs and the kibbutzim in meat production,
where the advantages of scale are greater. In fruit
the kibbutzim specialize in bananas, apples, and
pears and the moshavim more in citrus, peaches, and
wine grapes. This specialization is caused by locational, water, and investment reasons.

There is also differentiation between veteran
and new moshavim. The new moshavim have all the
flower production and the major share of vegetables,
non-citrus fruit, and sheep and goat milk and meat,
which are items that require more labor, are new
branches, or are in settlements with locational advantages.

The private sector specializes mainly in citrus
and wine grapes, but it also produces a substantial
amount of grains and industrial crops. There has
been, however, a substantial growth in citrus production in cooperative settlements. In 1963/64, Tnuva
Export, the special cooperative for citrus fruit of

the cooperative settlements, accounted for 32 per cent of citrus exports.[34] The agricultural plan for 1965 indicated about half of the total area in citrus was in cooperative settlements.[35]

SUMMARY AND CONCLUSIONS

This chapter has traced the dynamic growth of the agricultural sector in Israel. The veteran cooperative settlements and private farms are at a European level of efficiency of organization and operation. The poststate settlements have also made great progress, but additional development is needed before they can be completely independent.

Rural life in cooperative villages has become a cult deeply imbedded in the national mores. This is evidenced by the large public investments in the agricultural sector, investments that have continued high in the face of competing claims of other sectors even though the sector is quite developed.

The moshav has evolved to occupy a specialized role in the commercial agriculture of the country. There are differences in the types of enterprises and in the method of farm organization and management among the moshav, the kibbutz, and private agriculture. A differentiation in the types of enterprises has also evolved between the prestate and poststate moshavim.

NOTES

1. Statistical Abstract of Israel, 1966, p. 5. This does not include the lands acquired in the War of 1967.

2. Rainfall data based on forty-year records from Haim Halperin, Changing Patterns in Israel Agriculture (London: Routledge and Kegan Paul, 1957), p. 3.

3. Statistical Abstract of Israel, 1968, pp. 415-16.

4. Ibid., p. 423.

5. N. Verlinsky, Tnuva (Tel-Aviv: Afro-Asian
Institute for Labor Studies and Cooperation, undated),
p. 17.

6. Calculated from basic data in Micheal Noam
and Haim Regev, National Income Originating in
Israeli Agriculture, 1952-1963 (Jerusalem: Central
Bureau of Statistics, 1964). (Mimeographed.)

7. Statistical Abstract of Israel, 1968, p. 241.

8. Israel, Bank of Israel Annual Reports,
1964 through 1966 (Jerusalem: Jerusalem Post Press),
pp. 251, 253, 284. The exchange rate was three
Israeli pounds per dollar.

9. Noam and Regev, op. cit., pp. 6-7, and Statistical Abstract of Israel, 1968, p. 162.

10. Estimated from unpublished Jewish Agency,
Histadrut, and Central Bureau of Statistics materials.

11. Statistical Abstract of Israel, 1968, p. 262.

12. Mundlak, op. cit., pp. 53-54.

13. Ibid., p. 35.

14. Ibid.

15. Production Yearbook, 1967 (Rome: Food and
Agriculture Organization of the United Nations, 1968).

16. Israel, Agriculture and Settlement-Planning
and Development Center, Five Year Plan for Israel's
Agriculture, 1964/65-1968/69, April, 1965, pp. 11 and
14.

17. Statistical Abstract of Israel, 1968, p. 312.

18 Calculated from data of Central Bureau of
Statistics.

19.   Zussman, op. cit., p. 5.

20.   Statistical Abstract of Israel, 1968, pp. 241 and 353.

21.   Ibid., p. 353.

22.   Ibid.

23.   Ibid.

24.   Ibid., p. 241.

25.   Mundlak, op. cit., p. 76.

26.   Ibid., p. 78.

27.   FAO State of Food and Agriculture, 1968, pp. 176-77.

28.   Ibid.

29.   Ibid., pp. 178-79.

30.   Ibid.

31.   Mundlak, op. cit., pp. 104-05.

32.   Statistical Abstract of Israel, 1968, p. 213.

33.   Ibid., pp. 204-05.

34.   Verlinsky, op. cit., p. 13.

35.   Israel Agricultural and Settlement-Planning and Development Center, Agricultural Plan 1965/66, March, 1965, p. 88.   (In Hebrew.)

CHAPTER **4** AGRICULTURAL PLANNING IN ISRAEL

The dynamic growth of Israeli agriculture did not occur just by chance. It was the result of co-ordinated comprehensive planning. This chapter is concerned with a review and analysis of this agricultural planning.

DEVELOPMENT OF AGRICULTURAL PLANNING

Obviously there was no scope for national or regional planning in the prestate period. Planning was then limited to a village and farm basis. Planning on a larger scale began only after statehood, when it became necessary to expand domestic food production for the rapidly increasing population and to settle many new immigrants on the land. Economic efficiency as a long-range goal was secondary, and its requirements were not clear. This resulted in poor planning and unrealistic forecasts. Unforeseen surpluses of certain products started to appear as early as 1954.

The first development plan was made in 1950 by a Committee for Joint Agricultural Planning, composed of representatives of the Ministry of Agriculture and the Settlement Department of the Jewish Agency. Their proposals were published in a mimeographed book entitled The Settlement of the Land.[1]

It included a four-year plan for agricultural development for 1951-54. The basic assumptions were unrealistic, overestimating (1) the number of new immigrant settlements, (2) amount of water available for agriculture, and (3) number of agricultural laborers required; and they completely misjudged the

differences in food-consumption patterns of the new
immigrants. The plan did not foresee any substantive
departure from existing types of dairy and vegetable
farming, nor did it seriously analyze, on the basis
of relative costs, what to produce domestically or to
import from abroad.

In 1952, a permanent organization, the Joint
Planning Center, was established.* The first seven-
year plan prepared by the center to cover the 1953-60
period was completed in 1953. Its basic assumptions
were similar to those of the 1950 plan. As a result,
it was criticized by Israeli agricultural economists
as well as by foreign experts in the country. The
plan was, therefore, revised, and in 1956 a new four-
year plan was published for the rest of the period.
The new plan was based on the following more realistic
assumptions: (1) a slower development of water resources, (2) a slower population growth, and (3) a
greater increase in the consumption of proteins because of the rise in the standard of living. It was
also realized that self-sufficiency per se was not
good economics and that it would be more rational to
help ease the growing trade gap by increasing agricultural exports, such as citrus, in which Israel had
some degree of comparative advantage.

The new planning center was not only interested in formulating better plans but also in implementing them. The agricultural possibilities of every
village in the country were surveyed for this purpose,
and plans were prepared for the most efficient use of
available land and water. The survey was published
in 1955 as "The Balance of Land and Water."[2] Six basic model types of farms were established, each with
output, input, and income norms based on actual field
data. That is, the country was divided into types of
farming areas with allowances made for regional differences. The basic types of farms established in

---

*Now called Agriculture and Settlement-Planning
and Development Center, but still referred to as Joint
Planning Center.

this plan were as follows: (1) fully-irrigated dairy,
(2) semi-irrigated dairy, (3) citrus, (4) field crops,
(5) hill farms, and (6) mountain farms. These basic
types of farms continue with modifications to the
present. Plans were detailed for every village according to the following considerations: (1) outputs
consistent with the requirements of the master plan,
(2) the most economical use of water, (3) provision
of all-year-round employment for the farmer and his
family, and (4) attainment of farm incomes equal to
that of the average urban working family. Thus coordination between macro and micro planning was established.

Delays in the implementation of irrigation
works together with surpluses of farm products in 1959
necessitated a new development plan. A comprehensive
plan to cover the 1960-64 period was prepared. The
effectiveness of this plan can be judged by comparing
some of the 1964 forecasts with actual results as
shown in Table 13. The estimates of cultivated area
and value of agricultural exports were quite close to
the mark. There were, however, deviations for specific products, smaller in the case of citrus and dairy
than for field crops. These deviations reflect pur-
poseful changes in the annual implementation programs
of the plan introduced by the planning authorities in
response to current conditions as well as deviations
from program goals by the farmers.

A new five-year plan was promulgated for the
1964/65 to 1968/68 period in 1965. A review of this
plan is presented in a later section.

REVIEW OF AGRICULTURAL POLICY

Up to 1954, the main problem was the expansion
of agricultural production, and, as previously indicated, the principal policies adopted included a comprehensive system of food rationing and price controls
so that farmers could freely expand production without fear of adverse price reactions. With the appear-
ance of surpluses after 1954 and the worsening of the
terms of trade for the agricultural sector, the

policies changed to control of surpluses by production, marketing, and land utilization quotas.   Policies were developed on a selective branch or commodity
basis.   Subsidies are given to compensate for production controls on commodities in surplus, such as milk
and eggs, and to encourage the production of new commodities, such as cotton and fruit for export.   A
comprehensive system of price controls is also in effect that represents, for many products, income support for the farmer in terms of fixed or floor prices.
These price controls are also important in stabilizing the national cost-of-living index that is used to
regulate salaries in both the public and private sectors of the entire economy.   For some products, however (groundnuts, for example), forward prices are
used to encourage production.

TABLE 13

Agricultural Plan Forecasts and
Attainments, 1964

	Forecasts	Attainments
Total cultivated area (thousand dunams)	4,000	4,100
Area in citrus (thousand dunams)	365	406
Milking cow numbers (head)	70,000	65,000
Value of agricultural exports (thousand dollars)	104,000	97,321

Sources: Forecasts from Joseph Ben-David, Agricultural Planning and Village Community in Israel (
(Paris: UNESCO, 1964), pp. 34-35; attainments: total
cultivated area, citrus area, and value of exports,
Statistical Abstract of Israel, 1965, pp. 364, 366, and
261; cow numbers from 1965/66 Agricultural Plan, p. 86.

Branch Summary

Perhaps the easiest way to review so complicated
a subject is to summarize the principal policies on a
commodity and branch basis. Such a summary follows:[3]

1. <u>Poultry, eggs</u>. This branch has been in surplus for some time. Marketing and price
   controls have been imposed. Substantial
   subsidies are paid to farmers as compensation for these controls. These subsidies
   amounted to about 12.5 per cent of the price
   received by the farmer in 1965. A substantial amount of egg production has been diverted to export.

2. <u>Poultry, meat</u>. Limitation of production is
   the principal instrument of control. A
   stabilization fund conducted by the Poultry
   Board is used to clear surpluses by market-
   regulation techniques, such as storage, and
   to maintain a minimum floor price for producers. As of 1965, about 70 per cent of
   its funds were used for the first purpose,
   and 30 per cent for the second.

3. <u>Milk</u>. There are marketing quotas that have
   been ineffective for the branch as a whole
   since output has been below the quotas. Subsidies are paid on a per liter basis, and
   the sums involved are the highest for any
   branch in the agricultural sector. In 1965,
   they amounted to about one-quarter of the
   price received by farmers. Prices are controlled.

4. <u>Beef</u>. Beef, for the most part, is a by-
   product of the dairy industry. The feeding
   of bull calves accounts for most of the
   domestic supply. The level of supply is
   below that of demand, and the price controls
   are for consumer protection. Protection of
   domestic production is attained by regulation of tariff duties.

5. <u>Vegetables</u>. This branch is generally in surplus. Production is controlled by land quotas, and there are guaranteed minimum prices. The Vegetable Production and Marketing Board clears surpluses by diversion to industrial use and by destruction.

6. <u>Fruits, noncitrus</u>. Planning has been quite successful in this branch that has expanded rapidly in recent years. Production is controlled by licensing of plantings. The licenses are based on five-year demand forecasts. There have been occasional small surpluses that have been disposed of by diversion to industrial use.

7. <u>Fruits, citrus</u>. This is an export crop where prices are determined by the European market. Plantings are controlled by licensing based on demand and price forecasts.

8. <u>Industrial crops, sugar beets</u>. Farm quotas are assigned equivalent to the capacity of the two factories in the country. Local production has supplied approximately 30 per cent of the country's consumption requirements.

9. <u>Industrial crops, cotton</u>. Subsidies are tied to production controls. Subsidies are paid to gins to keep down the price of textiles to consumers.

10. <u>Industrial crops, groundnuts</u>. Forward prices are set to encourage production. Small subsidies are given to the branch.

This seeming myriad of agricultural controls is conducted in a rather efficient and sophisticated way, particularly in terms of the coordination of the various types of controls. For example, poultry farmers are provided amounts of concentrated feed at subsidized low prices that are based on the previous year's receipts for eggs marketed through officially

approved channels. This technique is used to rein-
force the marketing controls. Should a farmer wish
to sell more than his marketing allocation, he would
have to buy his concentrated feed at higher prices
and market through nonofficial channels, where prices
may be higher or lower than officially approved channels, depending on the economic situation at the time.
Such illicit sales have been generally uneconomic
over the long run.

Subsidies

The role of subsidies in Israel agricultural
policy is important. Table 14 indicates that subsidies are paid on a wide range of commodities and commodity groups. The largest amounts are paid on milk
and eggs, two of the more important products of
Israeli agriculture. The dairy, in particular, has
been traditionally the basis of the diversified intensive farm. The subsidies on milk and eggs alone
accounted for almost 60 per cent of the total subsidies on output in 1966. Special subsidies are also
paid to new settlements to guarantee farmers minimum
price levels as soon as they begin to market their
produce while their production costs are high. The
subsidies cover the differences between the market
prices and the guaranteed minimum prices. Output
subsidies declined from IL 102.3 million in 1964 to
IL 91.2 million in 1966, a decrease of about 10 per
cent.

In addition, farmers receive indirect subsidies
on inputs such as water, fertilizers, and feed. Farmers pay reduced prices to the suppliers who are reim-
bursed by the government. The government also makes
compensatory payments to farmers for losses from
frost and drought. Factor subsidies paid to farmers
rose from IL 22.9 million in 1964 to IL 43.6 million
in 1966. The increase from 1965 to 1966 was caused
by a drought that necessitated more water and purchased fodder. Direct drought compensation payments
also rose greatly in 1966.

The importance of these subsidies can be judged
in better perspective when they are compared to the

TABLE 14

Agricultural Subsidies, 1964/65 and 1965/66
(Millions of Israeli Pounds)

Commodity	1964/65	1965/66	Per Cent Increase or Decrease	
			Subsidies	Subsidy per Unit of Output
Eggs	25.0	24.0	− 3.7	+ 5.0
Poultry	5.5	1.7	− 69.6	− 72.4
Cow's milk	32.8	29.7	− 9.4	− 17.2
Beef	1.2	2.4	+100.0	+116.2
Ewe's milk	0.3	−−	−100	−100.0
Fish	2.4	0.5	− 79.2	− 72.3
Cotton	14.7	7.6	− 48.4	+ 55.3
Vegetables and potatoes	13.0	9.2	− 29.0	− 58.4
Fruit	2.3	2.8	+ 21.7	+ 9.3
Peanuts	2.1	2.4	+ 14.3	+ 14.3
Sugar beets	5.6	5.3	− 5.4	−−
Tobacco	0.3	0.5	+ 56.3	+ 39.6
Wheat	4.3	4.0	− 7.0	+ 34.0
Miscellaneous	0.4	0.3	− 25.0	−−
Subsidies by Jewish Agency Settlement Dept.	1.4	0.8	− 42.9	−−
Total subsidies on output	111.3	91.2	− 18.1	− 20.3
Fodder	19.2	25.5	+ 33.1	+ 10.0
Water	13.2	15.1	+ 14.6	+ 5.1
Fertilizers	2.9	3.0	+ 3.4	+ 3.1
Total factor subsidies	35.3	43.6	+ 23.5	+ 7.6
Drought and frost compensation payments	0.2	13.8	+590.0	−−
Total subsidies	146.8	148.6	+ 1.2	−−

Source: 1966 Bank of Israel Annual Report, p. 282.

values of output and national income originating in
agriculture. In terms of the value of agricultural
output at market prices, the subsidies amounted to
about 10 per cent in the three-year 1964-66 period.
They accounted for less than 20 per cent of the national income originating in agriculture and somewhat
above 25 per cent of the aggregate net income of farm
operators in the same period.

Although the subsidies are high for a country
in chronic financial difficulties, some perspective
may be obtained by comparisons with other countries.
The agricultural sector is subsidized in practically
all countries. Compared to a sample of European
countries, the situation in Israel does not seem ab-
normal. Expressed in terms of per cent of value of
total agricultural output, subsidies are higher in
Finland, Switzerland, United Kingdom, West Germany,
Sweden, and France and lower in Belgium, Netherlands,
and Denmark.[4]

There is considerable sentiment among economists
and officials in the Ministry of Agriculture to reduce
subsidies. The highest subsidies, those on milk and
eggs, were both substantially reduced from 1964 to
1966. Of the thirteen items shown in Table 14, subsidies were reduced on nine. The decrease in subsidy
per unit of output fell 6.3 per cent from 1964 to
1965 and 20.3 per cent from 1965 to 1966. Increases
in factor subsidies and drought compensation payments
resulted in the small increases in total subsidies of
slightly over 1 per cent each year in 1965 and 1966.

There is considerable opposition to the reduction of subsidies by both farmer and consumer groups.
This may be an important constraint to their drastic
reduction. The current five-year plan confirms this
by indicating that agriculture will continue to be
subsidized, with possible changes in the extent of
subsidy policy and its structure. The indications are
that the amounts of subsidies in terms of agricultural output and farm income will probably be reduced
with the continued increase in production.

Factor subsidies, though less than output subsidies, are an important part of agricultural policy. Of particular interest is the subsidy on water, the principal physical constraint to the growth of Israeli agriculture. A scheme designed to equalize the cost of water has received considerable consideration and has had the strong support of the Settlement Department of the Jewish Agency. The cost of water varies greatly in the country, from two cents per thousand gallons in the Jordan Valley to thirty-four cents per thousand gallons in the Negev uplands.[5] Although this scheme is very controversial and is strongly opposed by many government officials and fiscal and industrial economists, subsidies for water will probably continue to be high. This is an important support to the moshavim where water is particularly expensive in the South, and in the hills and mountains of the Jerusalem Corridor and the Galilee.

NATIONAL ECONOMIC PLANNING

National economic planning for the entire economy came much later than agricultural sectorial planning. The Economic Planning Authority was established in early 1962, and in July of that year they published a four-year development plan for the 1963/64 to 1966/67 period. The three main objectives of the plan were (1) continued rapid growth of the economy and large-scale absorption of immigrants, (2) the gradual reduction of the import gap in the balance of goods and services, and (3) the development of the Negev and Galilee. The growth aim was an annual increase of 10 per cent in real national product to enable the absorption of seventy thousand immigrants a year. The target for the reduction of the import surplus was from about $400 million in 1961 to about $250 million in 1966.[6]

The Division of Physical Planning in the Ministry of the Interior has prepared a series of national physical plans, the main purposes of which have been (1) to distribute the population more evenly over the

entire country, (2) to decrease the relative proportion of the population in the coastal plain, (3) to
further the social and economic autonomy of rural
regions by establishing regional and district centers,
and (4) to protect agricultural land against urban
encroachment. A major instrument in promoting these
objectives was the preparation of general maps for
optimal geographic distribution of the population.
In addition, development priority maps have been prepared in cooperation with the Economic Planning Authority. This division has also prepared proposals
for the communication network, location of industry,
and parks and nature reserves.[7]

The aims of these national plans were social
and political as well as economic: diffusion of the
population, integration of immigrants in new communities planned as integral parts of larger regional developments, and the establishment of new settlements
for security reasons. The forecasts of the national
economic plans have been too optimistic, especially
on the numbers of immigration and the reduction of
the import surplus. Subsequent corrections have been
made in a new draft of a 1965 to 1970 five-year plan.
Although not all the proposals of the national plans
have been adopted, there has been a considerable
amount of coordination between national economic and
physical planning and planning for the agricultural
sector, particularly as regards the goals of agricultural planning, obtaining basic data from the national
planning bodies, and even in implementing agricultural plans, especially in regional planning and establishing new settlements.

AGRICULTURAL SECTORIAL PLANNING

Goals

The principal aims of agricultural planning are
delineated in the current five-year agricultural plan
as (1) promotion and stabilization of farmers' incomes, (2) improved efficiency of resource utilization
(3) establishment of new agricultural settlements.[8]
As in the national economic plans, these aims are social and political as well as economic.

The plan stresses raising farm income at a higher rate than that for the economy as a whole to close the income gap between farmers and urban workers. It also maintains that the pace of growth of incomes of farmers with less developed holdings should be faster than that for the better established farms. The main causal factor is expected to be the continued improvement of agricultural productivity.

Improved efficiency in resource utilization concerns the allocation of resources between agricultural and other sectors of the economy as well as among the various agricultural branches. These allocations are not decided by economic criteria alone. It is assumed that the place of agriculture in the national economy and its basic functions will not change in the period. Subsidies will continue at a lower level, and they will be used more as an aid to raise agricultural efficiency.

As to the allocation among branches, economic principles apply to those that have small subsidies or no price support. The production goals for these branches are planned at the level where market prices will be equal to the marginal costs of production. In highly subsidized branches deviations are recognized. As to the possibilities of foreign trade, the plan recognizes the need for stepping up production of products with a low-dollar exchange rate and slower development of those branches for which the dollar exchange rate is high. The plan stresses the role of increased productivity and new technology in improving resource utilization. The application of new technology depends on the maintenance of income levels and the constant development of the production units.

The plan does not make provisions for large-scale new settlement because of the limitations of additional resources for the agricultural sector and of the market demand for food, and because of the emphasis on raising farmers' existing incomes. It envisions some additional settlements, however, in the southern Negev and Galilee, mainly for reasons of national security.

Institutional Organization

The main national organizations involved in
planning and the implementation of planning are (1)
the Agricultural Planning Authority, (2) the Agriculture and Settlement-Planning and Development Center,
(3) the Production and Marketing Boards, (4) the National Water Council, and (5) the National Land
Authority.

The Agricultural Planning Authority was established by the Ministry of Agriculture in 1956. It
is composed of ministry officials, representatives
of the Jewish Agency, the National Water Council,
Land Authority, and other agricultural organizations,
including representatives of the settlements. The
Authority is responsible for all agricultural planning in the country: the extent of agricultural
production and the establishment of new settlements,
including the number and type.[9]

The executive arm of the Agricultural Planning
Authority is the Agriculture and Settlement-Planning
and Development Center. This center is responsible
for the preparation and publication of the national
plans and also has considerable responsibility for
their implementation. Its five main divisions and
principal functions are as follows:[10]

1. Production planning. Responsible for projections of production and means of production

2. Economic and statistical surveys. Responsible for economic analysis and price projections and policies

3. Detailed planning. Responsible for the im-
   mpelemtation of the national plan through
   the preparation of annual plans and the coordination of these plans with regional,
   branch, and settlement plans

4. Agricultural exports. Concerned with export
   market possibilities and their relation to
   production planning

5. Rural regional planning. Concerned with
   planning the type and location of agricultural facilities in the regions

The organizations chiefly concerned with the
planning and the control of supplies in the branches
are the branch production and marketing boards. As
of 1965, there were eleven such boards.[11] Their principal duties are (1) official representation of the
branch to the government, (2) planning production according to seasons, districts, and varieties to insure
the continuous and regular supply of the products of
the branch to local markets and industries and the diversion of potential surpluses to exports and other
uses, (3) organization of marketing, both local and
export, to equate supply with demand and to obtain a
fair average price to growers, (4) development of export markets, (5) improvement of the quality of produce, and (6) raising the professional standard of the
branch, principally by research and training.

The production and marketing boards use two
principal methods of operation: (1) actually consoli-
dating the marketing locally and/or abroad through
licensed contractors or agents and by making uniform
average returns to the producer, based on type and
quality of the produce and on the season in which it
is marketed but not related to the actual price received at any one market; and (2) dealing only with
the organization and direction of marketing, with
actual marketing operations carried out through normal trade channels. In the latter system, the boards
regulate markets through fixed or minimum prices,
equalization funds, and the diversion of market surpluses. Citrus, groundnuts, and cotton are examples
of the former type of operation, and vegetables,
milk and dairy products, fruit, and meat of the latter.

The actual organization of the boards include
all groups active in the branch: producers, marketing wholesalers, retailers, consumers, government
representatives, and industrial processors. Agricultural producers comprise at least one half of the
membership. These boards have legal status.

The National Water Council, Tahal, has extensive powers as regards agricultural planning through
its responsibility for developing the water sources
of the country. The National Land Authority holds
large reserves of land, and is responsible for their
land-use planning.

The regional and district offices of the Resettlement Department of the Jewish Agency and of the
Ministry of Agriculture together with settlement instructors and officers have considerable responsibility for planning and the implementation of plans at
the regional, settlement, and farm level.

Preparation, Forecasts, and Implementation
of National Agricultural Plans

The national agricultural plan was prepared in
four principal stages. The first stage involved col-
lecting the basic data, making economic surveys and
analyses, and preparing forecasts. The economic research covered such matters as the examination of the
dollar rate in tradeable outputs and inputs on the
international market and a comparison of alternative
production possibilities in the light of the main
goals of the plan. Forecasts were prepared of the production factors, local consumption, exports, and technological development. The second step was the
preparation of a preliminary production plan based on
the forecasts. The third step involved the preparation of the regional and agricultural branch plans,
the former in cooperation with the regional and district offices and the latter with branch planning
committees, including directors of the production and
marketing boards and directors of the specialized
branch and commodity divisions in the Ministry of Agriculture. These planning committees also helped in
the first preparatory stage. The final stage involved
adjusting the regional and branch forecasts and re-
vising the national production plan.

The implementation of the national agricultural
plan in effect amounts to an annual revision of the
plan in the light of new developments. Each year the
Planning Center makes a new master plan that includes

a review of the results of the previous year. It
also sets production goals for the coming year with
breakdowns by branch, region, and type of settlements,
and a further breakdown of cooperative settlements
between new (poststate) and old (prestate). These
branch, regional, and settlement goals are based on
consultations with branch committees and regional offices and include consideration of surveys of farmers' production intentions.

A basic frame of reference for micro planning
are the theoretical models of the different types of
farms. At present there are five principal models:
dairy, citrus, field crops, mountain, and hill farms.
These models, based on actual field data, include all
details of outputs, inputs, investments, and income.
They show what can actually be accomplished by an
average farmer. The net incomes are calculated to be
approximately equal for all types of model farms. A
more detailed adaptation of these archetypes to the
different regions necessitates a wide range of variations. In fact, the Joint Planning Center uses about
twenty variations.[12] These models are frequently revised to reflect current conditions and the latest
technological developments. The net income goals for
the poststate moshavim for the 1965-70 period is IL
6,500.[13]

As a matter of fact, there is a fairly wide
disparity in net income among the poststate moshavim
according to type of farm and region. As of 1965,
net income varied from about IL 9,000 per family for
fully developed poststate dairy farms in the coastal
plain to an average of IL 3,500 for mountain farms
and IL 4,000 for hill farms.[14] Part of this was due
to the fact that the latter types of farms were newer. They were not as yet in full development, their
orchards had not started to yield, nor had they as
yet received their full input quotas and egg allotments.

One of the basic guides for the implementation
of the national plan on a regional and settlement
basis is the objective to reduce the income inequalities among regions and types of farms and between the

new and old settlements. Efforts are made to supply
new irrigation water to the areas where there is the
greatest need and where planned quotas have not as
yet been fulfilled, particularly in the South and
areas where the cost of water is expensive. A major
part of the additional and unused marketing quotas
for eggs are assigned to the mountain and hill farms.
This is in accordance with the principle of comparative advantage. These farms are not the most efficient for poultry, but their efficiency, because of
natural conditions, is even less in other branches.

The implementation of the agricultural plan
also tries to modify drastic income changes that might
occur among different types of settlements because of
changing economic conditions. For example, the efficiency of milk production and the economies of larger
herds have increased greatly in recent years.[15] The
amount of water required per cow decreased from 2,000
cubic meters in 1960 to 1,200 in 1965. This has been
a result of the change in the feed ration from the
1960 ratio of 70 per cent field fodder, grown mostly
under irrigation on the farm, and 30 per cent concentrated feed, mostly imported, to 44 per cent fodder,
and 56 per cent concentrated feed in 1965. In the
same five-year period the number of work days for a
cow and calf has dropped from fifty to thirty-five
because of increased mechanization. These new developments have meant that for the economy as a whole
it would be better to shift milk production more to
the kibbutzim and moshavim with larger herds. But
through the control of the marketing allotments this
shift is being made on a gradual basis to protect the
income position of the moshav and to allow for the
substitution of other enterprises in moshavim with
smaller herds.

The implementation of the national plan to the
settlement and farm level is carried out by the regional and district economic planners in consultation
with settlement officials. In the case of the moshav
olim, the amount of credit offered farmers by the
Jewish Agency through the regional purchasing associations is governed by the needs of the farm plan.
This control is not perfect. Some farmers are able

to obtain additional credits from other sources and
thus change their farm plans. On the whole, however,
the implementation at the settlement level has been
effective.

In summary, neither the agricultural plan at
the national level nor its implementation at the regional, branch, and farm level is flawless. Planning,
nevertheless, has been effective. The national plans
are now worked out with considerable economic sophis-
tication, and much ingenuity has been shown in their
implementation to insure coordination of macro and
micro planning. At the national level, branch protection by the production and marketing boards and
the favoring of local products against competing imports have slowed adjustments. Yet the pace of the
adjustments has been quite rapid. The use of historical bases in marketing and production controls has
worked against the new settlements for some products.
Unused quotas, however, are given new settlements,
and additional quotas have been diverted, to a large
degree, to the new moshavim. On the whole, the efforts to maintain continual growth of output in the
agriculture sector, to improve its efficiency by increased specialization and the adoption of improved
technology, and to make viable the different types of
new moshavim diffused throughout the country are a
credit to the economic planning of the agricultural
sector in Israel.

LAND TENURE

The land-tenure system has been of particular
importance in the development of the cooperative sector of Israeli agriculture and has served as a subsidy
for the development of the poststate settlements, including the new moshavim. The nationalization of
land that effectively controls its use is an actual
achievement in Israel, not a nominal, political gambit
as in many developing countries. Of the total area
of Israel, 94.5 per cent belongs to the National Land
Authority, set up in 1959 to administer all the lands
formerly under the authority of the Jewish National
Fund and the State.[16] Taking into account only farmed

area, the proportion of privately owned land increases to 20 per cent.[17]   The National Land Authority
owns almost all the land reserves in the country.

The origin of public ownership of land goes
back to the establishment of the Jewish National Fund
by the World Zionist Congress. The purposes were essentially pragmatic. The first was to insure that
colonists who settled on land acquired by public fund
used it for making a living and not for speculation.
The second was to prevent the reversal of land
acquired by Jews to non-Jews. The Fund, therefore,
distributed the land in 49-year leases that were renewable and inheritable. The lease could be invalidated if the lessee did not settle on the land and
work it properly or if he hired non-Jewish labor.
Security was an important factor for awarding leases
to some form of cooperative or collective groups, as
protection of individual private farms was impracti-
cal.

Public ownership and administration of land
represents an important subsidy to settlers. Under
the Fund, after the settler acquired his lease the
average agricultural rent was fixed at approximately
2 per cent of the value of the holding.[18]   Until the
settler acquired his lease, that is, until the settlement is released from the administration of the
Settlement Department of the Jewish Agency, the land
is rent free. Before statehood the elimination of
rent made it easier for the Jewish farmer to compete
with the Arabs. After statehood, the rent-free system served as an incentive to attract people to agriculture. It also facilitated directing settlers to
areas that were important from a political or strategic point of view, though they may not have been
the best in agricultural terms. The rent subsidy
served as an equalizing scheme similar to water and
marketing subsidies.

The results of the nationalization of land have
been (1) farmers and settlements on national land are
in secure possession of their land and are as interested in the improvement of their farms as settlers on
private lands, (2) the land is alloted to the farmer

in equal proportions, the size varying with requirements of cultivation, (3) the use of the land is controlled, (4) rent-free land has been a subsidy to
new settlements to help equalize their economic position, and (5) it has reduced the cost of the development of cooperative settlements, particularly the
moshav, the most important type of poststate settlement.

There has also been a coexistence of nationalization of land with a significant private sector in
agriculture. Nationalization of land and the result-
ing economic and social benefits in the cooperative
sector have had considerable influence on improving
social and economic conditions for agricultural workers in the private sector.

SUMMARY AND CONCLUSIONS

This review of agricultural planning reveals
that it has been an important exogenous factor in the
success of the moshav in Israel, particularly the
postwar moshavim. Of particular importance is the
complete coordination of macro planning for the agricultural sector, the branches, and the regions, and
micro planning at the settlement and farm level. An
important purpose of the agricultural planning is to
assign adequate resources and sufficient output quotas
where there are production and marketing controls to
make the new moshavim viable in all parts of the
country and to approach the goal of equalizing net
income from the farm with the income of industrial
labor in the city. In addition, new branches of agriculture are being developed that are particularly
suited to the moshavim, and considerable effort is
being expanded to improve productivity. The planning
also includes free rents, equalization schemes for
water, and price subsidies. This is all consistent
with the goal of closing the income gap between the
prestate and poststate moshavim by increasing the income of the latter at a faster rate.

The nationalization of land has also been important to the success of the moshav. In the first

place, it has greatly reduced the cost of the development of the poststate moshavim. One of the more
important blocks to the functioning of land reform in
many countries has been the dissipation of public
funds in buying land from the owners, sometimes at
artificially high market prices. At the time of the
establishment of the State, the Jewish National Fund
had brought, at relatively low prices, 942,000 dunams
of mostly unimproved land for agricultural use.[19]

Not only has the nationalization of land been
an important factor, lowering the costs of the development of the settlements, but also public control
has set up the following basic conditions favorable
for the development of the moshav: (1) long-term
leases that are renewable and inheritable and contain
provisions for land use, (2) equality of holdings,
and (3) low levels of rent.

Many economists, particularly American-trained
Israeli agricultural economists, find many features
of the agricultural planning and the land tenure system objectionable. Professor Mundlak of Hebrew
University, as a result of his study on long-term projections of supply and demand for agricultural products in Israel, has claimed that agriculture in Israel
can function efficiently without government intervention and that the policy of intervention can be largely dispensed with. He considers this desirable, on
general principles, and practicable. On the problem
of land and water allocations, he stated that:

> The . . . problem [of] equating the mar-
> ginal contribution of resources among the
> various farms . . . is a rather difficult
> goal to achieve in the institutional
> framework of Israel agriculture. The dif-
> ficulty arises because land and water are
> not purchased in the free market but are
> allocated in fixed quantities to farmers.
> Since there are interfarm differences in
> efficiency, rigid allocation of small re-
> sources does not result in equal marginal
> contribution of resources. Consequently
> there would be a gain in output if

> redistribution of resources were allowed
> to take a place. This, of course, may
> violate the accepted notion that there
> should be equal distribution of resources
> resulting in equal distribution of income
> in agriculture. . . . Strict adherence to
> such a notion would require allocation of
> more of the resources to the less efficient
> farms so that the additional resources
> would compensate for their inefficiency.
> The absurdity of such a possibility only
> reflects the operational inappropriateness
> of the concept. If this is recognized,
> then one cannot escape the question: why
> not allow resources to flow to the more
> efficient farms?[20]

As a result of the analysis of a sample of
well-established moshavim and kibbutzim, Dr. Sadan,
a member of the Department of Agricultural Economics
of Hebrew University, concluded that the value of
the marginal product of land in the family farm in
the moshav exceeds the corresponding value in the
kibbutz and that the value of the marginal product
of labor in the kibbutz is higher than the labor market price level, which is still higher than the value
of the marginal product of labor in the moshav.[21] He
believes that specialization has been closing the
gaps. He suggested as policy measures that the self-
labor clause in the contracts between the land agency
and the settlers be eliminated, that rent could become instrumental in the distribution of land among
the various kibbutzim and moshavim, and that arrangements for transfer of land within the moshavim, at
least on a temporary basis, be made legal.[22]

Mundlak's policy suggestion on the elimination
of price and production controls would benefit the
older, better-established farms at the expense of the
newer ones. They would be in a better position to
make the adjustments to take advantage of market opportunities. His suggestions for elimination of price
and production controls and for redistribution of
land and water rights along with Sadan's suggestion
of a free market on labor would imply an exodus of

settlers from poorer villages and regions. This
would entail the economic burdens of finding new jobs
for displaced farmers and would result in the concentration of agriculture in fewer and larger producing
units.

Their evaluations and policy recommendations
are based on economic criteria only and completely
overlook the social and political goals of agricultural policy as well as the deeply ingrained economic, social, and political ideologies in the country.
Agricultural planning has been rationally based on
social and political ends as well as economic ones.
This dictates a diffusion of population throughout
the country, the necessity for a large number of
small, intensive family-sized farms, and support of
the postwar moshavim with a view to making them economically viable and as efficient as possible.

NOTES

1.   In Library of Settlement Study Center,
Rehovot.   (In Hebrew.)

2.   In Library of Settlement Study Center,
Rehovot.

3.   Adopted from an interview with Mr. Gad
Jacoby, Director of the Agricultural and Settlement-
Planning and Development Center of the Ministry of
Agriculture, and some of his principal staff assis-
tants.

4.   Haim Darin-Drabkin, "Aspects of Agricultural Planning in Western European Countries and the
USSR" (paper presented to International Symposium on
Role of Cooperative Organization and Rural Development, Tel-Aviv, March, 1965), p. 3.   (Mimeographed.)

5.   Raanan Weitz, "The Economies of Water Supply in the National Economy" (unpublished manuscript
in Settlement Study Center, Rehovot, November, 1964),
p. 4.   (Mimeographed.)

6. Benjamin Akzin and Yehezkel Dror, _Israel_, _High Pressure Planning_ (Syracuse, N.Y.: Syracuse University Press, 1966), pp. 72-73.

7. _Ibid._, p. 62.

8. _Five-Year Plan for Israel's Agriculture_, 1964/65-1968/69, 99. 9-10.

9. Haim Darin-Drabkin, "The Main Aspects of Agricultural Planning in Israel" (paper presented to International Symposium on The Role of Cooperative Organization in Rural Development, Tel-Aviv, March, 1965), p. 14. (Mimeographed.)

10. Information based on interview with Dr. Yehuda Landau, Director, Division of Rural Regional Planning.

11. For the following branches: (1) citrus, (2) groundnuts, (3) eggs and poultry, (4) cotton, (5) flowers, ornamental plants, and bulbs for export only, (6) vegetables, (7) fruit, (8) milk and dairy products, (9) beef and mutton, (10) wine grapes, and (11) tobacco. From Yaacov Berger, "Production and Marketing Boards for Agricultural Branches" (lecture prepared for Settlement Study Center, Rehovot, un-dated), p. 2. (Mimeographed.)

12. Weitz, _Agriculture and Rural Development in Israel: Projection and Planning_, p. 87.

13. Ranaan Weitz, "Future Administration of the Moshav" (summary of presentation to the Agricultural Center, Jerusalem, 1965), p. 2. (Mimeographed, in Hebrew.)

14. From files and interviews with Dr. A. Sklanevic, Director of the Division of Detailed Plan-ning, Agriculture and Settlement-Planning and Develop-ment Center.

15. _Ibid._ All the following dairy statistics are from the files of Mr. Sklanevic.

16.   Safran, op. cit., p. 61.

17.   Ibid.

18.   A. Bonne, "Nationalization of Land in Israel, A Successful Approach to Land Tenure in a New Society" (paper delivered to International Study Group on Problems of Individual and Group Settlement, Tel-Aviv, April–May, 1956), p. 3.   (Mimeographed.)

19.   Bonne, op. cit., p. 6.

20.   Mundlak, op. cit., p. 19.

21.   Ezra Sadan, "Agricultural Settlements in Israel, A Study in Resource Allocation" (unpublished Ph.D. dissertation, Department of Economics, University of Chicago, 1962), p. 55.

22.   Ibid., p. 57.

CHAPTER **5** ORGANIZATION, OPERATION,
AND DEVELOPMENT OF
MOSHAV OVDIM

This chapter is primarily concerned with the
moshav ovdim, particularly the prestate villages established before May, 1948. Some of the poststate
moshavim founded by Israelis and immigrants from
Western Europe, North America, and British Commonwealth countries have been similar in structure,
function, and character of settlers to the prestate
moshav. The majority, the moshvei olim, were not.
(The organization, operation, and development of the
moshav olim is presented in Chapter 6.)

STRUCTURE AND OPERATION OF MOSHAV SETTLEMENT

The structure and function of a moshav settlement is indicated in Figure 1. The chart presents a
generalized picture, as no two moshavim are exactly
alike. The moshav may have from fifty to one hundred
and fifty farmsteads, with possibly eighty as an average.[1] There are two types of members: the farming
members and the professionals who operate the village
services and are entitled to auxiliary farms. The
latter, on the average, constitute about 20 per cent
of the farming population.[2]

The chief administrative institution of the
village is the general assembly that meets about
every four to six weeks. Every member has one vote
in this village forum. The most important meeting is
the annual general meeting that considers the balance
sheet of the previous year, the budget of the coming
year, the reports of the executive committee and various special committees, and decides on matters of

FIGURE 1

Organization of a Moshav Ovdim

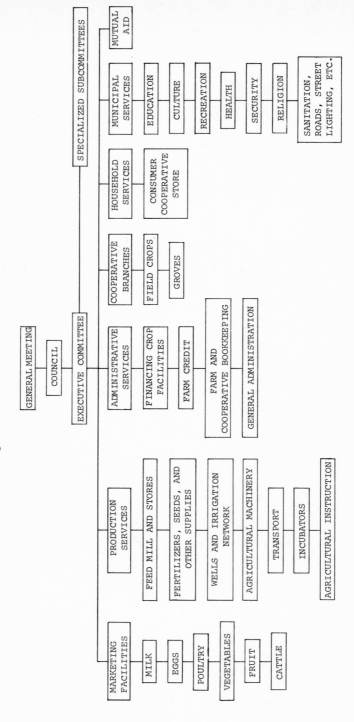

principle and future policy. The assembly elects a
council of eighteen to twenty-five members and the
executive committee or secretariat of five to nine
members, which is responsible for the current administration of all the affairs of the moshav. The
secretariat includes the accountant, treasurer, and
internal and external secretaries. The latter two
are the only farming members paid for their administrative work. Their jobs are full time, and their
farms are worked by hired labor during their period
of service.

Thus the most important problems of policy are
considered at the village assembly, while daily problems are handled by the council and executive committee. The executive committee is assisted by the
various special committees elected by the general assembly. These special committees act in the nature
of advisory bodies to the executive for the principal
functions of the settlement. There are usually special committees for control, education, cultural affairs, mutual aid, judicial affairs, and membership.
There are agricultural committees for each branch.

The executive committee meets weekly to deal
with the current affairs of the moshav. Problems of
greater importance may be referred to the council,
which deals with appeals against decisions of the executive committee. Appeals against decisions of the
village council may be brought to the general assembly. The general assembly meets when called by the
village council or when demanded by a certain percentage of members of the village.

The village cooperative performs seven principal functions: marketing, production, administrative,
household and municipal services, management and operation of cooperative production branches, and mutual
aid.

Almost all of the moshavim market their products
through the national marketing cooperative, Tnuva.
First-stage marketing operations are carried on in the
village. The types and extent of the facilities depend on the commodities produced in the village, the

amounts produced, and whether the facility services
other villages. Milk is weighed, cooled, and strained
in the cooperative receiving station, and in the better villages it is shipped to the town pasteurizing
plant by tanker and by others in cans. There may be
an egg storage facility. Grading is done by the
farmer himself, or the eggs are sold on a weight basis. The cooperative grades live poultry. There are
usually cold storage and grading facilities for fruits
and vegetables. Fruits, other than citrus, and vegetables are sold by the box. Citrus packing is now
generally concentrated in regional packing stations
owned by the national cooperatives. Cattle is often
sold through private channels, but usually by the
village cooperative.

Farmers purchase practically all their production materials from the village cooperative that keeps
stores of fodder, fertilizers, seeds, building materials, irrigation and other equipment, as well as
articles for repair of buildings and machinery. One
of the most important production services is the feed
mill. Most of the veteran cooperatives mix their own
feed. In many cases, the cooperative owns and maintains its water works and is responsible for the maintenance of the village irrigation system. Farmers
usually have their private tractors in the better
villages. There is a machine-tractor station, operated by the cooperative for heavy and specialized
equipment that is rented to farmers, as well as a
repair facility for farm equipment and private cars.
The transportation pool for trucks is important in
effecting economies in both marketing and purchasing.
Most settlements maintain an incubator service and
select the poultry breeding stock. Many have specialized farm instructors, often for fruits or dry farming, on a full- or part-time basis. Maintaining herd
books and production records is an important central
function. In addition, the cooperative may have a
communal service for control of diseases and pests
and for pruning trees of the individual farms.

Many of the cooperatives engage in communal
farming, most commonly on the unirrigated farm plots
where grains and hay are raised. The contiguous farm

plots are worked collectively as a unit for the entire
village. There is some common production for irrigated crops, particularly orchards. Plantations may
be planted in one plot by the whole village and
worked by the cooperative, at least until the trees
start bearing fruit. The cooperative may organize
irrigated pasture for the young stock to alleviate
overstocking of farms and may also arrange for communal herding of cattle on nearby natural pastures.

The administrative services are important. This
includes financing the cooperative facilities and
credit for farmers. One of the most important deter-
minants of the success of the village is the success
of the cooperative in handling its credit arrangements with farmer members. Strict control is necessary to avoid financial difficulties. Farmers must
market through the village cooperative, or debts will
pile up and turn into frozen debts. The village cooperative society acts as a banker. It receives
credit from supporting institutions and passes it on
to members based on need. Short-term credit must be
evolved quickly in the form of agricultural products
for sale and should not be used for longer-term investments. The banking system is geared to the cooperative setup of Israel agriculture.

The cooperative society keeps a unified account
of its own financial activities as well as separate
accounts for each individual member. The basic pattern of bookkeeping is prescribed by the audit union
to which each settlement belongs. Most cooperatives
give their members a monetary account of their transactions through the cooperative. The cooperative is
obliged by law to publish a yearly balance sheet of
its activities, which is audited by its audit union.

The credit arrangements operate in the following manner. Farmers obtain all their perquisites from
the cooperative stores on credit. These items are
charged to the farmers' accounts, and the farmers are
credited with the money received from their products.
The farmers' monthly balance sheets showing all credit
and debit entries give the details of their financial
position. If the farmer has a credit, he is free to

use his money as he likes, while a deficit in the
balance will be carried over to the account for the
next month.

If the farmer wishes additional credit for new
investments he applies to the executive committee.
If granted, it is not in the form of a loan for a
specified period but as additional credit on his current account. The rate of interest for the credit
has generally been lower than that charged by other
institutions. Other financial services provided by
the cooperative may include mutual fire insurance and
mutual livestock insurance.

A description of the functions of the three
most important administrative officers of the settlement follows.

The external secretary represents the moshav in
its contacts with supporting institutions such as
banks, settlement institutions, purchasing and supply
organizations, marketing organizations, etc. Within
the village he allocates internal credits to members
and to its joint undertakings. He works closely with
the accounting department and must be informed on the
business affairs of the cooperative and its members.
His responsibility includes checking that no members'
liabilities on current accounts and short-term loans
be allowed to go beyond a certain critical per cent
of annual turnover to prevent the accumulation of
frozen debts. He must balance the liabilities of the
cooperative according to the yearly plan.

The internal secretary manages the network of
the internal services of the village cooperative society. He handles the members' problems and the
proper functioning of the committees concerned with
economic and municipal affairs. He keeps a detailed
monthly record of the livestock inventory of the village and farm production plans, checking what is actually cultivated against the plans.

The main duties of the chief accountant are to
see that his department operates efficiently and that
the regular reports to the moshav management and its

members are prepared in time, not more than two months
after the event. He is responsible, in cooperation
with the settlement management, for drawing up the estimated income and expenditure budgets for the forthcoming period and to see that proper controls are
exercised on their implementation. His records indicate which holdings are not functioning economically
and which are not marketing their produce through the
cooperative. He is also responsible for seeing that
complete and correct records are kept of services and
stocks.

General administration, made up of daily business and contacts between the village cooperatives and
their members and the supporting institutions with
which the cooperative deals, is a heavy load for the
cooperative management. Despite the fact that production and consumption are on a family basis, the moshav
represents a closely integrated operation with frequent contacts among members and between members and
management.

The principal household service other than mutual aid is the consumer cooperative store in which
household shopping is done.

A large measure of economic security is given
by the mutual aid service. This provides emergency
help in case of sickness or other causes that prevent
the farmer or his wife from working their farm. Mutual help insures a fair subsistence level to members
at all times in case of hardship. There is no fore-
closure of mortgages or bankruptcy in a moshav. The
community stands by its members at all times.

Education is the most important of the municipal
functions. It extends from the nursery through kindergarten, elementary school, and high school. The
better moshavim pride themselves on their educational
facilities. The government provides but one year of
kindergarten. Some moshavim provide as many as three
years, including nursery school. They frequently
supplement the government stipend for teachers. All
educational services are free. Some of the moshavim
include high schools, often shared with other villages.

The education committee arranges for scholarships.
In some villages up to three years in high school are
provided free, and the family pays for the fourth
year. The education is a compromise between vocational agriculture and general education; however,
special emphasis is placed in the curriculum on agricultural values. Students may choose between a
general course and an agricultural course. The education committee also arranges for adult education
courses.

Cultural services usually include performances
and lectures that take place in the village hall.
Recreational activities include a cinema, swimming
pool, sports programs, and other organized youth and
adult activities.

Ordinary municipal functions, such as street
lighting, road building and maintenance, sanitation,
etc., are also administered by the cooperative. The
moshav is recognized by the government as a municipality responsible for its government and municipal
functions.

The moshav has autonomous judicial powers on a
local level. A local judge functions as a justice
of the peace and adjudicates conflicts among members
as well as between individuals and village authorities. There are regular channels of judicial appeal
for conflicts not settled at the local level.

The services provided by the cooperative are
paid by the farmers in three ways: (1) deducting fees
from sales, (2) adding fees to the expenditures for
supplies and services, and (3) imposing direct taxes.
The latter is uniform for all farms. Costs differ
widely from one moshav to another, depending on the
number of farms in the village and the amount and
efficiency of the services performed. In well-
organized villages costs of services represent 11 to
15 per cent of annual sales.[3] Absolute costs of services are highest in the best developed villages.
They are relatively the lowest, however, when compared to value of output per farm.

A comparison of the structure and function of
the moshav with its four basic ideological principles
shows the following: (1) settlement on national land-
operative; (2) use of cooperatives whenever possible
--with minor exceptions, operative; (3) mutual aid-
operative; (4) no paid labor on family farms--only
partially operative. Use of hired labor is an academic matter because of the general conditions of
full employment. The well-established, better moshavim have a small pool of paid labor whose members
are distributed to the farms as needed. They are
utilized during emergency periods. Members must obtain permission of the cooperative to use hired labor
as well as to work for salary outside the village.
In the past, at the request of the government, the
older moshavim have hired immigrant labor for agricultural training. Most of the common labor in the
village services is hired.

FARMING IN THE MOSHAV

The layout of farms in the moshav has evolved
to increase the efficiency of agricultural operations.
In the first moshav, Nahalal, the individual plots
project back of the houses, which are arranged in a
large circle. The municipal buildings such as the
school and assembly hall, the buildings housing the
centralized technical and business facilities, and
houses and small plots for the permanently employed
workers are located in the center of the circle. All
farm houses face a circular road that connects them,
and other roads cross the inner circle to connect the
circular road with the communal buildings.

There is great variance in the planning of each
moshav. The trend has been away from having the entire farm directly behind the homestead. There may
be six to eight dunams connected with the homestead,
while the rest of the land is in one or more parcels
within a large block of homogenous soil, thus safe-
guarding the equality of land for farmers and making
the planning of proper crop rotations and collective
cultivation activities requiring heavier equipment
easier.

A fundamental matter is the extent to which the moshav as a cooperative has contributed to the success of the individual members as farmers. The principal purposes of the cooperative society have been to bring the economic advantages of scale to a group of small farmers by helping farmers in their farm planning and in the implementation of their plans by improving agricultural practices, developing improved breeds of livestock, and by freeing the time of farmers from nonfarming activities so that they can devote most of their time to farming and increasing output on their plots.

The economies of joint buying and joint sales and the use of pooled transportation for those operations are obvious. The economy of farm storage to obtain market-price advantages is also obvious. The operation of village milk-cooling facilities, tank trucks, and incubators at cost made possible the rapid growth of the livestock industry in these settlements when it was most profitable in the decades of the 1940's and 1950's. Animal breeding was largely controlled by the cooperative, which supervised insemination services and owned bull stations. These services, which resulted in higher output and incomes, have since been transferred to regional organizations. The cooperative has been responsible for the rationalization of a better poultry branch by selecting breeding stock and by scheduling the incubator service to fit with farmers' production plans. The village feed mill has been one of the most important services in developing the livestock branches. It has not only made it possible to obtain feed from supporting cooperative institutions at lower prices, but also it has enabled producing better mixes at lower costs. Savings obtained in the management of the village irrigation system and in the collective operation of the communal dry-farming enterprise are also obvious.

The value of the cooperative services depends, to a large degree, on the efficiency of their operation which, in turn, frequently depends on the amount of business transacted. Savings have been the economic rationale for villages combining to use

cooperative services and in the formation of regional cooperatives. An economist of the Ministry of
Agriculture, who has specialized in the analysis of
the organization of the cooperative services, has
concluded that even where the absolute costs of cooperatives services have been high they were justified from an economic point of view. They made it
possible for the farmers to concentrate entirely on
production, which enabled output to rise. High expenditures on services were then low in relative
terms when compared to total output.[4]

In the well-established moshavim the individual
farmers are responsible for making their production
plans. There are, however, numerous constraints.
First of all, there are production and marketing allotments for a number of commodities. These quotas
are distributed to the village and by the village
executive committee to the individual farmers. The
village cooperative thus coordinates national and
local planning. In this respect, it carries out policies dictated by national interests, even when they
may be against the settlers' short-term interests.

The individual farmer also may not be able to
raise products for which there are no village first-
stage marketing facilities and for which he may have
difficulty obtaining credit outside the village cooperative. For some products, however, such as beef
and grains, there are no production limitations. Thus
while the farmers have complete freedom on how to manage and operate their farms, there are fairly stand-
ardized types of farms within the village as a result
of the production and marketing constraints. With the
development of the settlement, however, different
types of farms have evolved, some much more intensive
than others. To some degree, this has been dictated
by the amount of family labor on the farm, as the
basic farm unit must remain intact. It cannot be
subdivided or enlarged unless there is a complete reorganization of the standard size of farm for the village as a whole. In many of the established villages
two-family farm units are common, and two or sometimes
more farms are farmed as a unit when operated by family members. This allows for more intensive cultivation on some farms than others.

In the older, well-established moshavim assistance is given farmers not only in auxiliary services, but in actual farm planning and management. Physical output/input norms and income norms are available for all farm branches. The income norms are also calculated on a man-day and cubic meter of water basis for all branches. Thus the basic data are available for the farmer to make his budget and plans for the farm. In addition, the cooperative keeps herd books and production records of cattle and poultry and marketing records of all commodities. Farm instructors, either members of the village or supplied by the agricultural extension service, help with the improvement of farm practices and with the keeping of farm records to aid in the choice of enterprises and to appraise the profitability of combinations of enterprises.

It has been indicated in Chapter 3 that the average net income for the veteran moshavim in 1965 has been estimated at from IL 9,000 to 10,000 per year. The economic research unit of the Histadrut estimates it at IL 10,000. The Settlement Department of the Jewish Agency is somewhat more conservative, estimating it at IL 9,000. In any event, this income cannot be calculated on an objective statistical basis. The annual reports to the audit union are not useful, as not all output and sales are completely reported.

This income estimation is on a farm basis. There are two or more families on many farms. Other farms may not be worked intensively because of the age of the operator, or may be worked by the cooperative itself on an interim basis, or may even not be worked at all for members who are on leave from the village on government or institutional jobs. In many instances, farmers have off-farm incomes that can be quite substantial. Thus many farms are really part-time farms.

Although the moshav does not try to equalize incomes of its members, it attempts to limit extreme variations in standards of living. It assigns each member plots, equal in size and/or quality. The prohibition of hired labor may also be a factor, although

this regulation was relaxed in the early 1950's in
deference to the special needs of mass immigration
and to the necessity for rapid increase in farm production. Also, the mutual aid service, provided by
the cooperative society in cases of illness and other
emergencies, places a floor on members' incomes.

Yet there is a sizeable variation of farm income within the villages. An accurate measurement
of this may be seen from the results of a tabulation
of the frequency distribution of net farm income for
1954, based on a random sample of 189 farms in fifteen villages. The sample also included middle-class
moshavim and can be considered representative of the
income situation of moshavim in the entire country at
that time. The results shown in Table 15 indicate
variations ranging from a net loss in two farms, only
1 per cent of the population, to an average of IL
14,000 to 14,999, representing 2 per cent of the population. The average for the sample as a whole was
IL 4,873 or $2,707.

There are no objective national statistics data
on the size distribution of income in established
moshavim in more recent years. There is a plethora
of data, however, indicating that the spread is large
and might even be increasing.

The distribution of gross income in current
prices for 1964 in one of the most successful of the
prestate moshavim was as follows:*

---

*Figures obtained from moshav accountant. These
gross income figures represent value of sales less
current expenses for production materials and services
except depreciation of current assets and income, old
age, and employment security taxes.

Israeli Pounds	Number of Farms
Up to 9,999	5
10,000 - 19,999	10
20,000 - 29,999	4
30,000 - 39,999	11
40,000 - 49,999	14
50,000 - 59,999	10
60,000 - 69,999	9
70,000 and over	13
Total	76

In these examples the lower-income levels may merely represent income from part-time farming, and in the upper-income levels the farm may include two or more families. On a per capita or family basis the variation in family incomes is considerably less than that shown by the figures. In the village figures for 1964, the five farms with incomes under IL 10,000 represent farms where the heads of families do not live on the farms but occupy public service posts. The income shown represents their share of the proceeds from the collective cultivation.

Available statistics indicate that income variations within the villages is greater than that among the villages. In a 1961 farm-income study based on a random sample of fifty-four farms from five moshavim, Lowe showed that the variability of net income expressed as index numbers with the average farm in each village equal to 100 was as follows:[5]

Village	1	2	3	4	5	Average All Villages
Average farm	100	100	100	100	100	100
Best farm	164	232	196	156	311	218
Worst farm	26	21	39	35	49	36

A comparison of the variation in net income of the average farm in each village with the average for all five villages, again expressed in index numbers, was as follows:[6]

Village	1	2	3	4	5	Average
Average farm	100	98	86	50	163	100

TABLE 15

Frequency Distribution of Net Family Incomes
on Moshav Farms, 1954

Level of Income, Israeli Pounds	Number of Farms
Net loss	2
0 - 999	12
1,000 - 1,999	26
2,000 - 2,999	25
3,000 - 3,999	28
4,000 - 4,999	27
5,000 - 5,999	18
6,000 - 6,999	10
7,000 - 7,999	6
8,000 - 8,999	8
9,000 - 9,999	8
10,000 - 10,999	4
11,000 - 11,999	5
12,000 - 12,999	2
13,000 - 13,999	4
14,000 - 14,999	4
Average 4,873	Total 189

Source: Gershon Kaddar, "Family Farms in Cooperative Villages" (paper presented to FAO-sponsored
study group on Problems of Individual and Group Settlement, Tel-Aviv, April-May, 1956), Appendix, p. 15.
(Mimeographed.)

Within the five villages the variation in net
income from the best to the worst farms ranged from
11 to 1 to 4.5 to 1. Among the moshavim the average
net income in the best village was 3.3 times higher
than the average in the worst.

To what extent do veteran moshav farmers follow
economic rationality in the management of their farms?
How important is the factor of management in moshav
farms? How responsive is management to changes in

economic conditions? To what degree is the moshav
cooperative responsible for the improvement in management? Answers to these questions, at least as far
as a small sample of farmers in better than average
prestate moshavim are concerned, can be obtained from
a farm management analysis of sixty-six farms in six
villages for the period of 1954 through 1958.[7]

These farms were primarily devoted to livestock,
which represented 90 per cent of their total output,
about 35 per cent from cattle and 55 per cent from
poultry.[8] Their average size was about fifty dunams,
half of which was irrigated.[9]

The study estimated the effects of the various
inputs on production by fitting a Cobb-Douglas production function. The coefficients of the function
elasticities measuring the percentage change in output associated with a 1 per cent change in inputs,
are indicated in Table 16. If the farms operate under competitive conditions and adjust inputs to maximize profits, production elasticities represent the
proportion of the total output paid to each factor.
The results of the table may be interpreted as follows
At equilibrium or optimum point of output an increase
of 1 per cent in the use of raw materials is associated with an 0.58 per cent increase in output. The
explanation is similar for all other input factors.
The table indicates that 69 per cent of the total
output is attributable to capital inputs, mostly in
raw materials, and feeds for poultry and cattle.
About 11 per cent of the total output is attributable
to labor, and 20 per cent, the residual output, to
management.

The study then investigated whether farmers
adjusted their factors of production to the production
optimum--that is, whether the value of the marginal
product of each factor was equal to its respective
market price. Table 17 shows a close agreement between the value of marginal products and corresponding market prices. This indicates that the farmers
adjusted to market conditions, particularly by adjusting inputs to factor prices. There has been a gradual adjustment to the equilibrium point, particularly
in labor and raw materials.

TABLE 16

Estimates of Production Elasticities:
Selected Moshav Farms

Input	Elasticity
Capital	0.687
Value of cattle	0.005[a]
Value of livestock structures	0.100
Raw materials	0.582
Labor	0.115
Land	0.007[a]
Total for all inputs	0.795
Management (residual)	0.205
Total	1.000

[a]Not significant at the 20 per cent level. Other figures are significant at the 5 per cent level.

Source: Gershon Kaddar, "Family Farms in Co-
ooperative Villages" (paper presented to FAO-sponsored
study group on Problems of Individual and Group Settlement, Tel-Aviv, April-May, 1956), Appendix p. 18.
(Mimeographed.)

The study measured farmers' response to market
conditions directly in the case of the poultry branch.
It differentiated between the short-run response,
where some fixed factors limit the response, and the
long-run response, which takes into account changes
in the level of these factors. The short-run response is determined mainly by the price ratio of
product to feeds and the initial capacity of the
poultry runs. The short-run supply elasticities of
these two variables were 0.6 and 0.4.[10]

This indicates that a 1 per cent increase in
the price ratio of product to feeds, with the capacity
of runs being fixed, was associated with a 0.6 per
cent increase in the quantity produced within the
year.[11]

The short-run supply functions for both eggs
and poultry meat, indexes constructed so that the
geometric average of all the values is equal to one,

fluctuated greatly from one year to the next. The
indexes for eggs were as follows:[12]

1955	1956	1957	1958	1959
0.789	0.883	0.813	1.244	1.420

The figure of 0.789 in 1955 is a function of
the prices and capacity of poultry runs in that year
and indicates that the supply of eggs was nearly 79
per cent of the average amount that would have been
produced had prices and capacity remained constant.
The rise in productivity is an important factor in
the upward trend of the short-run supply function.
The high increases in 1958 and 1959, however, are also due to the elimination of price uncertainty through
an agreement signed in October, 1957, between the
government and marketing agencies.

TABLE 17

Value of Marginal Product and Factor Prices,
Selective Moshav Farms, 1954-58
(1954 IL per Factor Unit[a])

	Labor		Raw Materials		Livestock Structures	
	VMP[b]	Price	VMP[b]	Price	VMP[b]	Price
1954	3.02	4.75	1.16	1.06	0.29	0.27
1955	3.58	4.95	1.16	1.06	0.30	0.27
1956	4.36	5.75	1.16	1.06	0.30	0.27
1957	4.51	6.00	1.11	1.06	0.27	0.27
1958	5.12	5.97	1.05	1.06	0.28	0.27

[a]Factor units are as follows: for labor, man-days;
for other items, IL purchased.

[b]VMP = value of marginal product.

Source: Gershon Kaddar, "Family Farms in Cooperative Villages" (paper presented to FAO-sponsored
study group on Problems of Individual and Group Settlement, Tel-Aviv, April-May, 1956), Appendix, p. 20.
(Mimeographed.)

The long-run analysis traced the effect of changes in the level of production on capital production investments. When production increases at any given capacity, pressure is created to increase capacity. Until this is accomplished, there is a gap between available capacity and the desired one. The study estimated the closing of this gap at an annual rate of 50 per cent.[13] This means that if output goes up as a result of price changes, productivity increases, or removal of uncertainties, the capacity of the durable factors considered as fixed in the short-run would increase at a relatively rapid rate. An upward shift in capacity causes the short-run supply function to shift, and, therefore, at any given price output increased. This dynamic process of adjustment of output and capacity converged quickly in the case of poultry to a new equilibrium point where the long-run effect of a change in prices was 1.67 times as large as that of the short-run effect. If the short-run supply elasticity of price was 0.6, the long-run elasticity would be 1.0. Thus if the government price controls on eggs raised supply in the short-run by 50 per cent, its long-run effect would be an 83 per cent increase.[14]

Another important contribution of the study is the attempt to measure statistically the effect of management on production organization and output. Mundlak's sample showed that the most efficient farm produced 58 per cent more than the least efficient from a fixed bundle of resources.[15] Better management was also positively correlated with the use of more inputs. His coefficient for measuring management efficiency, therefore, was ten times higher in the best as compared to the least efficient farm in the sample.[16]

The wide variations in productivity of the farms in the sample were reflected in net incomes. Arranging 94 per cent of the farms in the sample (excluding the two farms with the highest and the two farms with the lowest incomes) the upper limit was seven times that of the lower limit. The analysis indicates that about half the range can be explained by management productivity effected in two ways: by obtaining more output per unit of input and through the use of more inputs.[17]

The sample on which this study was based was a subsample of the national sample used by the Falk Foundation Project in 1953/54. The average net farm incomes of this subsample in current Israeli pounds were as follows:

1954	1955	1956	1957	1958[18]
5,600	5,700	6,400	7,300	8,500

For the two subsequent years that were not included in the analysis, the average net farm incomes were: 1959, 6,600, and 1960, 8,900.[19] The average net income of the subsample in 1954 was 15 per cent higher than the average for the total sample of the 189 farms that was assumed to be representative of the veteran moshavim for the entire country.

The principal conclusions to be drawn from this study are that farmers in the better than average moshavim were quite rational in their farming operations, following the tenets of production theory in combining the factors of production to maximize returns, and they were responsive to the market situation. Management was isolated and measured as an important factor contributing to output and income. Despite the fact that the average farm income in the samples was high, there was a large variation among the farms. Although this study is somewhat dated, the conclusions are probably still valid for veteran moshavim.

To what extent did the moshav cooperative society contribute to the success of the farms in this study? It was precisely in livestock that the cooperative makes its greatest contribution to member farmers, supplying their most important item of expenditure, feed, at low cost. The incubator service, the village dairy, and the insemination service all played an important role in helping the farmers improve their incomes. One of the villages had a large unirrigated area in grain communally farmed.

The record service to farmers participating in
this study was also important in improving the performance of the farms. Farms began to keep records
for data not available in the cooperative books.
Farmers' records were returned to them in the form
of an annual report, including an analysis of the
profitability by branches compared to the previous
year and comparing actual working days to accepted
norms. The farm visits grew more and more into farm-
management instruction sessions.

DEVELOPMENT OF MOSHAV AS AN INSTITUTION

Relation of Success of Cooperative
to Success of Moshav

The present analysis is concerned with the assumption that the success of the moshav depends on
the success of its cooperative. This is central in
the development of the moshav as an institution. It
is believed by many, it is even accepted as dogma in
Israel, that a strong cooperative is synonymous with
a successful moshav. This assumption is examined
historically both for the established moshav ovdim
and the poststate moshav olim. The change in the
role of the cooperative is considered over time, with
some indications as to possible developments in the
future.

The moshav is a dynamic institution constantly
evolving with changing economic and social conditions. The role of the cooperative has evolved with
the development of the moshav and is quite different
in the moshav olim than in the moshav ovdim, is quite
different now in the moshav ovdim than it was in the
past, and it may well be quite different in the future.

The answers to the following questions are basic in the analysis of the relation of the success
of the cooperative to the success of the Moshav. Was
the exogenous factor of the large increase in demand
for food in the 1940's and early 1950's primarily

responsible for the success of the moshav ovdim? How
important was the cooperative in this success?

Of about fifty moshvei ovdim established by
early 1949, thirty-five, or 70 per cent, evolved into
successful agricultural communities.[20] The pioneers
who founded the early moshavim not only were volunteers but also had agricultural training before they
organized and settled their villages. Many of the
dropouts occurred during the difficult preparatory
period before settling the village. The early years
of settlement in the 1920's and 1930's were also
years of intense physical hardship, when the settlers
converted malarial swamps and land that had been fallow for centuries into viable villages. The cooperative was the center of social cohesion for the group
and played an important economic role in the distribution of the meager resources and in farm planning
and development. The settlement authority supplied
the initial investment and facilities and was responsible for the physical planning of the village. It
did not, however, take an active part in the management of the village until the postwar years of mass
settlement of untrained and unprepared immigrants.

The moshavim with better management and stronger cooperatives concentrated early on a few selected
high-income branches, mainly livestock and livestock
products; for until the founding of the State they
did not have to produce all the staple foods. These
specialized items were those in which they could compete with the Arabs. This concentration necessitated
strong cooperative management for the development of
the dairy branch, and later the poultry branch, and
for the development of irrigation. It also necessitated good control of cooperative investments and
farm financing to expand agriculture. When the substantial increases in demand came in the 1940's and
early 1950's, the moshavim with the strongest cooperatives were able to develop output the quickest
and respond to the market situation for the benefit
of all the members. The main functions of the cooperative in the economic success of the village were
obtaining credit, making the capital investment in
production facilities, farm planning, and improvement

of agricultural practices that made possible the
rapid development of member farms. While the large
increase in demand was an important exogenous factor
in the success of the moshav, a strong cooperative
was the enabling institution through which the factors filtered through to the success of the village
and its farm members.

The cooperative was not only important for the
economic success of the village, but also for its
social success in providing the amenities that the
members wanted and inducing the children of the original settlers to live permanently in the moshav as
farming members. To a large extent, this was made
possible by the economic prosperity in the villages
that could support two families on the farm plot. The
first priority in social planning was the school. The
members were also interested in maintaining a high
level of cultural activities, adult educational programs, libraries, and organized tours to the cities
for concerts and other events.

To a certain extent some moshavim with less
social cohesion and less developed cooperatives were
able to get along if they could use the economic services and schools of neighboring moshavim. In some
moshavim, particularly those close to cities, members
did not market their products through the cooperative,
thus weakening its financial position. If the land
was good enough and outside village facilities were
available, the moshav could keep going up to a certain
point. If the village, however, were to remain as a
viable unit, the better and cooperative farmers had
to be protected from the self-seeking ones, and the
failure of the cooperative would mean the failure of
the village.

In the case of the moshav ovdim, the conclusion
is quite positive that prosperous settlements have
been distinguished by well-run cooperative societies.
The effectiveness of the cooperative depends chiefly
on the business ability of its managers and the re-
sulting confidence that the settlers have in their
leadership. There are many examples of the differential rate of growth, indicating that the success of

the moshav depends on the success of the cooperative.
Nahalal, Kfar Yehoshua, and Beth Shearim are neighboring moshavim in the Yizreel Valley. In fact, the
latter settlement was formed from lands made available
from the other two. Nahalal and Kfar Yehoshua became
successful agricultural communities with strong cooperatives. Beth Shearim had a much weaker cooperative,
and although some members developed into good farmers,
it was not able to develop as fast as the other two.
The social amenities of the village are at a lower
level, and the differences in the farm incomes of the
members are much greater.

At the beginning of 1962, the settlement authority decided to accede to the request of the inter-
moshav committee and help manage a number of moshavim,
whose economic and social difficulties were such that
neither they nor their parent movements were able to
solve them. The basic difficulties were bad financial management of the cooperative and the farms, unpaid debts to the moshav by members who had left, and,
in some of the moshavim, bad farm management. Many
of these settlements were founded in the 1940's during the period of the price boom by members lacking
the degree of social solidarity and communal motivation of the earlier pioneers. These settlements could
survive the period of high prices in the early 1950's,
but when the agricultural terms of trade worsened in
the late 1950's, they could not continue on their own.
One of these settlements, however, was of the early
pioneer type where bad financial management of the
cooperative was responsible for the near failure of
the moshav.

On the other hand, a cooperative alone could
not overcome all the basic difficulties in the evolution of a sound agricultural village, such as poor
agricultural conditions, overfragmented plots, and
poor farmers. To a certain degree, it can ameliorate
these conditions by concentrating on such products as
poultry, that depend less on soil fertility, and, with
outside help, improvements could be made in the layout
of plots. However, the moshav had to meet certain
minimum levels in its physical and human ecology for
the cooperative to function and help promote the village to an economic and social success.

Historical Development of Moshav Ovdim

The purpose of this section is to trace the development of the moshav to the present, to analyze the recent tendencies in the development of the moshav as an institution, and to appraise the direction of further development.

Nahalal, A Micro Example

Nahalal, the first moshav ovdim, is used as a micro example of the development of the moshav.[21] This is not a typical moshav, as it is better than average. It is not, however, the best, at least in terms of economic performance and possibly by other criteria. It has the most extensive records and illustrates aspects of the development of the successful prestate moshavim.

Nahalal lies in the center of the Western Yizreel Valley, about 100 meters above sea level. It is about fourteen miles east of Haifa and about six miles west of Nazareth. It has an average rainfall of twenty-one inches. The average annual temperature is 68°F, with daily averages in summer of 73 to 80° and in winter of 55 to 57°. Temperatures drop to freezing only a few times at night in winter and early spring, and in the summers the maximum temperature may reach 104°. The soil is of a heavy clay loam type, deficient in lime.

The settlement was founded in a swampy area that had to be drained to become habitable. Two previous attempts to settle in the area in the first two decades of the century, one by local Arabs and one by German Templars, failed because of malaria.

The site was occupied in 1921 by a vanguard group of forty-eight men and eight women. The other women and children of the group remained behind for security and health reasons. The first settlers lived in tents while they built wooden huts for all the families. Within a year all the families moved to the village. At first they all worked together with 180 hired workers on the drainage scheme financed by the Jewish National Fund. They also built the farm buildings. The land was then parcelled out with each family moving to its plot.

Of the eighty members of the group that founded Nahalal, practially all were members of the Hapoel Hazair, a Zionist non-Marxist Socialist party. Every member of the group already had ten to twelve years' experience as an agricultural worker in the country. Many came from the first kibbutz, Degania. They had undergone the privations and hardships of The Conquest of Labor, and as veteran pioneers in their mid-thirties they were embarking on a bold new experiment. The first presettlement group included Eliezer Joffe, the ideologist of the moshav, an American trained specialist in market gardening, and Palestine's first poultry expert. All the women were experienced farm workers.

The moshav received a hereditary leasehold from the Jewish National Fund of a total land area of 9,250 dunams, 2,312.5 acres. The land unit per family was originally 125 dunams. In 1926, 500 dunams were given to a girls' agricultural school founded by the Canada Hadassah. In 1936, more land was given for the founding of the village Beth Shearim. In 1965, there were seventy-six agricultural holdings of one hundred dumams each. There were fifty small plots of about two dunams each for the nonfarmer professional members of the community. Of the 8,374 dunams in 1964, 7,977 were in cultivation and the remainder in roads and communal built-up areas.

Total sales by the village cooperative in 1964 amounted to 3,683.3 thousand Israeli pounds.* They were distributed as follows:

---

*The value of sales varies greatly among the prestate moshavim, depending to a great extent on the number of farms in the village. Audit Union records indicate that the better moshavim in 1965 had more than two million IL gross sales through the cooperative. At least one had over five million.

	Per Cent of Value of Total Output
Milk	15.8
Hatching eggs	9.3
Poultry meat	19.1
Turkey poults	8.3
Vegetables and potatoes	1.8
Fruit (noncitrus)	7.4
Citrus	2.9
Beef animals	25.4
Miscellaneous	10.0
Total	100.0

Almost 80 per cent of total sales was from livestock and livestock products, with the sale of meat animals the most important, poultry for meat, second, and milk, third. The importance of the various products has varied considerably over the years.

The net income per farm in 1964 was conservatively estimated at IL 15,000. This is considerably above the IL 9-10,000 average for the moshav ovdim for the entire country. Most of the farms, however, support two families.

The growth of the village can be gauged by the following cooperative-sales figures:*

		Israeli Pounds
1945	-	99,947
1950	-	282,337
1956	-	1,106,750
1964	-	3,683,800

The increase in intensification of farming can be gauged by the increase in land under irrigation. The figures in dunams were as follows: 1945, 1,200;

---

*In 1945 and 1950, the exchange rate was 2.8 IL to the dollar; in 1956, 1.8; and in 1964, 3.0.

1950, 2,544; 1956, 3,292; and 1964, 3,625. About half of every farm is now under irrigation, and the remainder in dry farming is cultivated by the cooperative, although the family can work their dry farming holding themselves if they wish. The whole dry-farming area, however, is planned and operated as a unit.

The population of the moshav has increased as follows: 1922, 365; 1945, 620; 1951, 630; and 1959, 684. Most of the second generation of the original settlers have remained to farm in the village. The population of the moshav can now be considered stable.

The head of cattle has grown as follows: 1922, 88; 1925, 213; 1930, 395; 1935, 363; 1940, 447; 1946, 657; 1951, 946; 1956, 871; 1961, 1,090; and 1964, 1,214. The increase in animals in recent years is the result of the growth of a new enterprise, the farmlot feeding of young bulls that are sold as yearlings for meat. The number of animals sold was 154 in 1956, 550 in 1961, and 741 in 1964. The income from the sale of meat animals increased from IL 1,352 in 1945 to IL 437,600 in 1964.

The amount of milk produced is increasing, but the number of farms in dairying is falling sharply. This is in line with the growing concentration of milk production in larger herds throughout the country.* Originally all the farms had dairy cattle. In 1964, forty-eight farms had dairy cattle. In 1965, the number had been reduced to thirty-four. The dairy herd has remained practically stable since 1946, from 348 in that year to 368 in 1964. The litres of milk produced has increased from 1,056.6 thousand in 1945 to an estimated 2 million in 1965. The increase in productivity has been most spectacular in the

------

*In Beer Tuvia, the most important dairy moshav in the country, the number of farmers producing milk decreased from 82 in 1964 to 64 in 1965, while the number of cows remained the same, and the production of milk rose. (Data obtained from village farmer.)

dairy branch, from 600-800 litres per cow in 1922 to
5,800 in 1965. It is considered uneconomical to have
a cow producing less than 4,000 litres. All the
dairy farmers have milking machines and modern mechanized equipment.

The number of eggs produced in the poultry enterprise has been falling in recent years, but the
sale of birds for meat, a relatively new enterprise,
has been increasing. The figures on egg production
in thousands of units are as follows: 1945, 551.8;
1955, 3,141.0; 1961, 5,800.0, and 1964, 4,479.0. The
sale of poultry meat in tons has risen as follows:
1945, 8.6; 1950, 167.7; 1956, 201.4; 1961, 200.0;
and 1964, 337.0. Raising turkeys has become a profitable new enterprise. In 1964, 129,000 turkey poults
were sold by the cooperative.

Fruit plantations, which were greatly reduced
during World War II, have increased sharply in recent
years from 302 dunams in 1951 to 1,216 in 1964. This
plus the move out of dairying is an indication that
some farms are going to a part-time farming operation.
Fruit requires labor for only a few months during
harvesting. Cultivating and spraying is handled communally.

There has been a small increase in vegetables
from 270 dunams in 1945 to 455 dunams in 1964. Most
of this increase has been specialized production in
which returns are good. Seventy dunams were used for
seed production and a hundred for melons.

A distinct diversification in types of farming
has evolved in Nahalal, with sizeable differences in
incomes from the various types. This diversification,
the differentiation in pattern of agricultural production, is one of the more important recent trends
in the development of the moshav ovdim. In Nahalal, it
has produced four distinct types of farms. The model
types in 1965 were as follows: (1) specialized dairy
with twenty or more milk cows; (2) mixed dairy-poultry
farms that on the average had about twelve milking
cows, five hundred chickens for eggs, and one thousand
chickens for meat; (3) turkey and beef farms that had

about three thousand turkeys and ten to fifteen bulls
for meat; and (4) poultry and beef farms that included about ten bulls for fattening, and produced both
regular and hatching eggs that were sold to the cooperative in return for chicks. The average net incomes on these farms in IL for 1965 were as follows:
dairy, 18,000; mixed dairy-poultry, 15,000; turkey
and meat animals, 35,000; and poultry and meat animals
10,000.

This diversification has come about because of
a number of factors. One of the more important is
the amount of labor available on the farm. The egg-
meat animal type requires the least and is suitable
for older couples with no children on the farm. The
turkey farms require more labor, and there are many
production risks such as disease. The dairy farm
represents a full-time operation, and the trend to
concentration of herds will probably continue. All
the farms have supplementary enterprises in addition
to their main ones, particularly orchards, many of
which in 1965 had not yet come into production. In
the main, however, there has been an increasing specialization of the farms, with the main sources of
income from fewer enterprises.

Besides a growing diversification in the types
of farms, there is a large variation in the intensity
of cultivation within farms in the village. The differences in labor requirements of the four principal
types of farming are large. Part of the variation in
intensity of cultivation is caused by off-farm city
employment of moshav residents. Five farms in Nahalal
are not worked at all. Usually people working full-
time in outside jobs are employed in the institutions
supporting cooperative farming or on special government assignments. In the 1962-68 period, about 12
per cent of the population of the moshavim were employed in such services.[22]

Of the seventy-six farms in Nahalal, members
from twenty obtain a substantial part of their income
from off-farm work. To some degree this is accounted
by the fact that in double-family units there are not
enough means of production to keep all family members

working on the farm. Thus even in good intensively
cultivated farms some of the members may obtain supplementary income by working in the cities. In many
instances, off-farm work means paying less attention
to the farm, keeping some chickens, and planting the
farm in orchards where irrigation is available. The
growth of nonfarm income and part-time farming is a
second important development in the moshav ovdim.

Nahalal has a complete line of production services for farmers maintained by the cooperative society. An important factor in the development of the
moshav has been the integration and expansion of
these services to serve more than one village. Under
the regional approach, in the new moshavim many services, both economic, social, and municipal, are operated on a regional basis through the regional
councils and regional purchasing associations. Consolidation has also affected the well-established
moshavim, so that some services can be operated more
efficiently with more economies of scale. Thus Nahalal is classified as a rural center, in addition to
being a moshav ovdim, as it performs the functions of
a rural center for neighboring villages in much the
same way as the new rural centers in the regional organization that has been developed since 1955. Nahalal has a regional agricultural and normal school.
The elementary school serves four villages. The dispensary services the area of the regional council.
The feed mill services three other villages besides
Nahalal; the transportation pool, two. In some respects, however, the importance of the central services has been reduced. Every farm in Nahalal has a
private tractor. The machine tractor station, however, is still important, servicing the farmers with
specialized equipment such as caterpillar tractors,
hay balers, combines, etc., and even supplementary
small tractors.

Nahalal maintains extensive social and municipal
services. It supplements the year of kindergarten
and eight years of elementary education required and
financially supported by the government, with two additional years of kindergarten and three years of
secondary education at its own expense. It has funds

to award university scholarships. It has an extensive adult education program, maintaining a public
lending library and organized lectures. Theatre performances are held once or twice a year in the moshav
assembly hall, and bus trips to theatre and concert
performances in town are regularly organized. The
moshav maintains a cinema where shows are held twice
weekly. It has a large swimming pool and promotes
all sports activities.

The housing is definitely superior, not only
to workers' housing but to the average housing in the
cities. They contain all modern appliances and sanitary facilities. Most families or groups of families
have a private automobile.

Before statehood, the population pattern in
Israel was one of excess concentration in the three
principal cities and environs and complete decentralization and self-sufficiency in collective and cooperative villages. This was not a difference between
metropolitanism and provincialism in the usual sense
but between competing different scales of social values, those of the inhabitants of the big cities and
those of rural cooperation. The improvement of roads
and transportation, the rise in the standard of living, and the development of regional planning has
promoted the integration of village into town life.
In the case of the veteran moshav, such as Nahalal,
it has meant increased employment in cities, more
part-time farming, to some degree, the differentiation
of social values within the village, and the growth
of individualism.

In summary, although Nahalal is not the perfect
average village, it illustrates the three principal
current tendencies in the moshav ovdim: the increasing differentiation in the pattern of agricultural
production, the growth of nonfarming income and part-
time farming, and the integration of the village with
the surrounding area.

Although the power of the executive committee
is still quite strong, there has been a growth in individualism in the moshav ovdim, probably more in

those less successful than Nahalal. An indication
is provided in the opposition to the cooperative law
that was being discussed in 1965 and 1966. This law
was supported by the two leading parent movements of
the moshavim, particularly the Moshav Movement, the
most important one, which is attached to Mapai, the
leading political party in the country. Its purpose
was to legalize the identity of the moshav and the
cooperative, and to give legal sanctions to the parent movements in certain relations with individual
moshavim. The law has been strongly opposed by some
of the political parties and even by some members in
veteran moshavim as curtailing their fundamental lib-
erties. Legalizing the identify of the cooperative
and the municipality is opposed by those who claim
that they can be removed from the moshav cooperative
by infraction of the cooperative society rules but
not from their homes in the village that are legally
their own. Strangely enough, one of the opposition
leaders was the son of Eliezer Joffe, the ideologist
of the moshav.

Macro Review

There have been some interesting macro economic
studies, particularly in the economic development of
the established moshav. Kadar, in 1954, as a result
of a study of a representative national stratified
sample of 183 prestate moshav farms, including middle-
class moshavim, concluded that six types of farms had
been developed. The types and sample village average
net incomes for each were as follows:[23]

	Net Income Israeli Pounds
Partly irrigated family farm	9,634
Irrigated specialized dairy farm	6,300
Citrus Belt farms	
Citrus-poultry farm	10,700
Mixed farm	4,790
Vegetable-orchard farm	2,600
Specialized poultry farm	--

The partly irrigated farm is of the Nahalal type. The variations in types of farms have increased considerably since 1954, although approximations of most of the earlier types still exist.

A summary analysis of the characteristics of the average family farm in 1954 is shown in Table 18. The mode is shown with the arithmetic means of indicators of economic performance. The arithmetic means are higher as they are more influenced by the larger more successful farms. Assets and economic performance have increased considerably since 1954. Many of the farms were doing quite well at the time, especially those that had adequate livestock. About 81 per cent of all sales were through the village cooperative.[24] The financial condition was good because of the poststate inflation that gave the farmers the opportunity of repaying the original settlement loan and other debts at nominal prices. About 75 per cent of cash income came from livestock and livestock products. The farms where livestock and livestock products were most important generally had higher incomes.

The average net family farm income from this 1954 project investigation was IL 4,800 per farm or IL 11 per family labor day. The net income required to cover reasonable living expenses, including some new investment and taxes, was estimated at IL 3,000. Using these figures, the study revealed that about 20 per cent of the old established farms failed to cover expenses.[25] The main causes for insufficient income were: (1) bad agricultural conditions, particularly insufficient water supply, overfragmentation, shallow soils, and distance from markets; (2) weak village cooperatives; and (3) settlers unsuited for farming.

The main factors influencing profits were: prices, production efficiency, and scale of operation. As for the first, while milk and egg prices were at the same level as in the United States, poultry meat prices were twice as high and beef about three times as high. If the prices on the latter two items were reduced to the United States level, the net income of the average farm would fall from IL 4,8000 to IL

3,000.[26] While dairy and poultry yields were high,
labor efficiency was not. This is partly explained
by the small unit of production that could not be
offset by the cooperative. The study, as expected,
showed a close correlation between farm size, labor
input, and net income. The correlation between labor
input and net income was positive up to a certain
point: eight hundred eight hundred standard working
days. Labor inputs above this level lowered net income per farm.[27] There was a positive relationship
between number of cows and net income per cow.[28] With
the limitation on the size of the farm, enlargement
of the scale of operations was achieved mainly by
denser stocking based on imported feed, bringing more
land under irrigation, and extending the area of
labor-intensive crops.

The standard for a well-developed farm adopted
in this study was 450 man-days per annum. Using this
standard, an examination of unit production data from
the records of all the moshvei ovdim of the workers'
agricultural cooperative audit union revealed that
only the settlements established before 1935 could
be considered fully developed. Those established between 1936 and 1947 included many farms that were
underdeveloped.[29]

Lowe continued economic investigations on a
subsample of the 1954 national sample that included
about seventy farms in six villages. In terms of
income, this sample as a whole was about 15 per cent
above average, although not all the farms and villages
were above average. The development of these farms
from 1954 to 1960 is shown in index numbers for 1960
with 1954 equal to 100. The index numbers for growth
in physical output by commodities was as follows:
milk, 163; cattle, 246; eggs, 198; poultry, 206;
fruit, 575; and vegetables and potatoes, 38. The
quantity increase in all output with 1954 price weights
was 187. The increases in the same period in physical
quantities of principal inputs were: feed produced
on the farm, 163; feed purchased for dairy, 244; feed
purchased for poultry, 180; and man-hours of hired
labor, 56. The quantity index of inputs at fixed 1954
prices was 176. The changes in cultivated area,

TABLE 18

Details of Average Moshav Farm, 1954

	Arithmetic Mean	Mode
Physical area, dunams		
Total farm area	42.2	
Of which irrigated	20.0	
Cropped area, dunams		
Total	46.1	
Irrigated fodder	12.3	
Vegetables	7.0	
Fruit orchards	3.2	
Unirrigated field crops	21.6	
Miscellaneous (chiefly groundnuts)	2.0	
Livestock, head		
Cows	2.9	
Young cattle	2.9	
Laying hens	367	
Capital (IL[a], including share in cooperative assets and debts)		
Total (full replacement value)	25,178	
Net worth (depreciated replacement value)	16,006	
Debts	1,487	

Economic performance, IL[a]		
Total output	13,254	11,300
Total expenditure (including depreciation at replacement values)	8,381	5,600
Net income	4,873	4,400
Labor input, days		
Total	572	
Family labor	450	
Hired labor	122	

[a]1.8 IL to the dollar.

Source: Gershon Kaddar, "Family Farms in Cooperative Villages" (paper presented to FAO-sponsored study group on Problems of Individual and Group Settlement, Tel-Aviv, April-May, 1956), Appendix, p. 11. (Mimeographed.)

family labor force, and net income were as follows:
unirrigated area, 56; irrigated area, 136; family
labor, 92; and net income, 159. The absolute increase in average net farm income was from IL 5,600
in 1954 to IL 8,900 in 1960.[30]

The development of these farms in this period
is quite impressive. It was carried out by increases
in intensity of farming through expansion in irrigation and by increases in productivity. A number of
farms developed into two-family and father-and-son
units and leased land from neighboring farms. There
was also some reparcellation to accommodate sons returning from military service. The decrease in labor
was accounted partly by contraction of the vegetable
branch, which has high labor requirements, and partly
by increases in efficiency.

The intensification of farming in this sample
during the period studied necessitated heavy capital
investments. Average additional investments in farm
property amounted to about nineteen thousand pounds
per farm, about half of it in livestock and half in
buildings and equipment.[31] These investments were
financed by restitution payments received from Germany, from special development budgets given by settlement institutions, to some extent by borrowing
from the village cooperative, and to a greater extent
by reinvesting profits in the farms.

The conclusion to be drawn is that in the better than average prestate villages there was a substantial development of farming in the 1950's and an
improvement in the farmers' economic position.

The capital-assets structure of the established
moshavim in the early 1960's, as indicated by Lowe,
is shown in Table 19. The current figures, of course,
would be considerably higher. The variability from
highest to lowest would be just as great, if not more
so. Lowe also asserts that 70 to 90 per cent of the
assets were acquired over the years as equity and that
farmers owed no more than 20 to 30 per cent in the
form of medium- and short-term loans.[32]

TABLE 19

Capital Assets[a] of Typical Farms of
Established Moshavim
(Israeli Pounds)

	Average	Highest	Lowest
Cow shed with equipment	10,500	15,000	6,000
Poultry houses with equipment	8,700	17,000	4,000
Irrigation network	1,600	2,200	600
Machinery and tools	3,200	9,000	400
Orchards	6,000	8,000	4,000
Dairy herd	14,000	18,000	10,000
Total production assets On the farm	47,000	71,000	36,000
Share in production assets of cooperative	6,500	12,000	3,000
Total production assets	53,500	80,000	40,000
Dwelling house	25,000	40,000	6,000
Share in consumer assets of the cooperative	2,500	5,000	1,000
Total consumers' assets	27,500	44,000	7,500
Total assets	81,000	115,000	47,500

[a]At renewal value.

Source: Yehuda Lowe, "Kibbutz and Moshav in Israel: An Economic Study," in R. N. Dixey, ed., International Explorations of Agricultural Economics (Ames, Iowa: Iowa State University Press, 1964), p. 136.

In summary, farmers in the successful prestate moshavim have done quite well compared to workers in the city. Within the moshav, however, there are wide differences in income, largely because of differences

in managerial ability and labor supply. This has led
to a diversity in the types of farms within a village
and a concentration of the more intensive and profitable types of farming in fewer farms, particularly
in the case of dairying. This is made possible by
the fact that the milk-marketing quotas are allotted
to the village, and the quotas are reassigned to fewer farmers. Farmers lease land from other village
members and also buy quotas from them. The latter
two practices, though illegal, are quite common and
represent ways of enlarging the farm. The amount of
part-time farming in established moshavim is expanding. Exact statistics on its importance are unavail-
able. It may be that in about one third of the
farms, the major part of income comes from outside
agriculture, and some of these farms, or part of them,
are not farmed at all. This estimate may well be on
the conservative side.

It is hard to establish whether the proximity
of the city is a bad or a good thing. While it has
allowed farm incomes to be supplemented, it has
greatly affected the social values of the village.
For a number of people it has been possible to obtain
the best of both worlds: good housing and social amenities in a pleasant rural environment and increased
incomes from specialized city jobs. In some cases,
earnings from city jobs have been reinvested in farms.

The families of the older moshavim were generally small. There has been a problem of how to assure the continued working of the farm in the parents'
old age, and, in some instances, after their death.
There is a problem of inheritance rights as more
adult children marry. Regulations in the constitution of the Moshav Movement are quite clear on this
point. The family legally is not the ultimate owner
of the farm. Its right to hold it depends on the
willingness to work it by family labor. This rule is
not completely enforced. The holding cannot be divided up among the children. The oldest or any other
child is not entitled to inherit the farm automati-
cally on the death of the parents, nor may parents
will farms to any of their children. Children who
wish to farm have a legitimate claim for land, and

the moshav endeavors to meet this claim. On the
death of the parents, if the children are unwilling
to work the holding themselves, it reverts to the
moshav for allocation to a new member, who pays the
family for improvements.

As of the early 1950's, some 70 per cent of
the adult children in the established villages remained in their parents' village, while 10 per cent
became farmers in other moshavim or kibbutzim.[33] In
well-developed villages, such as Nahalal, almost all
the children remained. In the poorly-developed
moshavim most of the children left. A problem arises
when the second child marries. One solution is for
the village to receive supplementary holdings of
land or to keep supplementary holdings in reserve.
This has been possible only in some districts. Another, where conditions are favorable, as in Nahalal,
is to have two-family homesteads on single plots.
A third solution is the establishment of new moshavim
by children of working age. This has been achieved
only on a small scale. The problem of farm inheritance in the moshav is still controversial, and a new
law has been under consideration.

The central role of the cooperative in the success of the village has been stressed. In strong,
well-established villages the council and executive
committee still play a large role. With the growing
diversification of agriculture within the village,
the increase in members who obtain their primary
source of income outside the village, and the growth
of functions of regional authorities such as the regional councils and regional purchasing associations,
there is growing resentment of the power of the executive committees and councils and more scope for
individual activity.

Some authorities believe that there will be a
schism between farming and nonfarming members in the
moshav. In some of the villages the nonfarming members are substantial and may outnumber the farming
members. The locus of much of the administration
of farming activities may change from the village to
the region and from national cooperatives to regional

cooperatives. Regional marketing cooperatives based
on a single commodity or related commodities may take
the place of the national cooperatives. Farmers can
thus have more control over their operations and compare results with other regions.

There may be a need, therefore, of separation
of the municipal affairs of the village from the cooperative economic affairs that are primarily of concern to farmers only. There could be different
village councils and executive committees with prescribed powers. The moshav may then evolve more in
the direction of a private village or moshava with
strong cooperative features of particular concern to
farmer members. Facilities outside the village for
servicing farmers have increased, and farmers can
manage many activities on their own more easily than
in the past--financing, for example.

In any event, there is strong pressure to limit
the scope and powers of the moshav council and executive committee and to separate municipal from economic cooperative functions. There certainly will be
changes in the future structure and operations of the
moshav ovdim because of the growing diversity of interests of its members. Whether it will go as far as
indicated is still problematical.

NOTES

1.   Yehuda Lowe, "Kibbutz and Moshav in Israel:
An Economic Study," in International Explorations of
Agricultural Economics, Roger N. Dixey, ed. (Ames,
Iowa: Iowa State University Press, 1964), p. 133.

2.   Ibid.

3.   Yehuda Lowe, "The Economic Structure and
Functions of the Village Cooperative in Moshavim"
(lecture delivered to Settlement Study Center,
Rehovot), p. 5.   (Mimeographed.)

4.   E. Sternberg, "The Cooperative Society's
Services in the Moshav and Evaluation of their

Economic Efficiency" (paper presented to International Symposium, The Role of Cooperative Organization in Rural Development, Tel-Aviv, March, 1965), p. 15. (Mimeographed.)

5. Yehuda Lowe, "The Variability of Income of Family Farms in Cooperative Villages in Israel" (paper presented to International Symposium, The Role of Cooperative Organization in Rural Development, Tel-Aviv, March, 1965), p. 2. (Mimeographed.)

6. Ibid.

7. Yair Mundlak, An Economic Analysis of Established Farms in Israel, 1953-1958 (Jerusalem: Falk Project for Economic Research in Israel, 1964).

8. Ibid., p. 131.

9. Ibid., p. 117.

10. Ibid., p. 30.

11. Ibid.

12. Ibid., p. 31.

13. Ibid.

14. Ibid., p. 32.

15. Ibid., p. 21.

16. Ibid., p. 74.

17. Ibid., p. 22.

18. Ibid., p. 15.

19. Yehuda Lowe, "Economic Analysis of Established Family Farms in 1959/60 " Ministry of Agriculture, Agricultural Publications Division, 1952, p. 1.

20. From interview with Mr. Benjamin Kaplan, Assistant Director General of the Settlement Department of the Jewish Agency.

21.   Data obtained from village archives and settlement accountant.

22.   Statistical Abstract of Israel, 1965 and 1968, pp. 305, 266.

23.   Kadar, op. cit., Appendix I, pp. 4,6,8,9.

24.   Ibid., p. 13.

25.   Ibid., p. 15.

26.   Ibid.

27.   Ibid., Appendix I, p. 14a.

28.   Ibid., p. 14b.

29.   Ibid., p. 14.

30.   Yehuda Lowe, Economic Analysis of Established Family Farms in 1959/60 pp. 1 and 4.

31.   Ibid., p. 5.

32.   Ibid.

33.   Korn, op. cit., p. 52.

CHAPTER **6** ORGANIZATION, OPERATION,
AND DEVELOPMENT OF
MOSHAV OLIM

POSTSTATE SETTLEMENT IN THE MOSHAV

This chapter is primarily concerned with the
moshav olim, specifically the moshav founded for new
immigrants who arrived in the country after independence in 1948. As already indicated, the structure,
function, and development of these poststate moshavim
have been quite different from the moshav ovdim.

Poststate agricultural settlement, for the most
part, has been a closely directed and closely controlled settlement of immigrants, two thirds of whom
came to Israel from Moslem countries in the Near East
and North Africa. At the same time there has been
some continuation of volunteer pioneer settlement by
immigrants from Western and Central Europe, America,
British Commonwealth countries, and by native Israelis who established villages similar in operation
and function to the moshav ovdim. The Israelis included about 1,500 families, who settled in agriculture in the 1952-54 town-to-land movement, and
children of farmers in veteran moshavim, who have
founded five new moshavim.[1]

Rural settlement played an important role in
the absorption of the new immigrants. More rural
villages were founded in the first few years of statehood than in the previous seventy. Well over half of
the moshavim in the country were founded in the first
three years after the establishment of the State.

The principal aims of this new rural settlement
were (1) the increase of agricultural production, (2)
the provision of immediate employment for immigrants,
and (3) the decentralization of population and

development of new areas in the country, including
border areas. The authorities wanted to continue
rural settlement within the framework of the cooperative sector, and the new immigrants were free to
choose between moshav and kibbutz. The highly organized and collective structure of the kibbutz was
obviously unsuited for the new immigrants from traditional Moslem societies, many of the immigrants
being from Communist countries of Eastern Europe and,
the former, inmates of displaced persons camps. The
relatively flexible, cooperative framework of the
moshav was, therefore, chosen as the standard ab-
sorptive unit.

The planners modified the moshav economy according to the needs of agricultural production, and
the immigrants from different cultures brought about
changes in the moshav framework more in comformity
with their habits and traditions. The confrontation
of the moshav structure, along with the economic,
social, and organizational expectations of the authorities responsible for its maintenance and the
predispositions brought to the situation by the settlers in all spheres of activity constituting the
moshav pattern, involved mutual interactions that
resulted in a completely new type of village and the
development of settlers (or at least a significant
share of them) into modern commercial farmers in a
Western democratic setting within the short space of
less than a generation--that is, within ten to fifteen years. The process is still going on. The
progress of these moshavim and the results accomplished have been the most dramatic and important
development in postwar Israeli agriculture.

There was a minority who chose to settle in the
kibbutz. They were, for the most part, either Israelis long established in the country or immigrants
from the West who were more prepared for adaptation
to kibbutz life.

The great needs in the 1949-51 crash period of
settlement were to feed the population and to provide
immediate employment for a mass of immigrants for
whom there were no other economic activities.

Most of these new immigrants were housed in crude
temporary billets. Many were sent to abandoned Arab
villages. Substantial areas of irrigated lands were
given to the new farmers. Agricultural cultivation
was divided into two categories: (1) villages that
could be developed by irrigation methods and (2)
those based on the exploitation of already existing
Arab crops of olive trees, fig trees, and vines plus
additional dry-land cultivation. The budget for the
farmer in both types of settlements was fixed at IL
500 that was then the equivalent of $1,400.[2]

In 1954, after the emergency crash period of
settlement, it was realized that settlement policy
had to be implemented more carefully in line with
national goals. The first need was for systematic
national agricultural planning and the implementation
and integration of the plans at the farm level with
regional and national goals. The second was that to
decentralize the population, especially to settle
the new areas not previously inhabited by Jews, it
would be necessary to evolve a system of comprehensive regional planning in which agricultural settlements would be basic and linked up with the total
economic development of the region. The third was
that, to have viable immigrant settlements, it was
necessary to change the structure of the moshav to
help the new immigrants evolve into commercial farmers who would want to settle permanently in their
villages.

Development of National Agricultural Planning:
Implementation and Integration
at the Settlement Level

The subject of national agricultural planning
has already been covered in detail. The present concern is its relation to the structural adjustments
in the new moshavim. The main effort from 1948 to
1954 was to expand the production of fresh foodstuffs
with which Jewish farmers had considerable experience:
milk, eggs, vegetables, and fruits. Village instructors supported by the national moshav organizations
worked out production programs for these commodities
with the new settlements, emphasizing the commodities
for which the village was most suited.

The Settlement Department of the Jewish Agency
promulgated a rather grandiose plan in August, 1950,
looking forward to a population of two million in
1954 with 25 per cent of it engaged in farming. It
also defined the different types of agricultural
farms that would be needed. The plan was expected
to provide for the country's entire food needs except
for corn, meat, and fish.[3]

The unrealistic assumptions in this plan were
realized when surpluses started to appear in 1954.
By 1955, the new Joint Agricultural Planning Center
had worked up a system for implementing national agricultural plans at the micro level and had begun to
draw up a new national plan.

Implementation of national planning at the village level was a sine qua non for the development of
comprehensive regional planning and for the consolidation and very existence of the new settlements in
protecting and expanding their markets. Regional
industries and processing facilities depended on local
supplies that had to be assured. It, therefore, became necessary to prepare annual village plans and to
provide the necessary perquisites and services so
that the annual plans would be implemented. The village plan had to be integrated with regional and national plans. This involved a complicated planning
apparatus and the reconciliation of the needs of the
new villages with those of the established old ones.

The basis of planning at the village and farm
level have been the model-farm types. The details
and variants of these farm types have been under constant review and are changed as necessary in order
to fulfill the goal of equal income opportunities
among the various types of farms and the income for
farming in general and that of urban workers. Changes
in the model-farm types and in the details within the
types are dictated by changes in general economic
conditions, changes in the demand for agricultural
production, and in the supply of the basic factors of
production, particularly land and water allocations.

For the 1965-75 decade there are five principal
model types of farms which are planned to yield an

average net income of IL 6,000-7,000.[4] The principal model types are dairy, field crops, citrus, hill,
and mountain.

The model for the dairy farm is based on thirty-
one dunams of land, three for the farmstead (the rest
under irrigation), twenty-two for forage crops for
the dairy herd, and six as a citrus grove. The average amount of water allocated would be approximately
seventeen thousand cubic meters per year. This model
is based on an annual production of forty thousand
litres of milk as compared to twenty-four thousand
in 1965.

The model for the field crop farm is based on
sixty dunams of irrigated land in comparison with
the pre-1965 forty to forty-five dunams. Fifty-
three dunams are for industrial crops and vegetables,
five for a citrus grove, and two for the farmstead.
Poultry raising and merino sheep may be supplementary
branches. It is planned to allocate nineteen thousand cubic meters of water per year for this farm
type compared with sixteen thousand cubic meters in
1965.

The citrus model farm is allocated thirty
dunams of land and 17,600 cubic meters of water.
Twenty dunams are intended for the grove and the remainder for vegetables and specialized crops suited
for the area.

The hill farm is planned for fifteen to twenty
irrigated dunams and ten to twelve unirrigated dunams
for field crops such as tobacco and seed crops. It
includes a poultry flock of four to five hundred
birds and ten to twenty head of sheep.

The mountain farm is somewhat smaller, containing about ten to twelve dunams in fruit plantations.
The smaller land allotment is compensated for by an
increased poultry flock of 800 to 1,200 birds.

These models are used mainly as a guide for
planners and to indicate what average net incomes
are possible under average performances in different

types of farms in different parts of the country. In
actual practice there are many variants to these
models. For the country as a whole, many dairy and
citrus farms are more developed than the models and
are yielding higher incomes. Incomes on the average
field-crop farm were, however, as of 1965, somewhat
below the model type. This was caused by the fact that
many of the plantations were young and not yet bearing, and the farms had not received full water and
land allotments because of delays in irrigation plans.
Incomes as planned by the model farms are, however,
practicable.

Development of Comprehensive Regional Planning

Before the establishment of the State there
could be no comprehensive regional planning, as the
settlement authority did not have entire regions at
its disposal. Agricultural villages were established
singly, frequently at long distances from each other.
They were thus unable to cooperate in the organization of essential services; consequently, each village maintained its own vital economic and social
facilities in order to be able to exist independently
of its surroundings. Only in a few cases, where a
number of moshavim had been founded in the same area,
were joint institutions--a district school, for ex-
ample--practicable.

The situation changed following the establishment of the State. Concentrated settlement on a
large scale became possible. But although agricultural settlements were founded in large clusters, the
settlement authorities continued to work according to
conventional methods. Because of the urgency of mass
settlement within a short period of time many mistakes were made. The experience gained and the problems generated by unplanned settlement led to new
methods of planning and development and to a system
of comprehensive regional planning.

In the 1949-51 crash period of settlement many
villages were founded without any preliminary planning or detailed soil surveys. This often resulted
in the establishment of settlements without a sound

economic basis. Only in the South, the Negev, was
there any preliminary planning. A soil survey of
the area was made and geographical maps were prepared.
The number of agricultural units in the settlement
were determined in accordance with the soil survey.
Later a committee consisting of representatives of
the settlement authorities, the Settlement and Technical Departments of the Jewish Agency, and the Ministries of Agriculture, Interior, and Defense
determined the site for farm buildings. Planning of
each village, however, was made separately, without
taking into account the structure of neighboring settlements. This sometimes resulted in the establishment of villages in the same area that practiced
different types of farming so that they could not
make use of common services. The type of farming in
some of these villages was later changed in conform-
ity with the regional plans. Such changes created
considerable problems in the development of the village.

The first steps towards regional planning were
introduced in the Negev in the second 1952-54 consolidation period where groups of three to five settlements called "garinim" (nuclei) were founded. Each
village comprised eighty to a hundred farm units.
The settlements were built as close to each other as
possible with a common service center in the middle
of the group within walking distance of each village.
Its function was to serve as the location for the
services and institutions of the surrounding settlements, such as the school, tractor station, marketing
facilities, stores, etc. Two groups of villages were
founded on the basis of such principles at the end
of 1952 and in 1953. Single settlements, however, were
still being founded, both in the Negev and other regions.

The garin method demonstrated the advantages of
planning a number of settlements together. Its limited range, however, prevented the development of
services to a high level. A new system, therefore,
comprehensive regional planning, was promulgated by
Dr. Ranaan Weitz, Director of the Settlement Department of the Jewish Agency, in 1954 and initiated in
the South in the Lakhish zone in 1955.

In each moshav settlement in Lakhish there are about eighty farm units. There are only a few services in the village: the general store for daily provisions, kindergarten, a local clinic with a nurse, a synagogue, and, sometimes, a recreation room.

A rural center serves a group of four to five moshavim (five to eight in other regions) and is conveniently located for all of them. In it are located the district school, clinic, bank, post office, a civic center for cultural and youth activities, and cinema, often the headquarters of the regional council and economic services such as sorting and packing stations, machine tractor stations, garages and repair facilities, etc. Inhabitants of the rural centers are employed to run the services. A rural community composed of a number of agricultural villages with a rural center is called a "Composite Rural Community."

A further link in the composite rural structure is the provincial regional town, the urban center that serves a number of composite rural communities. It is the location for industries processing the agricultural production of the district such as cotton gins, oil presses, sugar refineries, other industrial plants, commercial enterprises, banking and insurance companies, secondary school, government offices, central garages and workshops, etc.

Such overall regional planning facilities assessment of the dimensions of the various branches of agriculture to be developed in the region and the determination of the size of industries for the processing of local farm produce of the packing houses, stores, etc. to be erected in the rural centers. Regional planning helps the farmer obtain higher incomes. Joint services are usually better and cheaper than separate village services. A wider scope of municipal and cultural services are made available. It enables professional specialists to settle in the rural regions. Teachers, technicians, nurses, physicians, and other public workers who would not live in the villages are willing to settle in the rural centers or provincial regional towns.

The regional structure has a social aim no less important than its economic one. The patriarchal family structure of newcomers from the Oriential coun- tries, which is supported by kinship groups, hamulas, made it impossible to settle different ethnic groups in the same villages. A strict and definite separa- tion of the ethnic groups is, however, against the national policy of integrating the different groups into a single nation. Regional planning has facili- tated settling each village with one ethnic group, insofar as possible, and, at the same time, has pro- moted frequent contacts in the common institutions in the centers that have gradually broken down the bar- riers separating the immigrants. An important factor has been the association in the school at the rural center of the children from all the ethnic groups.

The regional approach to settlement has now been established in the Lakhish area that comprises about 300,000 dunams of arable land, in Adullam, a region of 100,000 dunams, of which twenty thousand are cultivable, extending northeast of Lakhish to the Jerusalem hills, and in the Tasnach area in the north near Emek Yizreel that includes about eighty thousand dunams.[5] Other settlement areas are being transformed to the new structure insofar as possible. One of the principal methods is through the construction of rural regional centers for common services and other eco- nomic, social, and political functions and the setting up of regional cooperative-service organizations.

As of 1965, forty-five rural regional centers were established, and another sixteen were planned for operation in the course of the next five years.[6] These rural centers differ in scope and organizational structure. There are three main types: (1) subregion- al village group centers, the rural centers of the composite rural community already described, that com- prises twenty-five of the forty-five centers,[7] (2) nonresidential centers that are particularly suited to the needs of the kibbutzim, and (3) interregional centers organized by several regional councils to ob- tain economies of scale for larger plants. All re- gional centers are located on nationally owned land rented to rural regional councils. This means that

the farmers themselves are involved in the decisions
on the development and management of the centers.

All the new settlement areas are being developed and perfected in the framework of comprehensive
regional planning. This includes the B'sor region
in the Western Negev near the Gaza Strip where there
are 350,000 dunams of fertile land available for further settlement, particularly suited for export crops
such as citrus fruit, winter vegetables, and groundnuts, but where the limiting factor is water. A
second area under development is in Central Galilee
where there are seventy thousand dunams available for
intensive cultivation in hill-and mountain-type farming units after fairly extensive land reclamation.
The third area is the Arava, a long narrow strip extending from the southern shore of the Dead Sea to
the Red Sea coast. This will be an area of limited
settlement because of the lack of water and large
areas of good lands. Because of market, water, and
financial limitations the development of these areas
will be gradual.[8]

The comprehensive regional planning approach
to settlement has incorporated many features that,
since 1955, have become standard settlement policy:
(1) detailed physical planning of the moshav along
with its facilities and the farming units as well as
well as the rural center and its facilities in the
context of the economic needs of a region; (2) planning and implementation of settlement activities by
a professional team of a wide variety of experts do-
miciled in the region and working with a professional
team at the village and rural center levels and with
the elected representatives of the settlers themselves; (3) a more careful selection of immigrant
farmers and sending them directly to the village after arrival in the country; (4) a transitional training period for the new farmers before they assume the
responsibility of operating their own farms; (5) the
delegation of responsibility to farmers in stages until they are able to assume independence and collectively run the affairs of the village; and (6) the
integration of industry with agriculture in the region
to provide better markets for farmers and increased
incomes for farmers' families.

The comprehensive regional physical planning for a region has involved the following stages:

1. Detailed topographic land and soil surveys and mapping.

2. Determining the types of settlements and types of farms by the expert committees of the Settlement Department of the Jewish Agency and Ministry of Agriculture. For example, the hilly eastern area of Lakhish bordering on Jordan was found suitable for extensive kibbutz farms. Thus, for both economic and security reasons, kibbutzim with well-trained Israeli farmers were chosen as settlements in this area.

3. Division of the region into sections, each suitable for a village of seventy-five to a hundred families.

4. Determining the site of the village within the section and its approval by a committee of representatives of the Ministries of Interior, Health, Agriculture, and Defense. Special attention has been paid to the requirements of communications, drainage and water conduits, soil conservation, and distances within the village and between the villages.

5. Detailed architectural planning of the residential quarter in the village and of the various centers, and approval of the plans by the committee. Before these plans are submitted detailed blueprints were prepared of the public buildings and the farm structures required by farm type, and the extent of production to be carried out in the village and the region.

6. Division of the village land into farm plots in accordance with the type of farm, with the field roads, waterways, and the principles of soil conservation and irrigation. Since the farms in the Lakhish area were of the industrial type, attempts were made to create larger irrigation blocks in order to facilitate cooperative effort and more efficient mechanization techniques such as deep plowing and spraying.

7. Mapping out the regional water systems with a blueprint of the distribution of the water to the village lands, and approval of the various plans by expert committees. Every farm unit in the village is equipped with a water meter.

8. Planning of the agricultural production and employment for the settlers on a monthly schedule. Determining the correct crop rotation is very important, as not more than 16-17 per cent of the total annual water allocation may be used in any one month. Consequently, crop rotations must be determined by the farm planners working with the regional water planning department. Annual water schedules were drawn up from water norms, the requirements of different crops in the various months of the year.

9. Field marking of the plans by surveyors and commencement of their execution.

This brief resume indicates the complications of the administrative apparatus in regional planning. Proper horizontal organization of the agencies concerned in regional development is basic. As soon as the decision to settle the Lakhish area was taken, a special team was formed for the planning and implementation of the project. All the personnel required (architects, engineers, agronomists, economists, sociologists, administrators, etc.) were organized as a team within the administrative framework of the Settlement Department of the Jewish Agency. For this purpose the settlement authority separated the region from the other administrative regions and accorded it the status of an administratively independent body with wide authority in implementation and budgetary methods. The team worked out of a headquarters in the development town of Kiryat Gat. The closeness to the settlement region made for better understanding of local problems and for closer contact with the settlers.

Since 1954, the authorities have been more careful in selecting immigrants for settling in moshavim. The institutions mostly concerned with screening the settlers have been the national moshav organizations.

Although there have not been sufficient candidates
for settlement to provide the best type of screening,
the immigration authorities who worked in North Africa to screen the settlers for Lakhish tried to select
only families where the provider was between eighteen
and forty years old. Considerable educational work
was done to describe village life in Israel. The
immigrants underwent medical treatment in the transit
camps in North Africa and France. On arrival in
Israel they were sent directly to the village. Unlike
the prestate settlers their agricultural and social
training started only after reaching the village.

Every effort was made to settle in one village
only those from the same town, village, or area in
their country of origin so as to eliminate, as much
as possible, the difficulties of language and adjustment and to facilitate the settlers' taking over the
administration of the community by increasing their
feeling of self-confidence in their new environment.
The authorities learned through experience that this
necessitated relatively comfortable conditions for
the new settlers. The attempts in 1949 and 1950 to
offer the settlers only the barest minimum, in the
hope that their desire to settle on the land would
forge the necessary links to bind them to the land,
were failures.

The Lakhish regional planners benefited from
the earlier experiences in poststate settlement and
decided that development should be phased over a prolonged period and that the problems of each stage
should be anticipated.

The first stage involved the first large-scale
experiment in a managed farm system whereby most of
the land in the village was managed by a public or
private company as a large training farm for the settlers, who were paid the prevailing agricultural
wages. The profits, if any, were divided among the
settlers, with the settlement authority sustaining
the losses. After 1956, the settlers not only participated in the profits but also shared losses.
Centralized operation was gradually brought to a minimum in a few years, while the settler's farmstead
was gradually enlarged.

In Lakhish the settler was provided with a
standard house including the basic furniture and kit-
chen equipment. He was also allocated about four
dunams of land of the forty odd to be ultimately giv-
en him. The contractor agreed to employ the settlers
to develop and work the land in accordance with the
crop rotation scheme and water schedule planned by the
settling authority. The earnings of working about
twenty days a month for the contracting authority
were supplemented by raising vegetables on his own
land for home consumption as well as marketing.

After a year the plan called for allocating
another thirteen to fourteen dunams of irrigated land
and the area cultivated by the contractor was accord-
ingly reduced. The settler was then supposed to derive about half his income from working as a laborer
for the contractor and half from working his own land
In the third year an additional area of land was to
be allocated to each household, and the contractor
gradually withdrew until by the fourth year the settler was farming his twenty dunams independently, although still under the control and supervision of the
settling authority. By this time the entire income
of the settler was supposed to come from working the
land. Families that had fallen behind in developing
their farms were allocated outside work to supplement
their income, while needy cases were helped from a
special mutual aid fund.

The intermediate stage started from the fourth
year and was to end about the seventh year when the
settler should have all his capital investment in
housing and equipment. In the Lakhish area the great
er part of the budget in the intermediate stage was
allocated for irrigation equipment to bring the total
area under intensive cultivation from thirty-five to
thirty-seven dunams. The agricultural instructor
still assisted the settler in this stage in farm operations. The settler has been regarded as a licensee
in both the introductory and intermediate stages. He
was authorized to use all equipment even though the
settlement authority retained complete ownership.

The final stage was to be reached not less than
ten years after the establishment of the settlement.

The climax of this stage was reached when the settler
and his wife signed the agreement of transfer of ownership. That is, the settler accepted all responsibility for all items contained in the inventory and
was now regarded as a debtor to the Jewish Agency
until he completely liquidated the loan. Capital
loaned to the settler by the Jewish Agency was now to
be repaid over a period of thirty-five years at a
3.5 per cent interest.

The actual stages of development, particularly
the intermediate stage, have often been prolonged
beyond the original schedule because of unavoidable
delays in capital advances and irrigation. There also has been the sad experience of village freed from
Jewish Agency guidance but needing to return some
years later when they faced financial difficulties.
There are advantages of remaining under Jewish Agency
guidance in not having to pay income tax and obtaining credit under more favorable terms. Seventy-four
moshavim, however, were released from Jewish Agency
control in 1967, and sixty-six were scheduled for
release in 1968.[9]

The economic activities in the provincial towns
and rural centers are not only for servicing farmers
in the villages, but also to employ members of the
village and the sons and daughters of farm proprie-
tors who cannot be absorbed in agriculture. One of
the most important reasons for regional development
has been the dispersion of national industry within
the development regions, using local raw materials
and supplying perquisites for local production. The
regional purchasing associations and regional councils are active in the development of such industries.

Parallel with the development of the agricultural sector in Lakhish, efforts were made to develop the
regional town of Kiryat Gat. The planning and actual
building of this town were also carried out by a special team that worked in close contact with the planners of agricultural settlement. The development of
Kiryat Gat deviated considerably from the original
plans because of the pressure of mass immigration.
Instead of becoming a small outling town serving only
as a center for services and for the processing of

agricultural produce of surrounding settlements,
originally planned for eight thousand inhabitants,
the town expanded to 16,300 persons by 1968.[10] This
called for additional sources of employment, especially the introduction of industrial plants not necessarily connected with the agricultural production of
the rural hinterland. According to the revised plan
the town is eventually to accommodate a population
of thirty thousand.[11]

     In addition to the industries in the provincial
town and processing and service industries for the
farmers in the regional centers and elsewhere, beginnings have been made with the help of supporting
institutions for the establishment of linked and
auxiliary types of industries to augment farm income.
Some marginal agricultural areas have a season that
is too short to secure an adequate living for the
farming population, and a suitable industry can fill
the gap by providing jobs in the slack season. An
example is tobacco farming in the northern highlands.
There is a slack season from October to February. A
plant was established for sorting, grading, and fer-
menting the tobacco leaves in this period. With some
additional branches tobacco farming and limited industrial processes result in a balanced and profitable
program for the farmer.

     There are auxiliary industries unrelated to agr
cultural production that may be promoted in rural
areas for the purpose of absorbing surplus manpower.
A number of enterprises of this kind have been established: one for the production of copper and brass
objects d'art, one for silver and other ornaments in
a regional center, and another in a moshav itself,
the first instance of industry in a moshav, for the
repair of jute sacks and production of other packing
materials. The distinguishing feature of an auxiliary
plant as compared to an ordinary factory located in
an urban industrial center is that its labor requirements are adjusted to the surplus manpower available
in the rural areas.

     Only beginnings have been made in the develop-
ment of such industries. In certain areas, particularly the hill and mountain areas of Galilee and the

Jerusalem Corridor, there may be opportunities for further development. The introduction of industry within the settlement is contrary to moshav ideology that considers the moshav to be a purely agricultural community. Whether it is practicable in supplementing rather than impeding the agricultural development of the village remains to be seen.

Need for Change in Moshav Structure

The previous chapter expanded on the moshav as a cooperative society with limited liability established to promote farming as the occupation and source of living for its members. Although the family is the basic unit of production and consumption, the moshav structure provides for the economic and social needs of its settlers. The organizational structure of the moshav ovdim demands members interested in agriculture, capable of working hard and improving their performance, members interested in cooperative living who can subordinate individualistic tendencies for the good of the cooperative and the community, and educated members competent to manage the cooperative and the public affairs of the village.

It soon became obvious that fundamental changes were needed in the structure of the moshav olim to maintain its very existence as an agricultural community and to protect those members who wished to become farmers from those who did not. Unlike the prestate settlers who founded the old moshavim, the new settlers lacked experience and training in agriculture and, in many cases, were not strongly motivated to become independent operators. This resulted in poor management of many of the farms. Special provisions were needed to tide the settlers over the first few critical years, for training them to become independent farmers, and to supply them with the necessary services to reach this goal.

The average size of farm was small, and there were fewer means of production than in the older moshavim. This meant a smaller output and turnover. Many members did not farm their plots. If the village

cooperative were to perform the services of the older moshavim, the farming settlers could not meet the
costs of the services from their relatively small
output. Because of the tight financial situation the
cooperative could not pay their members on time. This
induced the settlers to sell their produce to private
traders for immediate cash payment. Thus a vicious
circle was created whereby the position of the cooperative was further impaired. In addition, the cooperative was exploited by those who did not expect to
remain in the community but received credits for one
or two years of operation and then left the village
without repayment.

The immigrants from traditional societies in
the moshav olim were unfamiliar with the principle of
delegation of authority to elected officials and associated democratic practices underlying moshav self-
government procedures. They were neither equipped to
handle the responsibilties assigned them by the moshav
ovdim organization and ideology nor motivated to
adapt to the roles the community type prescribed.

Changes had to be made in the moshav structure
to transfer the locus of village services to a group
or regional basis. The villages had to be administered and serviced on a tight basis to assure their
success or at least to keep the settlers who wished
to remain in agriculture. The local village council
was still regarded as of importance as a possible
cohesive force in the development of the village. The
village cooperative was reduced to a precooperative
institution that, with the development of the village,
would be in a position to take on duties that could
be better and/or more cheaply performed at the village
level. The moshav olim became an administered community. Until its independence, the success of moshav
olim, as modified by the quality of its land, special
economic conditions, and the quality of its settlers
depends on the nature of its guidance in meeting the
needs of the settlers and developing them into progressive farmers. The evolution of the moshav olim
precooperative to the cooperative of the moshav ovdim
is a possibility for the future that is just beginning
to be realized. The role of the cooperative even in

a successful moshav olim is more limited than that
in a moshav ovdim.

Structure and Operation of Moshav Olim

There are far greater differences in structure
and operation among the moshvei olim than among the
moshvei ovdim. In the average moshav olim the number of facilities is likely to be fewer, and much
greater use is made of regional facilities or secondary cooperatives, and even private facilities, often
by the farmer acting directly on his own behalf rather than through a village official. The analysis of
the structure and operation of the moshav olim is in
terms of the services needed for moshav farming as
indicated in Figure 1 of the previous chapter. The
presentation of a macro view is more difficult for
the moshav olim than for the moshav ovdim, as there
are greater variations in structure and operation.

The physical centralization of service facilities in rural centers and regional towns has been
indicated in the analysis of the development of comprehensive regional planning in the new regions of
the country. Three new types of regional organizations have developed that provide many facilities and
services that have been traditionally in the province
of the village itself. These are the regional purchasing associations, regional councils, and the regional development associations.

The regional purchasing associations are active
in group purchasing, credit, to an increasing degree
in marketing, and conduct various processing and service operations. This has been entirely a poststate
development. There were thirty regional purchasing
associations in the country in 1966, of which eleven
serviced moshavim, each on the average of twenty to
thirty villages.[12] The national settler associations,
particularly the Moshav Movement, were primarily responsible for setting up these purchasing associations.
Each moshav contributes share capital. The moshavim
in the region are represented by elected members in
the boards of directors.

The purchasing associations pass on savings to farmers by mass purchasing. Perquisites are obtained through them on credit based on the production plans of the village as worked out by the economic planners. The purchasing organizations have also been responsible for operating the consumer cooperatives in most of the new villages. They encourage the village to take over the cooperative when it is in a position to do so. They also make consumer loans for such items as refrigerators and stoves and for ceremonial occasions such as bar mitzvahs and weddings. All such loans are backed by co-signers. Most loans before 1965 were for a one-year period. New longer term loans have been made in recent years, for example, two-year farm credit loans to increase poultry production so that the village may obtain higher allotments in subsequent years. The loans are based on the village plans and have village endorsements. The purchasing associations charged 6 per cent for credit in 1965, lower than would be obtained from other sources.

The purchasing associations have a good reputation on the credit market as they have the mutual guarantee of member settlements. Closely associated with the moshavim, since they are organized on a regional basis and have frequent contact with the settlers, these organizations serve as representatives for the settlements to the government in the case of subsidies, payments for damages caused by natural elements, government loans, etc.

The directorate of the purchasing organizations, as indicated, is elected by representatives of its member settlements. In addition, there is a joint secretariat for all purchasing associations that is concerned with coordinating their activities on a country-wide scale as well as representing them jointly in dealing with government agencies, the Histadrut, banks, and other institutions.

New developments have emerged in recent years. Many purchasing associations have added processing and other service enterprises to their basic purchasing and credit functions. They have constructed large

feed mills, installations for produce sorting, refrigeration warehouses, and slaughterhouses. A second
important development has been their entry into the
marketing of agricultural produce. This is only natural for the commodities for which they have processing and first-stage marketing facilities. Some of
the regional organizations serve as regional agents
of the countrywide marketing institutions in certain
types of produce. In many of the newly established
agricultural settlements, where the local cooperative
is weak because of the lack of efficient leadership,
the individual settler can bypass the local cooperative both in the purchasing of supplies and the marketing of produce and deal directly with the regional
association.

Regional councils are the municipal bodies of
the agricultural regions. They are located at rural
and regional centers. Each comprises about ten to
twenty settlements. In 1965, there were 49 regional
councils embracing 650 settlements.[13] They report to
the Ministry of the Interior. Only about half their
budget, however, is from the Ministry. The rest
originates from the settlements and council economic
activities. Each settlement elects a representative
to the regional council which in turn elects its director. Council terms are for four years.

The regional council is principally concerned
with (1) general administration, (2) local services
such as sanitation, public security, upkeep of local
roads, fire brigades, public buildings, and gardens,
etc., (3) state services such as education and culture, hospitals, social aid and welfare, and religious services, (4) public utilities such as water
supply, and (5) increasingly in recent years, with
economic services and functions. The regional council itself administers many activities and also provides space and facilities for activities supported
and operated by other entities. It is concerned with
the efficiency and quality of all its activities for
the service of its member settlements.

The social, administrative, and municipal services are very important in the development of the

moshav olim. The council runs the district elementary school for children aged six to fourteen, operates the buses for transporting the children to and
from the schools, and supplies hot school lunches.
It is also responsible for the cultural activities
of the settlements in the area, which include youth
activities, adult education, and libraries. Adult
education includes evening classes held in the school-
rooms in winter, agricultural subjects, and village
administration. The youth center arranges education
and cultural activities for adolescents above compulsory school age but not yet liable to military service. Evening classes are held for those who have
not completed their elementary education and in agricultural subjects. There are classes for girls in
home economics, hygiene, and cooking. The youth center also serves as a club for adolescents and adults,
offering leisure-time activities and classes.

The council operates the community health center serving the entire district. The center is supported by the Kupat Holim (sick fund) of the Histadrut
The center engages in both therapeutic and preventive
medicine and is responsible for the health of the
family and community as a whole. It is staffed by a
doctor and a nurse. The doctor receives patients in
his clinic daily and visits the village mother-and-
child welfare centers frequently. The nurse runs the
clinic, supervises the village nurses, and is responsible for the medical care, preventive measures, and
health education in the district school.

The regional council has a benevolent fund for
mutual aid in case of emergencies, extending short-
term loans without interest. The council also provides
a public legal advisor. It also includes a religious
council concerned with providing for the settlers'
religious needs. An itinerant rabbi who visits the
village on schedule is in charge of this service.

One of the more important administrative services in the moshav olim is the district accounting
service developed by the settlement authority at the
rural centers in conjunction with the regional councils. The maintenance of the accounting and control
service at the village level proved unsatisfactory.

Centralization of the accounting services for the
Negev at Jewish Agency regional headquarters at Beersheba was not successful because of the difficulty of
contact and identification with the villages and
farmers in the utilization of the accounts for the
analysis and improvement of farm operations. Decentralization of the accounting services to a district
level is proving successful. The accounting service
prepares a monthly statement for the farmer and a
quarterly statement for the village. Annual statements for the farmers in the Northern Negev were made
for the first time in 1965, in addition to the annual
statements for the village. The use of the annual
farm settlements will be helpful in improving planning
and performance at the farm level. There are little
if any savings in cost over preparation of the statements at the village. The main advantage is the preparation of more accurate and detailed statements.

A common economic service at the rural center
is the tractor section, operated as a subsidiary of
the settlement authority for leasing tractors and
heavy equipment to farmers in the settlements serviced
by the council. Its aim was to reduce the investment
of the village in heavy equipment and to supply technical knowledge in mechanical operations. The ultimate aim was for it to be taken over by the settlers
on a cooperative basis. This process is now going on.
The tractor stations made arrangements with the villages for the collective cultivation of dry farming
lands. This operation also is now being taken over
by the villages on a regional cooperative or settlement basis.

The regional council supports a fruit and vegetable marketing center operated under the jurisdiction of Tnuva, the national cooperative marketing
association. Other marketing facilities operated by
the regional council include cold storage plants,
poultry slaughterhouses, etc. The shops for agricultural supplies are maintained at the center by the
regional purchasing association. The councils frequently operate bakeries and laundries.

The regional councils are undertaking increasing economic activities, more in the case of the

kibbutz than the moshav, but substantially in the
case of the latter. They have promoted and become
partners in industrial activities. They and the regional purchasing associations have promoted regional development cooperatives for the moshavim.

For example, the duties of the development cooperative in the Lakhish area, started in 1964, were
(1) to conduct the communal cultivation of dry farming for villages in the region, (2) similarly to conduct the communal cultivation of the village orchards
in the area, and (3) to conduct a transportation cooperative. The trucks in the transportation cooperative are the property of the individual farmer in the
moshavim and are pooled and leased for use in the
region. The cooperative was planning to operate a
tractor pool in the same way. It has been found that
the pooling of privately owned equipment for serving
the area works more efficiently than the machine-
tractor station operated by the settlement authority.
In this connection it engages in the mass purchase
and sale of petrol for farmers. The cooperative was
also preparing to organize an enterprise for the export of flowers to Europe.

The regional development corporation is another
instance of a secondary cooperative organized for the
new moshavim, subscribed to by their share capital,
and represented by the moshavim on the board of directors. This is an example of a secondary cooperative taking over duties from the settlement authority
and conducting them more efficiently on a cooperative
basis with direct participation and control by the
moshavim themselves.

The committees of the regional council in which
the settlers are represented through the village committees commonly include agriculture, leadership,
control, welfare, culture and education, and contracts
and bids. The effectiveness of the regional councils
vary. They provide services for the village more efficiently, including services that could not be provided by the villagers themselves. Examples of the
voluntary surrender of duties from the village to the
regional council include (1) regional schools--cheaper

and better than village schools; (2) water supply--
local wells no longer sufficient; (3) drainage; and
(4) health control. In many instances cooperation
through the regional council has helped the new
moshav develop a sense of community responsibility
and cooperation in improving village services.

The regional council is a two-tier authority
with the village council the first tier. The main
difficulty frequently is in the village council.
This had led to the transfer of local services such
as garbage collection, street lighting, and maintenance of roads from the village council to the regional council. Attempts are made by education to make
the village assume those duties that it could perform efficiently itself.

The regional councils, like the regional purchasing associations, are organized on a national
level; they represent the interest of the villages
before government agencies, the Histadrut, banks, and
other institutions, and channel government and other
assistance to the villages. In their industrial and
economic companies they cooperate with the regional
purchasing associations at the national level, dealing with government institutions, Histadrut, and
other institutions in obtaining guidance, assistance
in legal matters, taxes, and technical problems.

Besides the basic capital investment the settlement authority maintains supervised credit programs that are coordinated with the village production
plans. At first the loans were made directly by the
Settlement Department. After bad experiences with
such loans their issuance was shifted to private banks.
Half the revolving funds needed for these loans are
contributed by the bank. The settlement authority
guarantees the bank 100 per cent of its money in the
event of failure of repayment. The loans are made by
the bank at 6 per cent interest. The borrower must
provide three sureties: two neighbors and the village
secretary. This new system of short-term credits has
completely changed the attitude of the settlers towards loans. The refund of loans rose from 35 per
cent to 95 per cent, and the requests for loans fell.[14]

This has helped to make more money available by the
settlement authority for other development needs.

Normally the moshavim, as all villages in the
cooperative sector, sell through Tnuva, the national
marketing cooperative. Sales are usually handled
collectively through the village cooperative. Tnuva
operates on a commission basis, and it may take a
number of months for returning the proceeds from sales
through the village cooperative.

This system was not adaptable to the new
moshavim, where the village cooperative was weak. The
settlers were not educated in cooperative marketing,
and they needed immediate cash. The problem of selling outside Tnuva channels was especially acute in
fruits and vegetables, where farmers could market directly to dealers at a nearby town, or dealers would
come to the village to buy.

To alleviate this problem, Tnuva, with the financial cooperation of the Settlement Department and
the Ministry of Agriculture, set up in 1956 a subsidiary Nov that bought produce from the farmer for cash
based on prevailing market prices. Nov assumed the
responsibility for premarketing activities: sorting
and grading performed at the rural center or village
by a settler trained by Tnuva, transporting the produce to the Tnuva regional centers, and billing the
farmers individually. In cases where there was a
surplus over the sums paid, Nov returned the monay
to the village to show the advantages of cooperative
marketing. Through educational campaigns Nov has
started to transfer the villages over to marketing on
a commission basis but still provides premarket services and individual billing. About twenty villages
were handled on this basis in 1965.[15]

While the Nov arrangement has had some effect
in reducing marketing outside cooperative channels,
there is still a fair share going on for some commodities. Cooperative settlements are no longer legally
obliged to market through Tnuva. About fifteen villages in 1965 did not.[16] Even well-established villages such as Nahalal, that market through Tnuva, use

other channels also, but in an organized way including all farmers through the village cooperative. In
the moshav olim a certain amount of private selling
is tolerated since credits are obtained by co-signers,
and money returned to the regional purchasing association can be used for future moshav activities. In
the village such selling is usually organized by
family groups, consisting of two or three groups in
the village. With the consolidation of the village
even such marketing may be done on a community-
cooperative basis.

In addition to the reorganization of the village services to suit the needs of the new settlers,
the moshav olim has been given many other special
benefits: price, transportation, water, credit subsidies, and volunteer help from the older settlements
to improve its agriculture and social and cultural
services.

There are now a minimum of service facilities
in the individual moshav olim, especially those in
the comprehensive regional planning projects. There
has been, however, a constant evaluation of the administration and types of services offered. There
has been a change in some services from centralized
administration by the settlement authority and the
national marketing agency to a regional cooperative
organization in which the villages have more direct
control. This has occurred in communal farming, communal orchards, transportation and machinery pools,
and in the marketing of certain commodities. At the
same time beginnings of transferal of administration
from national and regional organizations to the village level have taken place, for example, in the
maintenance of water supplies, consumer cooperative
stores, and the cultivation of village orchards.

The case of water supply offers an interesting
example. In many new villages some settlers did not
pay their water bills, and the water supply for the
entire village was turned off. Arrangements were
then made for supplying and billing each farmer individually in return for an extra fee. The water
company, through the regional councils, arranged,

for still another additional fee, to keep the village
water networks and meters in proper condition. Steps
were then taken by the settlement authority and the
regional councils to organize water associations, in
which the consumers themselves would be members, to
handle all matters pertaining to water. This has
helped the better villages to take over the maintenance of their water supplies and thus obtain savings
on this service.

Unlike other developing countries, the postwar
settlement problem in Israel has been to move people
from town to country rather than to find employment
for the surplus farm population in the cities. There
was a security need to settle the borders and the
entire country and to have a rural population larger
than that dictated by economic considerations alone.
In addition to the numerous difficulties encountered
in the transfer of urban population to the land, in
Israel there have been the additional difficulties
of adjustment to a life that was centuries ahead of
that in the immigrants' countries of origin. The need
for the State to integrate all immigrants into one
nation imposed a heavy burden of social nonagricultural problems on top of the many sufficiently complex agricultural problems.

In order to meet these difficulties in the
moshav olim, extension work in Israel is organized
not only to help in the agro-technical and economic
aspects of farming but in the social adjustments of
the settlers as well. It is not confined only to
educational activities, but is also concerned with
the actual implementation of settlement activities
and with the planning and supervision of settlement
operations. Extension work as a whole has been designed to achieve these main goals: (1) to encourage settlers to adopt a more positive attitude toward
the idea of working their own land and to build up
self-confidence in their ability to do so, (2) to
foster sound agricultural practices and develop a
secure village economy based on adequate family income from individual holdings, and (3) to promote
active cooperation among the farmers and to pave the
way for independence of the village and the gradual

transfer of authority and responsibility to the settlers' own elected body, the village council.

Extension work is carried on at three levels:
local, district, and regional. The following description is primarily concerned with the organization of
extension in the Lakhish region. It operates in the
same way in other regions where comprehensive regional planning has been adopted and with variations,
since 1956, in other areas.

The village in its intermediate stage has a
team of five extension workers: the general instructor, agricultural instructor, home economic instructor, kindergarten teacher, and nurse.

The general instructor acted as the over-all
guide and mentor to the village. Initially he headed
the staff team and served as the village general secretary, both for internal and external affairs. His
influence was mainly to develop a democratic atmos-
phere in the village, especially through the election
of a village council to make and execute village policy. The general instructors have usually been chosen
by the national moshav organizations from veteran villages. While they have played a role in the development of the moshav olim, they have not been a complete
success. They are now being phased out as the villages achieve economic maturity, and those remaining
have responsibilities in more than one moshav.

The agricultural instructors' main task has
been teaching the settlers to perform elementary farm
operations and the timing and coordination of all
branches of farming. Their role has become more important over time. They service one village and generally remain in it until it reaches an independence
stage. Most agricultural instructors are quite young,
and many are of Oriental origin. They, as well as the
social instructors, have taken courses conducted by
the settlement authority, including sociology and village development. They generally work with the best
farmers and use their development as examples to the
others. All farmers are visited every two weeks, and
their technical problems are discussed. In many

moshavim the agricultural instructors perform the
functions of the internal secretary in the veteran
village. Originally the settlement authority thought
it best for the agricultural instructor to live in
the rural center and devote full time to his job. As
their salaries were not high, this was not a success,
and there was a large turnover. Most agricultural
instructors in recent years have, themselves, farmed
in a neighboring village. Their success as commercial farmers has enhanced their prestige as instructors.

The job of the home economics instructor is to
promote a stable, healthy family life, quite important because of the revolutionary changes the family
undergoes in resettlement. She emphasizes family
budgeting and teaches the women skills such as sewing
and food preservation. She encourages the women to
strive for a higher standard of living, and, in cooperation with the nurse, instructs them in mother and
child care. Home economics instructors usually serve
a number of villages.

The village nurse is concerned with both the
treatment and prevention of disease. She visits the
homes of the settlers regularly and instructs all
families in methods of health and hygiene. She administers the village first aid clinic and decides
when patients have to be referred to the doctor in
the rural center. She works with the village committee on all matters concerned with public hygiene and
supervises the hygiene of the children attending the
kindergarten.

The work of the community team has changed emphasis with the development of the village, and quality rather than number of instructors has become more
important. The extension work of the community team
has been important in the development of the village,
and in transforming poor villages to good ones.

Extension work at the district level has worked
out of the health center of the rural center. The
team has included the district physician and nurse,
the social worker and director of social activities

of the regional council, the secretary of the rural
center, a representative of the school staff, and a
community worker who heads the team. The main object
of the district extension work is to coordinate efforts, exchange information, and encourage cooperation
among all team members to improve the quality of the
instruction and guidance by the local instructors.
The work at the district level frees the local extension workers for many more immediate, practical, day-
to-day tasks. The results of this team work have in
general been positive.

Extension work at the regional level has operated from the regional office of the settlement
authority and is concerned mainly with providing technical expertise and over-all economic planning. The
regional extension workers, including specialists in
all branches of farming, irrigation, and farm management, visit the moshavim on a regular schedule and
keep local personnel informed of agronomic and technical developments. The regional farm planners constantly examine and try to improve the profitability
of farm enterprises and the farm unit. The extension
service has realized that in the new villages group
activities and mass media used in veteran moshavim
and kibbutzim are relatively ineffective and has emphasized individual instruction by personal farm
visits. The regional specialists thus work closely
with the village agricultural instructors.

In addition, agricultural specialists in both
the new and old regions have been constantly striving
to develop new species and products in the many research substations scattered throughout the country.
The development of new products and new methods of
culture is of particular importance in the new development regions. The agricultural instructor frequently uses demonstration plots in the village, often with
the cooperation of selected farmers.

What then remains as the function of the village
council in view of the decentralization of services
outside the village? The growth of regional cooperatives and district services has developed leadership
in the villages, and the settlers can actually see how

cooperative activity in which the village takes part
increases their incomes and improves their services.
They can see that these new regional institutions are
set up and operate not for profit but are organizations in which the settlers participate for the welfare of the villages in the area.

The village council is the vehicle by which
representatives are chosen for the regional cooperatives and for the district committees of the regional
council at the rural center. It is also the instrument by which the services in the village are conducted, by which local taxes are collected, and through
which a united front is presented to district, regional, and national authorities. It is the unit
through which the village can assume additional local
functions. It is still important in the economic and
social consolidation of the village. Under the regional structure decisions on principle taken by the
village council must be ratified by the regional
council and are then binding on the village.

In any event, a council with a secretary and
treasurer is needed to conduct the affairs of the
village. The duties of the external and internal
secretaries may be combined in one person. One of
the instructors or a representative of the settlement authority may take on one of these positions on
a full- or part-time basis, at least through the intermediate stage of village development. The village
secretary may also be responsible for some fiscal
matters, particularly the collection of local taxes.
Other fiscal and control aspects of the village are
diffused to the regional organizations, principally
the regional purchasing associations and the regional councils.

The village council in the moshav olim is generally smaller than in the veteran moshavim. It
corresponds to their executive committee, consisting
of five to seven persons. In the better Oriental
villages the council now consists of the younger,
more successful farmers. Each may be in charge of
one of the village services, such as operating the
consumer store or the dairy, and may receive a stipend

for his services. In addition, all the members operate their own farms. The council meets weekly, but
the general assembly meets two to four times a year,
less often than in the established moshavim.

Will the precooperative develop into a full
cooperative as in the established villages? There
is considerable doubt on this matter, since farmers
are able to deal individually with the secondary cooperatives, particularly the regional purchasing associations. The advantages of cooperative endeavor,
however, are being learned by the new moshavim, especially through their work with regional cooperatives
and associations. The final test of guided settlement, of course, will come after independence of the
villages, when it will be seen whether managed villages can dispense with outside guidance and manage
their own farms and affairs.

One of the tests of the new moshavim and a rationale for assisting their development within a cooperative structure may be the possibility of the
local cooperative framework to accommodate a reallo-
cation of holdings in order to allow for a rising
standard of living. The problem of the availability
of sufficient inputs is more acute in the newer
moshavin than in the older established ones. The size
of the family is larger. There is also more part-time
farming and a greater variability of incomes from
farming. In some of the established moshavim consolidation of holdings for larger units is being undertaken by the cooperative. Whether this could be
possible in the moshav olim is conjectural.

While the future structure and functions of the
new moshavim when they are independent cannot be fore-
cast with any degree of certainty, the success of
their development to independence has been due principally to the pragmatic approach of guided development by the settlement authority as aided by other
institutions. This has involved changing the structure of prewar moshavim, first, by changing the locus
of basic services from the village to outside the village, and, second, from national institutions to regional institutions in which the settlers share

control. It has also assisted the villages to perform
their more limited duties competently and to help
them gradually reassume those duties that they can
perform more efficiently. Both the settlement authority as well as the other institutions supporting settlement have modified their policies to meet the
needs of the new farmers and to ease the administrative burden of the moshav olim.

Guidance at the village level in farm planning
has been strict. It has been necessary, however, to
protect the postwar development of the moshavim and
for the maintenance of the agricultural structure of
the country as a whole.

The over-all problem of guided development that
culminated in comprehensive regional planning was how
to initiate an evolutionary process through which heterogeneous ethnic groups would fuse, ultimately
emerging as a closely-knit, cooperating community of
agriculturalists skilled in modern technology and
planning techniques. Although mistakes have been
made, the guided development of settlement has evolved
pragmatic solutions that have developed settlements
into successful agricultural communities. The process
is not complete, and continued development of the
settlements and even new settlement planning on a
limited basis will call for a continued pragmatic approach to changes in the structure and functions of
the moshavim.

Investments in Moshav Olim

The standards of investment in the four principal types of farms in 1960 prices are shown in Table
20. On the average, the capital invested by the settlement authority to the final period has been calculated to be IL 30,000 at 1960 price levels. Prices
in 1967 were over 30 per cent higher.[17] The investment costs in new settlements are constantly rising.
In 1965, they were as high as IL 50,000 in the Upper
Galilee and in the Arava areas of the South Negev.[18]

Repayment of the investment begins only when
the total allocation of IL 30,000 has been advanced.

As indicated, the period of repayment is thirty-five
years, and interest of 3.5 per cent is charged over
that period. No interest is charged until the whole
of the IL 30,000 has been invested.

TABLE 20

Average Investment in Principal Types
of Moshav Farms
(Israeli Pounds, 1960 Prices)

	Hill Farm	Dairy Farm	Field Crops Farm	Citrus Farm
Housing, road access, and electricity	10,150	8,645	8,675	8,675
Farm buildings	7,540	5,440	5,180	3,560
Irrigation	4,500	3,160	4,480	3,790
Livestock	2,050	2,170	1,650	1,050
Tools	1,190	1,670	1,820	1,470
Plantations	6,000	3,000	2,400	6,000
Circulating capital	800	1,000	2,000	1,000
Water	1,000	1,000	1,000	1,000
Miscellaneous	3,850	2,915	2,795	1,985
Total[a]	37,500	29,000	30,000	29,500

[a]Rounded.

Source: Benjamin Kaplan and Avsholom Rokach,
"Rural Resettlement in Israel" (paper presented to
Interregional Technical Meeting on Rural Resettlement
conducted by the International Labor Office, Ashkelon,
April-May, 1965), pp. 14-15.

In addition to the investment of the IL 30,000
per farm unit, the government and the settlement
authority together invest an additional IL 15,000
per farm unit in public works such as regional water
schemes, roads, forestation, etc.[19] This sum is not
repayable by the settler. On the other hand, communal services in the village and investments in communal building are debited to each farm unit and are
repayable. These sums are not included in Table 20.
They amount to IL 1,330 for field crop farms in the
Lakhish area.[20]

In order to make the maximum use of the resources given by the settlement authority, an additional investment of 30 per cent over the IL 30,000
is required. This additional investment is expected
to be provided by the settler himself, either by in-
vesting accumulated profits or by a special development loan given by the Ministry of Agriculture after
the agricultural settlement authority has completed
its capital investment. Development loans have been
available at an interest rate of 7 per cent and are
repayable over a ten-year period.[21]

The total cost of agricultural settlement runs
much higher than these basic investments. It includes, in addition, the administrative overhead of
the institutions involved in settlement and all the
additional subsidies to the new settlements.

DEVELOPMENT OF MOSHAV OLIM

Full-scale guided administration of the moshav
olim by the settlement authority in conjunction with
the other institutions did not evolve until 1955.
While the system of comprehensive regional development
was developed primarily for settling new areas of the
country, many of its basic principles in administered
moshav development, particularly micro farm planning
and consolidation of moshav services to district and
regional bases, were applied to the already existing
moshvei olim throughout the country. Substantive
economic development of many of the new settlements,
particularly those settled by immigrants from Moslem
countries, did not really begin until 1955.

This does not mean that there was no guidance or planning before 1955. In the first two years of crash settlement after the founding of the State, the new settlements produced little surpluses for market. In the consolidation period of 1952-54, the settlement authorities were mainly concerned with the single-settlement approach and greatly underestimated the period needed for the economic development of the new villages. The settlement authorities made capital investments in the new moshavim based on the needs of the various types of farming, but the amounts were insufficient, and the settlers were not properly trained to use the capital to best advantage. They misused farm machinery, and they did not adapt easily to dairy and poultry farming.

The national moshav organizations supplied volunteer instructors, mainly older men from the veteran settlements, particularly in the period of 1952 to 1954. The number, however, was insufficient. The instructors often had difficulty in adjustment to the situations in the new moshavim, particularly where the settlers were of Oriental origin.

As the progress of the new villages was slower than expected, the authorities realized that more instructors were needed and that they should live in the new villages with their families for a longer period of time. The older instructors were, in fact, commuters, returning to their own villages on weekends. It also became evident that there had to be a differentiation of instructors for the various social, economic, techno-agricultural, and home adjustment problems of the settlers. The new instructors were second generation volunteers from the established villages and also from the kibbutzim. By the end of 1954, there were 250 instructors in 40 moshavim, 217 of them from the veteran moshavim.[22] These instructors worked mainly in the Negev and the Jerusalem Corridor.

The new instructors volunteered for a period of two years. In 1956, further mobilization of instructors on a more permanent basis was carried out by the settlement authority from a variety of sources:

the Jewish Agency itself, the national moshav movements, former kibbutz members, and graduates of agricultural schools. The candidates agreed, after about
a year of study, to work for a certain number of years
in the moshavim. The courses for moshav instructors
organized in 1957 were for eight months, six for theoretical studies and two devoted to practical work.
The subjects scheduled included rural administration,
economics, sociology, farm management, and technical
agriculture. The practical exercises included study
of moshav operations and administration of different
types of moshavim in different stages of development.
As the courses progressed, the participation of young
people from the new immigrant families increased. By
1957-58, the systemization of more effective instructor leadership on a professional basis had been accomplished.

In 1954, the contribution of mutual aid by the
veteran villages took on a new form--that of mutual
sponsorship, which reached its culmination in 1956.
Forty villages participated in this program, mainly
in the areas of more concentrated veteran settlements.[23] The veteran moshav adopted the nearest immigrant moshav and visited it regularly (at least
once a week) to help solve its social and economic
problems. The sponsorship committee consisted of a
representative of the village council, the consumer
cooperative, one or two of the member committees, and
a representative of the youth. Although they dealt
with all the problems presented them, they were mainly concerned with the organization of the consumers'
cooperative, mutual aid, and educational and cultural
activities. The home-defense units of the Army also
sponsored twenty young moshavim.[24] This was over
and above the volunteer contributions of soldiers in
the field of education in the immigrant moshavim.

Although the volunteer work was helpful on an
emergency basis, it failed to meet many of the basic
needs of the new settlements in a systematic way. It
gave the settlement authority and supporting institutions time to reorganize their own services, to study
the problems more carefully, and evolve solutions for
them.

The organization of managed farms for unsuccess-
ful villages was first proposed by the Moshav Movement in late 1953 to the settlement authority.[25] Many
new moshavim had ceased agricultural operations. The
settlers considered the village as a place of forced
residence. The new approach of managed farming for
the village as a whole by the settlement authority or
a private contractor to reintegrate the settlers in
agriculture was first tried in 1954 on a limited
scale. Adopted in the Lakhish region in 1955, it has
since been applied on a national basis as the standard way of absorbing settlers into agriculture, the
first stage in guided settlement. The burden of the
first few years of settlement was thus shifted from
the village cooperative to the settlement contractor.

As previously indicated, general economic progress by 1954 in most of the immigrant villages, especially those of the Oriental settlers, was not
very satisfactory. The number of people who had left
the villages was very high, particularly in the newer
areas of the country, the Negev, and the Jerusalem
corridor, where settling conditions were difficult,
and many villages had ceased agricultural operations
entirely.

In 1954, a detailed study of moshavim estimated
the net farm income of all poststate moshavim in that
year to be IL 1,000, as compared to IL 4,800 for the
prestate established farms.[26] The poststate moshavim
included 179 moshvei olim and twenty-five new moshavim
settled by Israeli residents. The average number of
man-days worked per farm for the immigrant moshavim
was 195 compared to 260 for the poststate moshavim
settled by natives.[27] According to the standard of
450 man-days required for a well-developed farm, all
the new moshavim were underdeveloped. The average
income estimate of IL 1,000 for the moshav olim may
have been liberal.

The study indicated that even in the better
poststate farms income was barely sufficient to provide for a modest standard of living. This was as-
cribed to insufficient capital, lack of experience,
and deficient cooperative organization. The main

income of the new settlers was from outside work.
Their farms could be regarded only as auxiliary
farms.

A study of the Department of Agricultural Economics of the Hebrew University Faculty of Agriculture is very insightful as to conditions in the
better-than-average poststate immigrant moshavim in
1954. It includes a detailed economic and social
study of twelve moshavim of settlers of European
origin in densely settled, good agricultural areas
in the country. As a check it also included three
backward poststate moshavim of Yemenite settlers in
the Jerusalem hills, the Jerusalem corridor, and the
Negev, three new areas of settlement where development was only in its initial stages.

The educational level in the European moshavim
was about the same as that for the entire country at
the time. About half the heads of families had elementary education, and more than a fifth, secondary
education. About a third of the immigrants had been
engaged in primary and secondary occupations, 11 per
cent in agriculture, and 24 per cent in industry and
other handicrafts in their country of origin (about
half in tertiary occupations), while the others had
either no specific occupation or were at school.
Over two fifths came directly to the moshav on arrival in the country and only 8 per cent from temporary
billets. Over 40 per cent received some sort of preliminary agricultural training. The average size of
family was 4.1 persons.[28]

In the three Yemenite moshavim, 98 per cent of
the man had received a traditional home Jewish Bible
education. Almost 60 per cent of the women were illiterate. About 70 per cent of the heads of families
had been craftsmen of various kinds, 18 per cent had
engaged in trade, and 6 per cent were farmers. Almost
70 per cent of the Yemenite settlers came to the village from temporary billets, and the other 30 per
cent were sent directly to the moshav. The average
size of family was 5.5 persons.[29]

Most of the settlers were recruited to come to
the moshav by the national settlement organizations.

About half claimed they had chosen the moshav for
economic reasons or because of their desire for independence.[30]

The net cash income from agriculture could
only be estimated for five of the settlements. In
four, it was between IL 1,300 and IL 1,600, while in
the other it was below IL 500 per family. The farm
produce for home consumption raised the income from
IL 500 to IL 700 per family. More than half the
settlers also performed outside work, almost 80 per
cent of these on a casual basis and 20 per cent as
public employees of the moshavim. The income of the
five moshavim including outside work varied from IL
2,000 to IL 3,300. In the same year the average income of the urban hired worker family was IL 2,500.
Thus the total average income in a better-than-
average immigrant moshav was more than that of an
average urban worker, although a substantial part of
this income came from nonfarm sources.[31]

The amount of own investment as percentage of
capital averaged 12 to 15 per cent. In the five
moshavim with income data the real burden of debt
payments varied from 4 to 41 per cent of the net farm
cash income and between 2 to 10 per cent of the total
family income. Including an estimation of farm wages
the settlers earned 4 to 11 per cent on invested capital, and profits ranged from IL 15 to IL 30. The
depreciated replacement value of the property exceeded the nominal debt by at least 60 per cent because
of the inflation.[32]

Of the twelve moshavim eleven were planned as
mixed dairy farms, with dairy, field crops, poultry,
commercial fruit orchards, and dry-farming branches.
The settlers, however, deliberately refrained from
developing mixed-farming branches. The settlers did
not develop mixed farms, choosing instead to specialize in a few branches. About one third of the farms
had only one branch and half only two. This created
many different farm types. Thus the possible advantages of relatively homogeneous types of farms, with
greater efficiency in the village production and
marketing services, were obviated.

Dairy was the most important branch. Most settlers wanted large cattle herds that afforded a dependable income and the possible accumulation of large amounts of liquid capital. Vegetables represented the second most important branch. The capital output ratio in this branch was low, and it was labor intensive. Poultry served mainly as a source of self-supply. There was no poultry enterprise in 24 per cent of the farms, and in only 5 per cent were there more than a hundred laying hens.[33] This branch was underdeveloped because of lack of investment capital on the part of both the Settlement Authority and the farmers themselves.

The communal branches, orchards and grain farming, were poorly operated. They merely provided paid work for the settlers, who saw no advantage in this work compared to any other labor away from home. The orchards either had not reached the stage of bearing fruit or were abandoned or neglected. Grain farming was not profitable; yet, prices charged to the settlers for grain were the same as market prices. As a matter of fact, grain farming was changing from dry to irrigated culture. About 40 per cent of the area in the sample produced grain. The seasonal nature of this branch and the poor operation of communal cultivation were primarily responsible for its low level of performance.[34]

These farms were far from their stage of full development. The average plot for the settler amounted to 11.3 dunams, including common orchards, compared to 26.5 dunams according to the plan.[35] The settlers raised surplus amounts of vegetables on about half their crop acreage, thus creating difficult problems in marketing and in achieving proper crop rotations. The farmers were not able to use all the available water, mainly because of insufficient irrigation equipment.

The village institutions in the twelve moshavim were still being formed and defined, generally along the lines of the model of the moshav ovdim. Because of the lack of stability in the moshav municipal and economic institutions, there was a high turnover in

personnel. The main jobs were filled by members as
part-time workers on a short-term basis. The tax
system was not yet fully operational. Although the
collections were usually handled as deductions by
the moshav cooperative, payments were often in ar-
rears, the average debt per settler varying from IL
100 to IL 500.[36]

The principal economic institutions had not as
yet achieved efficient operations. The agricultural
machinery service had not been properly organized.
Ten of the villages had their own machinery organizations, while five (including the three backward
Yemenite villages) were serviced by regional tractor
stations. Neither method had demonstrated particular
efficiency, and it was hard to judge which was better. The settlers used three means of marketing: (1)
the national cooperative, Tnuva, (2) private dealers,
and (3) direct sales to consumers. Marketing was inefficient, and the cost of marketing high. The au-
thors believed that the economic activities carried
on in the immigrant moshavim by the several authorities were insufficiently coordinated.

On the social side a start in mutual aid had
been made in all the villages by either unpaid volunteer help in farm work, financial help, loans, or
a combination of loans and grants. Social cases
were supported by the village, sometimes with the
added assistance of outside authorities. All the
villages had a dispensary and nurse and were visited
by nonresident physicians. All the moshavim had kin-
dergartens, and most of them had elementary classes
in the villages with trained teachers. Some of the
adolescents received vocational training at agricultural schools.

The budget for cultural activities was inadequate, ranging from IL 15 to IL 21 per month for the
entire village. There were no youth organizations
in three of the twelve European moshavim and none in
the three Yemenite villages. The most important form
of entertainment was the cinema.[37]

Most of the economic development of the moshav
olim has been achieved since 1954. As already

indicated, the average net income from farming in
the 1964-65 period is estimated as about IL 5,500.
The Jewish Agency estimates IL 5,000 and the Histadrut, IL 6,000. The relative net farm-income position of the moshav olim as compared to the moshav
ovdim rose from less than 20 per cent in 1954 to 60
per cent in the 1964-65 period.* If the value of the
food consumed in the home and outside earnings are
added to their net farm incomes, total earnings of
farmers in the moshav olim are higher than those of
urban workers. Their housing and other social amenities compare favorably.

There have been no national economic studies
of the development of the moshav olim since 1954 or
of the farm management aspects of the new moshavim.
Only in 1964 was a national sample set up by the Institute of Farm Income Research to ascertain the development of national farm income on a yearly basis.
Unfortunately its work at present is limited to only
a few enterprises. There is a plethora of statistical data, however, at the district and regional offices and the headquarters of the Joint Planning Center
at Tel-Aviv. Practically all the farm-income data
is based on the use of income norms that generally
have a downward bias. The reports from the region
to headquarters have a downward bias, since their
main purpose is not just intelligence but to present
a case for additional capital investments and allotments of controlled products for the region. Similarly, the headquarters reports have a downward bias
to emphasize the need for additional capital investments in agriculture. There is sufficient material,
however, to appraise the income position of the moshav
olim and the rate of development as between different
regions and different types of farms.

The Central Region of the settlement authority
that extends from north of Tel-Aviv to the Lakhish

------

*The Settlement Department of the Jewish Agency
estimated a substantial improvement in the relative
net income position of the moshav olim by 1967, possibly by as much as 20 per cent.

region in the south has a farm accounting service to
help farmers improve their management practices. The
sample is not a random one and is limited to fifteen
villages near the regional headquarters of Rehovot.
Only four of the villages are Oriental settlements.
It, therefore, has an upward bias insofar as regional and national representation are concerned. It
provides material on the economic development of the
villages founded in the 1949-51 period that have a
good location and are well developed. Most of the
farms are of the mixed-dairy type and, in that respect, represent a bringing up-to-date of some of
the economic data of the Halperin-Yalon study of
1954. The latter study, however, included more farms
and was not restricted to the same region, although
most of the villages in the study were in the region.

As indicated in Table 21, the average net farm
income in this sample of forty-four farms was IL
7,037 in 1964. This figure does not include income
from communal orchards and communal dry farming, and,
therefore, net income is probably substantially un-
derstated.

The farms were generally of a mixed type, with
most of the income from livestock and livestock products. All but four farms had a dairy enterprise.
Twenty-nine had a poultry enterprise. Most had communal orchards, and many had communal dry cultivation.
A substantial number of the farms had private orchards
and a vegetable enterprise. There was a great variation in size of farm, from twenty-four to fifty-four
dunams including communal cultivation.

Table 21 shows that the size distribution of
income is skewed to the right. The six farms with
incomes less than IL 4,000 represent either social
cases where the head of the family was sick or where
he obtained most of his income from full-time outside
employment. Those that applied themselves to farming
on a full-time basis obtained good incomes.

Of the eleven farms with incomes over IL 10,000,
a quarter of the sample, all had dairy enterprises.
In eight, the dairy was the major enterprise. In two,

poultry was the major enterprise. Of these, one had
a large dairy enterprise that yielded an income only
slightly smaller than the poultry enterprise, and
the other, a much smaller farm, had a small dairy
enterprise. The eleventh farm in this group was also a smaller farm, with vegetables being the principal enterprise. It also included a medium-sized
dairy and a small poultry enterprise. The latter two
small farms were operated by Oriental settlers. Four
of the dairy farms did not include a poultry enterprise, and in two of them it was operated at a loss.
All eleven farms had orchards.

TABLE 21

Size Distribution of Net Farm Income of 44 Farms
in 15 Immigrant Villages, Central Region, 1964

Israeli Pounds	Number of Farms
Less than 0	1
0 - 999	2
1,000 - 1,999	0
2,000 - 2,999	1
3,000 - 3,999	2
4,000 - 4,999	5
5,000 - 5,999	4
6,000 - 6,999	7
7,000 - 7,999	5
8,000 - 8,999	3
9,000 - 9,999	3
10,000 - 10,999	4
11,000 - 11,999	2
12,000 - 12,999	3
13,000 - 13,999	1
Over 14,000	1
Total farms	44

Average net farm income, IL 7,037

Source: Accounting records of sample farms,
Settlement Department, Jewish Agency, Central Region,
Rehovot.

In thirty-three of the forty-four farms in the
sample, the dairy enterprise was the largest source
of income. In seven, the poultry enterprise was the
largest; in two, the orchards were the main source
of income; and, in one, the vegetable was the main
enterprise. Only four farms did not have a dairy
enterprise. These were small farms of Oriental settlers with less than ten dunams under cultivation.
In three of these poultry was the main enterprise,
and, in the other, the private orchard was the main
source of income. The net incomes in these four
farms ranged from IL 4,285 to IL 6,161. These were
probably units where farm income was supplemented by
outside work.

There was no strict relation between either
the size of the dairy herds or the number of laying
hens and broilers and the incomes from these enterprises. Performances and efficiency in these enterprises varied greatly. The yield of milk per cow per
year varied from 3,239 to 5,999 litres. The number
of eggs per laying hen varied from 175 to 270, and
the net income per ton of concentrate from the poultry enterprise varied from IL 160 to IL 235.

In conclusion, this sample of farms in better-
than-average, well-situated immigrant villages
indicates a very substantial progress in their agricultural development. Almost a third of the farms in
the sample had a net income of at least IL 9,000 or
more, as much as the average net farm income in the
average moshav ovdim. While many farms were on a par
with the average moshav ovdim, the sample as a whole
was not. Many did not have sufficient land resources
and capital investments. There were a substantial
number of social cases. As in the moshav ovdim, there
has developed a differentiation in the types of farming within the village and a substantial amount of
part-time farming. Most of the villages utilized
one or more of the facilities of a nearby moshav ovdim
that served them as a rural center. They were also
served by regional councils and purchasing associations.

This accounting service by the settlement authority in the Central Region is one instance of a

farm management and analysis service based on actual
accounts. As already indicated, such a service based
on district offices has recently become operational
in the Negev. There is farm management extension in
all regions using farm accounts but based mainly on
output, input, income norms, and the budget method.
There has been some experimentation with program planning and linear programming that does not necessitate
electronic computations, needs far less recording,
and can be explained to better farmers. A method
based mainly on a German model was adapted to Israel
conditions. The constraints in the new moshavim,
for example, that farmers will not sell their cows,
that poultry is not considered because of marketing
limitations, etc., are such that this method has but
limited practicability.

Variations of the dairy and citrus farms have
progressed most of all the types of farms. These
represent approximately 45 per cent of the total number of farm units in the immigrant settlements.[38]
An unpublished study by Dr. R. Weitz of 233 immigrant
settlements indicates that in 1963 net incomes in the
citrus type of farm ranged from IL 4,500 to IL 8,000,
averaging IL 6,200; in the dairy farms from IL 4,000
to IL 7,000, averaging IL 5,600; and in the hill
farms from IL 2,000 to IL 8,000, averaging IL 4,200.[39]
These are approximations based on the use of income
norms rather than detailed actual income and expense
accounts and probably have a downward bias. The incomes from field-crop farms probably are between
those of the dairy and hill farms. The dairy and
citrus farms were generally founded early in the
poststate period in good areas near well-established
settlements in the central and northern regions of
the country. They were the types of farms where
technical know-how was greatest and where less capital investment was required than in the other models.

Analysis of development by region gives a better picture of economic advance than by type of farm,
since the variations in the model types are very
great. Of the thirty-four immigrant settlements in
the Jerusalem subdistrict of the Hill Region, their
division by net farm-income grouping in 1964 was as
follows:[40]

Number of Settlements

Under IL 3,000	6
IL 3,000-3,999	7
IL 4,000-4,999	11
IL 5,000-5,999	8
Over IL 6,000	2
Total	34

The settlements with incomes under IL 3,000 were founded after the Sinai Campaign in 1956. About 40 per cent of their income was from poultry and 60 per cent from horticulture. All the settlers augmented their incomes with outside work, mainly from public works, and were to receive more land and more means of production from the settlement authority. In the IL 3,00-3,999 category, three of the settlements near Jerusalem had plots of three to six dunams on which the farmers conduct a small poultry enterprise. Many of the settlers worked in the city. Two moshavim on poor land were scheduled to receive large plots for fruit plantations in 1966, 1,160 dunams each. In the third IL 4,000-4,999 category, a number of the villages had substantial poultry enterprises that were to be increased. Other sources of income were vegetables and fruit. Many of the villages in the fourth and fifth highest income categories had well-developed poultry enterprises. The main sources of income in some of the villages were fruit plantations and vegetables.

If allowances are made for self consumption and the downward biases of the norms, it is safe to assume that in this district, the greatest problem area for settlement, the average net income from agriculture for the 1964-65 period was IL 5,000. Including outside work the average family income in the area was IL 6,000 or higher.

Based on data of a fairly large sample of villages, the net agricultural income per farm in the Negev Region, including the value of home consumed produce, was estimated for 1964-65 at about IL 5,500. This includes the Lakhish and Northern Negev areas.

The figures in current Israeli pounds for the agricultural development of Lakhish are as follows:[41]

	Average Net Farm Income	Administered Farm Wages and Relief Income	Total Average Net Income
1955/56	600	1,000	1,600
1956/57	900	1,500	2,400
1958/59	1,700	1,000	2,700
1959/60	2,400	500	2,900
1964/65	5,500		

Average total net family income including outside
work was well above IL 6,000.

Farm incomes in the Central and Northern Regions, that include the best and oldest farming areas
in the country, averaged higher than in the Negev
and Jerusalem subdistrict of the Hill Region. Farming in the Galilee district is similar to that in the
Jerusalem district, and incomes were probably at
about the same level. The sample already analyzed
in the Central Region is indicative of older immigrant
settlements in the Central and Northern Regions, although the average for these farms may be at a somewhat higher level than that for the two regions as a
whole.

The estimate of IL 5,500 as the national average net farm income for the moshav olim for the
1955-56 period, therefore, is considered reasonably
accurate, possibly even conservative.

The average, however, conceals a wide distribution both among and within settlements. The variations in income within the moshav olim, the number
of people in part-time farming, and the number of
social cases is much greater than in the moshav ovdim.
But even in some areas just being developed incomes
can be very high. In three villages in the B'sor
area near the Gaza Strip net farm incomes had, by
1965, reached a level of approximately IL 10,000. The
main crop, winter, off-season tomatoes, yielded a net

income of approximately IL 2,500 per dunam. The average family net income from the communal vineyards and orchards alone was IL 2,500.

Also, even within the newer moshavim in the comprehensive regional planning schemes, where individual unit plans are very similar, there are sizable variations as among villages and within villages. In one village in Lakhish one farmer had a flock of four hundred sheep and operated his unit with Arab help. He was able to buy up the sheep from other farms in the area because of a drought. Such instances of a kulak in a cooperative settlement are rather rare and certainly would not be tolerated in a veteran moshav ovdim. The authorities let such instances pass, as well as the leasing of allotments to other settlers, to show that high incomes can be obtained by hard work and good farming.

The ultimate test of whether the moshav is a success is whether the settler and his family wish to remain in the village on a permanent basis. Using the income test, considering total income from all sources, the moshav olim is definitely a success. Incomes are as high as those of city workers. The amenities in the village, including housing and schooling, compare favorably with those in the city. All homes now are at least forty-five square meters in size and include modern sanitary facilities, refrigerators, and stoves. A number of settlers have private tractors and trucks, which are leased by others when not used by the settlers themselves. Some settlers, even in 1965, had private automobiles. The settler in the village plays a more prominent role in municipal affairs than the urban worker.

The desire on the part of the children to remain in farming may not be as strong as in the moshav ovdim. The vacancy rate in 1966 was 5 to 10 per cent of the total houses in the village.[42] The size of family among Oriental farmers is much larger than that of the European settler in the moshav ovdim. Thus the increase in off-farm opportunities in regional development will help in keeping families in the village. Houses can be enlarged and additional houses built on

the unit so that children can commute to the regional
towns. Oriental farmers in the Negev are increasing
investments in their farms. The settlement authority
is encouraging enlargement of houses through a subsidy
on three quarters of the value of the enlargement.
Such enlargement is becoming quite common. In one
average village visited in 1965 at least twelve houses
were being enlarged.

Many of the immigrant units at present cannot
support two families as in the established moshav
ovdim. On the other hand, individual units are often
farmed cooperatively by fathers and sons, brothers
and relatives. As already indicated, the final
success of the villages will be judged by their performances after independence. Many of the villages
are already independent or are close to the final
stage, with a reasonably stable local government and
comfortable facilities. They will probably endure
in one form or another as permanene rural communities.

SOCIAL FACTORS IN DEVELOPMENT OF MOSHAV OLIM

The differences in the composition and social
background of the postwar, as compared to the prewar
settlers, and the changes in the moshav framework and
organization to meet these differences have been analyzed in detail. This section is concerned with
some of the social factors in the evaluation of the
administered moshav.

The postwar entrants to the moshav can be divided into three main groups according to their countries of origin and social background: (1) those from
the Middle East and Asia, (2) those from North Africa,
and (3) those from other countries, particularly
Europe, America, and Israel.

The immigrants from the first group continued
for the most part to preserve their traditional social framework based on the extended family, the
hamula. They had the most difficulty in adapting to
technological innovations. Their family tradition of

mutual assistance, however, helped in adjusting to
the system of village cooperation.

In contrast to the first group of settlers, a
large proportion of the second group had difficulty
in adjusting to village life and cooperation. Many
had lived in urban centers where both family ties and
traditions of mutual aid were weak.

Many of the settlers from these first two
groups were unable to make the necessary adjustment
to moshav life and left their villages. Their places
were taken by others. As the settlement authority
and other institutions made the changes in the moshav
structure and organization to meet the needs of the
settlers, adaptation to moshav life was eased. In
recent years these villages have attained stability
and a state of economic consolidation that has made
possible the advancement to the status of commercial
farmers.

The third group was heterogeneous, comprising
(1) Israeli army veterans, (2) children of veteran
moshav settlements, (3) immigrants from Communist
countries in Eastern Europe, (4) refugees from Jewish
communities that were destroyed in World War II and
from the displaced person camps, and (5) Zionist immigrants from Western Europe, America, and the British
Commonwealth who wished to settle in agriculture. Although there were differences in these five groups,
their villages progressed rapidly. The technical
training and cultural organization and background of
these settlers fitted the structure of rural settlement in Israel. Their main difficulty, particularly
the latter three groups, was in adaptation to hard
physical work.

The army veterans and children of the pioneers
in the veteran settlements were very similar to the
settlers in the moshav ovdim, and their villages became successful permanent settlements. The third and
fourth classifications were of a different nature.
The settlers were attracted to the moshav for economic reasons and by a desire for a plot of their own.
Many were only interested in making enough money to

invest in a business in town. An officer of the settlement authority estimated that only about a quarter
of their children would remain in the moshav. The
new immigrants to the moshav from advanced countries
have done well in the organization of their villages
but often not quite as well in farming. There has
been a certain amount of disillusionment, and a number of settlers have left the villages. Nevertheless,
they have founded good villages, and those that have
persevered have done well.

The differential rate of development in the
moshav olim according to ethnic origin is indicated
by the fact that twenty-three of the twenty-four villages that had achieved consolidation status by the
end of 1958 were of European origin. That is, of all
the villages established in the four-year 1948-51
period only these twenty-four had reached the stage
of full production, completed their basic investment
programs, established a stable municipal council, and
all resident instructors had been withdrawn.[43] Studies
indicated that even under the same soil and water conditions the nonoriental villages performed better.

A recent unpublished study of the progress of
new villages from 1958 to 1963 that includes a large
sample of 223 moshavim, 74 with settlers of Western
origin and 149 with settlers of Oriental origin, shows
that the Western settlements still rate highest in
performance. The settlements of the Asiatic ethnic
groups ranked second and those of North Africa, third.
The North African settlements, however, showed the
greatest progress from 1958 to 1963, followed by the
Asian settlements.

This study included measurements of ten aspects
of moshav performance: (1) proportion of total earnings from farming, (2) technical farming qualifications
as measured by yields, (3) adaptation to farm work,
(4) farmers' investments, (5) indebtedness, (6) use of
organized marketing, (7) social stability of village,
(8) stability of village committee, (9) status of
village institutions, and (10) cooperation between the
village and authorities. Admittedly some of these
items are hard to quantify, and the measurements were

quite subjective. In the analysis of overall performance the villages were stratified by the amounts
of water available and the quality of the soil. The
study indicates that the guided administration of the
moshav olim had helped the advancement of the Oriental
villages more than the European and has closed the
gap in performance among the ethnic groups.[44]

The thesis is that the primary reason for the
success of the moshav olim has been the guidance of
the settlement authority in cooperation with the
other supporting institutions. To achieve success,
there must be harmony between the development desires
of the authorities and the cultural horizons of the
settlers. This is basic since the moshav olim is a
highly administered and dependent community and, as
such, is susceptible to crisis, both from endogeneous
and exogenous sources.

One of the more important decisions in village
planning based on social factors was that of settling
villages with homogeneous ethnic groups, initiated in
Lakhish in 1955. The earlier theory, developed during the mass-immigration period, was that the best
path to quick integration was to settle culturally
different immigrants in the same moshav. The theory
was based on the premise that persons living in a
small community would be forced to adopt Hebrew as
their common language and that they would quickly give
up their old habits and assume new traditions. While
ethnic heterogeneity may have speeded up the tempo of
change in some situations, in many others it led to
factionalism and conflict. Therefore the policy was
changed to one of homogeneous settlement, with the
ethnic groups meeting in the rural center.

This policy shift signifies the adoption of a
different social theory: that assimilation is a slow
process and that speed in assimilation may be sacri-
ficed to community stability. In the new policy some
entire village groups emigrated as a unit and were
resettled intact. This is the extreme case of an organic community. More commonly the villages included
a number of kinship groups where members of each group
were previously engaged in cooperative activities, but

the different groups were unacquainted. In general
it was found that the more organic the village the
greater the degree of stability, with fewer settlers
leaving.

A second aspect of the villages is their fragile
character. Because of their small size should a kinship of eight or ten families leave a village and be
replaced by persons who are not kinsmen, the social
and political alignments of the village become reorganized. The small size of the moshavim make them
extremely sensitive to minor population shifts. This
explains the tendency to form more organic villages.

A community's demographic characteristics are
fundamentally important for rural planners who have
to face problems of both underpopulation and overpopulation. Underpopulation occurs when the village
community is unable to meet crop requirements adequately. For example, tobacco may be successfully grown
in hill areas. It is, however, labor intensive and
has failed in villages settled by European immigrants
where the families are small and settlers middle-aged.
The labor-intensive crops are more suited to the
larger Oriental families. To a considerable degree
the Oriental farmers are engaged in labor-intensive
crops in the industrial crop and hill types of farms.

Underpopulation also exists when the size of the
community restricts the growth of varied local services. This has been taken account of in the centralization of services in regional planning that has
already proven a success, particularly in social services such as education and health. New types of
regional services have also resulted in improved economic services for farmers.

Overpopulation occurs when resources are insufficient to meet villagers' needs. Because the farm
plot cannot be fragmented, agriculture may not be able
to provide a livelihood for all family members. Various solutions have been tried for absorbing surplus
population. One is to establish indistrial and semi-
industrial projects in the moshav or rural center.
The other is for the surplus population to take up

service functions in the rural centers and industrial
jobs in the regional towns. This has been one of the
aims of comprehensive regional planning: to provide
economic opportunities for the surplus farm population.

An important demographic aspect in the development of the moshav is that the home and the family
farm place a new emphasis on the nuclear family without breaking up the cooperative advantages of kinship
groups in economic and even political matters. The
new type of home was a factor in promoting change.

The moshav olim is an extreme case of directed
cultural change, where introducing innovation is the
central purpose of the administering group. Most of
the new immigrants assimilated agricultural skills
rather quickly and accommodated themselves to the new
ways of living. They learned the use of mechanical
equipment and complex irrigation and spraying practices. They readily accepted new ways of living and
consumption items, such as refrigerators, stoves, and
radios. In a majority of cases the acceptance of
these items represented an accommodation to a new cultural horizon. The relative ease of acceptance of
these new cultural horizons can be explained, to a
large degree, by the total change in social context
through the process of immigration from one culture
to another.

This does not mean that there have not been
serious problems in the adaptation to the moshav.
There have been many instances of community crises
and failures, because many settlers were reluctant
or opposed to becoming farmers and rejected the new
status and work that farming applies. The problem,
therefore, was not just one of technical innovation
but of changing roles, the degree to which the new
settlers were willing to accept a new life definition
and engage in new activities. The most successful
of the new Oriental moshavim were those where the
settlers came from small towns and villages, where
they were accustomed to hard work, and where farming
did not represent a lowering of their social status
in their new country. Yet, at the same time, some of

the most successful farmers, the most innovating
class, have been immigrants from the city who will-
ingly accepted their new agricultural role.

The implications of role shift for technical
change is illustrated in the acceptance of chicken
farming in Oriental moshavim in the Jerusalem area
at different time periods. When introduced soon
after the settlers arrived in the village, this enterprise ended in failure. The settlers slaughtered
the chickens and organized community feasts. When
reintroduced in the same villages some time later,
the settlers realized their importance as a continued
source of income, learned the proper techniques, and
reached high levels of egg production. They had
adopted a new role and adjusted their behavior to
conform with the necessities of their new life.

Age and cultural predisposition are key elements affecting role change. Younger persons are more
flexible than their elders. This explains the importance in selecting younger couples in the immigrant
settlements and concentration on the education of the
children in agricultural schools and the army for
becoming village leaders. Social research in Israel
suggests that the social composition of the community,
the type of leadership expressed within it, and the
relation between the settlers and the settlement authority have been important factors conditioning role
changes.

Group membership and group composition are important factors in a change situation, particularly
the kinship group that has tended to become a more
intensive unit and has assumed new functions. Kinsmen assist each other in harvesting fields, making
joint capital purchasing, and cooperate in crisis situations. Members of these groups receive psychologi-
cal as well as economic benefits. In the moshav olim
group membership is positively correlated with successful adaptation to farming.

The functions of community leaders are closely
related to the problems of group formation. Village
leaders may successfully bridge opposition between

various factions and play an important part in relation to innovation and social change. For new roles
to be adopted, the leaders must accept and sanction
them. They are also the important communication
agents to the other settlers.

A feature of the culture-contact situation in
the moshav olim was that status in the communities of
Oriental origin was related to age, wealth, and education. The motive of the moshav, with its emphasis
on egalitarianism, physical labor, and organizational
talent, altered the traditional system. In the more
organic villages there was greater emphasis on the
traditional status marks. In the earlier years, at
least, the village councils were dominated by the
elder family heads or by others who possessed traditional prestige symbols. When the importance and
rewards of labor and agricultural skill become recognized, both the old and new symbols become legitimate.
The two systems were represented by different age
groups. The young were drawn to the prestige lent by
agricultural success and accultivation, while the elders followed the traditional criteria. While there
have been periodic clashes between the groups, various
forms of reconciliation were generally made. The
young were gradually granted positions in village
councils and, in time, became the new leaders in the
village. The organization of regional bodies, the
councils and purchasing associations, not only provided better services, but gave further scope for the
advancement of the new leadership.

The third factor influencing the adaptation of
new roles is the relation between the new villages
and the settlement authority. Plans and policies appropriate to the settlers' desires and demands rein-
force the assumption of a new role, while if the
authorities' programs are ill suited to the settlers'
cultural expectations these policies damage the process of change. The settlement authority consciously
changed the structure and organization of the moshav
and reexamined and adjusted its own policies to help
the new settlers assume farmers' roles.

Dependence is an inherent problem of administered communities. The calculations and activities

of the nonvillage administrators greatly affected the settlers' lives. Thus crises were easily induced from the outside over and above the problems of cultural change. Planning had to be solidly based, and the implementation of planning had to be effective. This has been a challenge to the bureaucratic agencies involved in the development of the moshav, demanding dedication and efficiency on their part. Errors in policy and snags in implementation resulted in resistance to planning, open conflict with the settlement institutions, loss of initiative, and apathy. Sometimes the dependence relation has caused administrators to adopt new and unintended policies. Programs whose stated goal is village independence could become increasingly authoritarian. Rather than serving the villagers, such activities satisfied only the internal needs of a bureaucratic system.

Village independence has been positively valued by the settlement authority. The development of some moshavim has been retarded as a result of bureaucratic errors. In the earlier period some instructors did not sufficiently understand the inherent differences between the new immigrant settlements and their own and were in too much of a hurry to establish the village committees and institutions similar to those in their own villages. They channelled orders through elected leaders who were not the accepted leaders of the villages. In some cases, the settlement authority changed the entire agricultural plan in the village, from dairy to crop farming, for example, and the reasons were not sufficiently understood or accepted by the villagers.

There is an obvious dilemma. To what extent is community independence fostered by instituting dependent conditions? The planners themselves have tended to be conservative. They trust that the changes they have made in the structure and functions of the moshav olim will lead to the social solidarity that is necessary until the village is a complete economic success. This is particularly necessary in the more difficult areas of settlement, the Negev and the hill and mountain areas. They also believe that the village council will reassume functions that have been performed by others.

The most important problem is the differentiation between primary and secondary goals, that the
value of establishing a viable community is more important than the community's ultimate form of organization. The ultimate goal is the accommodation of
the settlers on their own terms. Change becomes permanent only when the actors accept and incorporate
the roles they are to play. To a considerable degree
this new agricultural role has been accepted in the
moshav olim.

NOTES

1. From Statistics Section of Resettlement
Department of Jewish Agency.

2. Yitzhak Korn, "Planning of New Moshavim"
(paper submitted at International Symposium on the
Role of Cooperative Organization in Rural Development,
Tel-Aviv, March, 1965), p. 2. (Mimeographed.)

3. Ibid., p. 3.

4. Ranaan Weitz, "Administration of the Moshav
in the Future." Summary details of types of farms
are also presented by Weitz in "Rural Development
Through Regional Planning in Israel," Journal of Farm
Economics, XLVII (August, 1965), pp. 639-40.

5. Benjamin Kaplan and Avsholom Rokach, "Rural
Settlement in Israel" (paper presented to Interregional
Technical Meeting on Rural Resettlement conducted by
the International Labor Office, Ashkelon, April-May,
1965), p. 12. (Mimeographed.)

6. Yehuda H. Landau, "Rural Regional Development in Israel," Agriculture and Settlement-Planning
and Development Center, Tel-Aviv, 1965, p. 3.

7. Ibid., p. 5.

8. Kaplan and Rokach, op. cit., pp. 16-17.

9.   Letter from Head of Settlement Department of Jewish Agency.

10.   Statistical Abstract of Israel, 1968, p. 31.

11.   From interview with Regional Director of Settlement Division.

12.   From the files of the Moshav Movement.

13.   Y. Gevirtz, "Rural Local Government in Israel," The Settler, IV (Winter-Spring, 1964-65).

14.   D. O. Fanimokun, R. S. M. Ezem, O. Olaniran, and D. A. Adeyemo, "Report on Organization and Management of Farm Settlements in Israel" (report by Nigerian students to Foreign Training Department, Agricultural Education Service, 1964), p. 39.   (Mimeographed.)

15.   From interview with Director of Nov.

16.   From interview with Director of Central Region of Tnuva.

17.   From Central Bureau of Statistics.

18.   Information supplied by Benjamin Kaplan, Assistant Director General of Settlement Department of Jewish Agency.

19.   "The Composite Rural Structure" (unpublished document prepared for OECD Course for Agricultural Planning and Regional Development, Herzlia, 1963), p. 33.   (Mimeographed.)

20.   Ibid., pp. 27-28.

21.   Ibid., p. 34.

22.   Korn, op. cit., p. 15.

23.   Ibid., p. 16.

24. _Ibid_.

25. _Ibid_., p. 5.

26. Kadar, "Family Farms in Cooperative Villages," p. 15.

27. _Ibid_., p. 14.

28. I. H. Halperin and D. Yaron, _Moshvei Olim_: _Survey of Immigrant Villages in Israel_ (Rehovot: Hebrew University, 1957, in Hebrew), pp. vii-ix.

29. _Ibid_.

30. _Ibid_., p. ix.

31. _Ibid_., pp. xii-xiii.

32. _Ibid_., pp. xiii-xiv.

33. _Ibid_., p. xi.

34. _Ibid_., p. xii.

35. _Ibid_., p. x.

36. _Ibid_., p. xii.

37. _Ibid_., p. xv.

38. From data of Agriculture and Settlement-Planning and Development Center.

39. R. Weitz, "Development Rate of New Settlements According to Ethnic Origins" (unpublished manuscript, Settlement Study Center, National and University Institute of Agriculture, Rehovot).

40. From records of Settlement Department, Jerusalem District.

41. Figures for 1955/56 through 1959/60 based on five villages. From R. Weitz, "The Economic, Organizational and Social Problems of Family Farms,"

National and University Institute of Agriculture,
Rehovot, 1961, p. 18.

42.   Estimate based on Settlement Department
data.

43.   Ben-David, op. cit., p. 116.

44.   R. Weitz, "Development Rate of New Settlements According to Ethnic Origins."

7

INSTITUTIONAL SETTING OF MOSHAV

An important factor in the success of the moshav in Israel has been its support by national institutions in administrative, economic, and social matters. Many of the principal institutions are concerned with the agricultural sector as a whole, the entire cooperative agricultural sector, or with the entire economic cooperative network in the country. This review is focused on their activities with the moshav.

JEWISH AGENCY

The Jewish Agency is the executive organ of the World Zionist Organization. The earlier review indicated the failure of early agricultural settlement in the nineteenth century because of the lack of national and international support. The development of the cooperative agricultural sector, both the moshav and the kibbutz, would have been impossible without the support of the World Zionist Organization, comprising the Jewish National Fund (its financial instrument responsible for the collection of donations by Jews from all over the world), and the Jewish Agency, its executive arm. Before the establishment of the State the Jewish National Fund was also responsible for buying lands for settlement and leasing them to settlers.

The primary functions of the Jewish Agency are:

1. Organization and implementation of immigration of Jews from all over the

world to Israel;
2. Absorption of immigrants into the country;
3. The reclamation of lands for agricultural, forestry, and nonagricultural uses;
4. Establishment and management of agricultural settlement;
5. Participation in development projects;
6. Encouragement of private investments supporting settlement; and
7. Promotion of higher education.

To implement its functions the Jewish Agency is divided into five principal departments: (1) administration, (2) immigration and absorption,* (3) education, (4) budget, and (5) agricultural settlement. Administration is responsible for coordination; immigration and absorption, for transporting the settlers to the country and, after arrival, for training them, finding them employment, and speeding up their social and cultural integration; education, for organizing education of immigrants; budget, for financial matters of the Agency; and agricultural settlement, for the establishment and maintenance of new settlements until they become self-supporting. The Agricultural Settlement Department has recently absorbed the responsibilities of a former technical department that was concerned with the architectural and construction work of the agency.

The Agricultural Settlement Department is the most important unit of the Jewish Agency, receiving in the 1963-66 period about half the total budget of the organization.[1]

Most of the functions of the Agricultural Settlement Department have been described in detail in the analyses of the development of the moshav ovdim and moshav olim. Specifically these functions are:

─────────────

*A new Ministry of Absorption was created in mid 1968 under the aegis of the Deputy Prime Minister. It seems, however, that the Jewish Agency will still retain a function in immigration activities.

1. Planning and setting up the time schedule
   for the establishment of cooperative
   agricultural settlements in the country;
2. Planning each settlement from the topographical, architectural, economic, and
   agricultural aspects;
3. Constructing the physical facilities of
   the settlement: building the houses,
   farms, and commercial buildings, paving
   roads, and installing irrigation, drainage, and lighting;
4. Assuring the livelihood of the settler
   during the early stages of his indoctri-
   nation into agriculture and until the establishment of his own farm;
5. Providing the agricultural, occupational,
   and organizational guidance for the settlers until the village reaches its final
   stage of development;
6. Supplying the means of production, capital
   investments, and credit until the village
   reaches its final stage of development;
7. Developing agricultural and general industry in areas where agricultural development is more difficult and slower to
   supplement the settlers' incomes and support the population in these areas;
8. Establishing rural and regional centers
   for joint economic and social services as
   part of a total regional plan;
9. Establishing plantations and citrus groves
   and bringing them to full yield before
   they are transferred to the settlers;
10. Providing for the common cultivation of
    dry farming before it is transferred to
    the village;
11. Assisting, with the aid of other public
    bodies, particularly through education for
    good citizenship, in molding the social
    and cultural character of the settlers; and
12. Assisting, with the aid of other public
    bodies, in establishing economic organiza-
    tions for servicing the villages.

The Agricultural Settlement Department has
worked closely with the Ministry of Agriculture in

matters of agricultural policy and services for the
new settlements. There has been complete consolidation of its activities in agricultural planning and
extension with the Ministry. The headquarters posts
of these activities are located in the Ministry of
Agriculture at Tel-Aviv. Many are supported by the
budget of the Jewish Agency. For example, as of 1966,
in the Agricultural and Settlement-Planning and Development Center the heads of the Divisions of Detailed Planning, Rural Regional Planning, and other
posts were on the payroll of the Agricultural Settlement Department. Theoretically these posts could be
filled by professionals on the budget of the Ministry
of Agriculture. The Settlement Department has been
more concerned with the work of these divisions as
they affected new settlements. In addition, the Director of the Center had to be approved by the Jewish
Agency before appointment.

The training Authority was set up in 1960 for
coordination of agricultural extension work in the
field, which was previously conducted separately by
the Settlement Department and the Ministry of Agriculture. In actual practice, however, the regional
offices of the Settlement Department conducted the
extension work for the new settlements and the regional offices of the Ministry of Agriculture, for
the established ones. In 1965, the field extension
work was consolidated. The same extension agents
were to serve old and new settlements, and the village agricultural instructors in the moshav olim were
to go on the budget of the Ministry of Agriculture.

The administrative structure of the Settlement
Department is indicated in Figure 2. Its functions
are decentralized in the four regional divisions that
have direct contact with the settlements. Most of
the personnel of the Settlement Department are attached to these regional offices and live near them.
Each region has the following sections: (1) planning,
(2) technical--mainly for irrigation and building,
(3) citrus and plantations, and (4) finance. Each of
these units receives professional directives from the
appropriate divisions of the department directorate.
They are under the direct jurisdiction of the Director
of the Regional Office, who has wide autonomy in

planning and implementation within the budgetary framework and settlement policy of the department directorate. The area of each regional office is divided into three district offices for convenience in serving settlements.

As of March, 1964, there were 1,462 employees in the Agricultural Settlement Department, including all employees stationed in the headquarters of the Ministry of Agriculture.[2] The number of employees is being reduced as the settlements gain maturity and functions are coordinated with and transferred to the Ministry of Agriculture and/or regional organizations.

The Jewish Agency and the National Federation of Labor are the most important autonomous public agencies in the country--states within the State, significant not only in the agricultural sector but in the entire economic, social, and political fabric of the country. This is due mainly to the prestate historic development of the country when autonomous public agencies had to be established to support the economic and social development of the Jewish settlers and supply the necessary services that were not forthcoming from the British Mandate and Turkish government authorities.

In the specific case of the Jewish Agency where the major portion of its funds originate from donations of Jews throughout the diaspora, it is a matter of considerable convenience that the donations be given not directly to a foreign government but as voluntary charity contributions to an autonomous public agency. The fact that the Settlement Department is not a regular government ministry gives it more flexibility in operations where many hard decisions with political implications have to be made. Such decisions would be more difficult in the Ministry of Agriculture which is closer to the electorate.

NATIONAL FEDERATION OF LABOR, HISTADRUT

General Services

The most important of the public autonomous institutions, the real state within the State, is the

FIGURE 2

Organization of the Agricultural Settlement Department

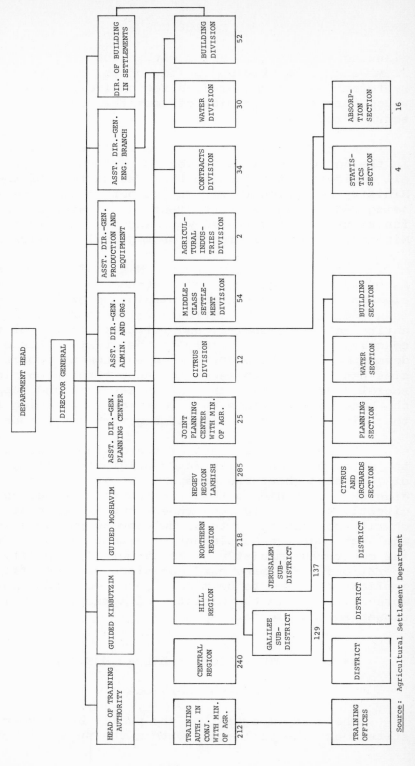

Source: Agricultural Settlement Department

National Federation of Labor, the Histadrut. It was
founded in 1920 to combine in one institution a number of organizations established in the previous decade to promote cooperation, mutual aid, and collective
bargaining. It is the organization for promoting the
labor economy of Israel, consisting of four distinct
activities: production, trade union work, social
services, and education.

From its very beginning the Histadrut acted in
its capacity as "The Cooperative Association of Jewish Workers for Settlement, Industry, Contracting,
and Supply." Its involvement in economic activities
beyond the traditional scope of trade unions arose
partly because of its socialist ideology and partly
out of necessity for creating employment for membership. It, therefore, encouraged members to organize
themselves into producers' cooperatives, bought fail-
ing businesses to save workers' jobs, and established
its own businesses. By means of its holding company
Hevrat Ovdim (the fellowship of workers), it controlled
in 1963 two thousand businesses and farm cooperatives,
employed a quarter of the country's wage earners, grew
75 per cent of the country's food, and accounted for
26 per cent of the gross national product. The Histadrut together with the State and its enterprises are
responsible for about half of the national production.[3]

The economic activities of the Histadrut in
production are of four types. The first consists of
cooperative companies in which Hevrat Ovdim has direct
ownership rights, such as Tnuva and Hamashbir Hamerkazi, the two most important enterprises in the agricultural sector. The operation of these enterprises
is based on hired labor and hired management. The
second represents the producer and service cooperatives that are members of the Histadrut Cooperative
Center. Most of the public commercial bus transportation consists of such cooperatives. They are organized on the principle of self-employment, although
hired labor is quite common. The third includes most
of the moshavim and the moshavim hashitufiyim. The
fourth includes almost all the kibbutzim.

The most important of the Histadrut social services is its health service, Kaput Holim.   In 1966,
it served about three quarters of the population.[4]
Most are members because the head of the family works
in the Histadrut or a Histadrut connected enterprise.
This service is extremely important to the agricultural settlements.   The settlements attached to the
religious parties which are not included in the Histadrut subscribe to this service.   In the middle-class
moshavim individual members are free to subscribe to
this service if they wish.

The education and cultural services of the Histadrut are quite extensive.   They include a mass
circulation daily paper, a large publishing house, a
cooperative film-distribution service organized together with the Moshav Movement and the national kibbutz organizations, and a similar service for books.
It has organized schools for training in agriculture
and cooperation, including a special school for students from underdeveloped countries.

The Histadrut has other miscellaneous activities
concerned mainly with the absorption of immigrants and
quasi-diplomatic activities with international labor
organizations.

Administrative and Financial Services
to Agriculture

The basic organization for the administrative
and financial functions of the Histadrut in the agricultural sector is the Agricultural Workers' and Settlers' Organization.   This organization is concerned
with the farmers in the cooperative sector, both
moshavim and kibbutzim, and the paid workers in the
private sector. Actually the organization was founded
in 1911, ten years earlier than the Histadrut, as the
spearhead organization for the "Conquest of Labor" by
the pioneer agricultural workers.   Time and the economic development of the country changed the agricultural population from a majority to a minority and
transformed the parent group to an affiliated group.
Nevertheless this agricultural union has preserved

its special character and has remained a country-wide
organization with broad autonomous rights. In 1965,
it included 230,000 of the total Histadrut membership
of over 800,000.[5]

The organizational structure is based on labor
councils, both in the settlements and private villages.
Membership in the organization, however, is individual
and direct. The highest authority is its agricultural
congress, the general convention that is held about
every four years. Election of delegates to the congress is held at the same time as the Histadrut convention elections. The delegates, 501, are elected
by a direct vote of the members on a system of proportional representation based on political party
strength within the Histadrut. The congress elects a
general council of 220 to 230 members that meets twice
a year. It also elects a central committee that, in
turn, elects the secretariat of the Agricultural Center, the executive body of the Agricultural Workers'
and Settlers' Organization.

The Agricultural Center is very important in
farm-settlement services and policy. It administers
a bank, Nir, for financing settlement activities. The
bank is under the jurisdiction of the Workers' Bank
of Histadrut, but its management is appointed by the
Center. The Center also includes the Nir Shitufi that
has two principal duties, a legal one that sets rules
and regulations for the settlements and a control and
advisory one of auditing the settlement annual reports.
Nir Shitufi thus has formal supervisory rights over
every agricultural settlement within the Histadrut
that are recognized in their constitutions. It represents the settlements in their dealings with external
groups and national institutions. It acts as a court
of appeal in any dispute between settlements and between settlements and Histadrut institutions. It has
the right to veto any decision of the settlement institutions that it considers to be an infringement of
fundamental cooperative principles. The device of
expressing the policy of the agricultural labor-
cooperative movement through Nir Shitufi, instead of
directly through Hevrat Ovdim, enables the agricultural sector to exercise responsibility in its own field.

The Agricultural Center, which in 1966 had 110
employees, has several departments, the most important of which is the Settlement Department. This
department is primarily concerned with the organization, financial, and technical needs of the cooperative sector. It includes twelve permanent executive
officers elected by the Center on full-time duty. Its
most important committee is the Economic Committee
that is mainly concerned with representational work
with government and other agencies on such matters as
price policies, subsidies, water allocations, etc.
There are also thirteen commodity-branch committees
under the jurisdiction of a member of the Executive
Committee that represent the interests of their particular commodity constituents. The Settlement Department also serves as a representational ageency
for the regional councils and regional purchasing
associations.

Other departments of the Agricultural Center
also have important functions. The Education Department has founded and supports agricultural schools
for both students from the settlements and adult
farmers. It issues a monthly publication that is the
principal agricultural journal in the country. The
Housing Department represents settlements in their
relations with the government on housing matters and
taxes. In summary, on the settlement side the Agricultural Center is mainly concerned with services,
representational activities, and with jurisdictional
problems between the settlements and Histadrut agencies.

The Center has committees for hired agricultural workers, dealing with wages and workers subsidiary
small holdings. Labor relations for workers in the
private agricultural sector are negotiated between the
Workers' Organization and the Farmers' Federation,
that represents the employers, with the support of the
Ministry of Labor. The Workers' Organization has a
membership of about 90 per cent of all the hired agricultural labor on the country.[6]

The Agricultural Workers Insurance Fund provides
for social benefits such as sick pay, severance pay,

pensions, and special emergency grants. Both employers and employees contribute to this fund, with the
employers' contributions considerably higher.

Economic Organizations Serving Agriculture

Before presenting a summary review of the
principal economic organizations of the Histadrut
serving agriculture, it might be well to note the
organizational relationship between Hevrat Ovdim,
the enterprise arm of the Histadrut, to which these
organizations are attached, and the Histadrut itself,
the parent institution and labor arm of the entire
Israeli economy. This is indicated in Figure 3. The
most important feature of the dual structure of the
Histadrut is that the same persons are delegates to
the conferences of both the Histadrut and the Hevrat
Ovdim and are members of their respective councils.
This means that the Hevrat Ovdim is controlled by
the same political forces as the Histadrut. Election
to the Conference of the Histadrut and the appointment of key personnel in the organization is based
on proportional representation in accordance to member voting based on political party lines.

At the executive level the General Secretary
of the Histadrut is chairman of the Hevrat Ovdim
secretariat. He is the most important personality
of both the trade union and enterprise production
branches. This split-personality outlook creates
problems of policy and economic efficiency of the
Hevrat Ovdim organizations, serving agriculture and
other sections of the economy as well. Actually the
personal relationship of the governing bodies goes
even further. The secretary of the Hevrat Ovdim and
six of the fourteen members of its secretariat are
also members of the governing committee of the Histadrut, the executive body of the Hevrat Ovdim.
Three other members of the secretariat of the Hevrat
Ovdim are managing directors of its more important
companies: Hamashbir Hamerkazi, Tnuva, and Solel
Boneh. As indicated, Hamashbir and Tnuva are the
two most important organizations of the Histadrut
serving the agricultural sector. A summary review
of their activities follows.

FIGURE 3

Organizational Chart of the Histadrut – The General
Federation of Jewish Labor

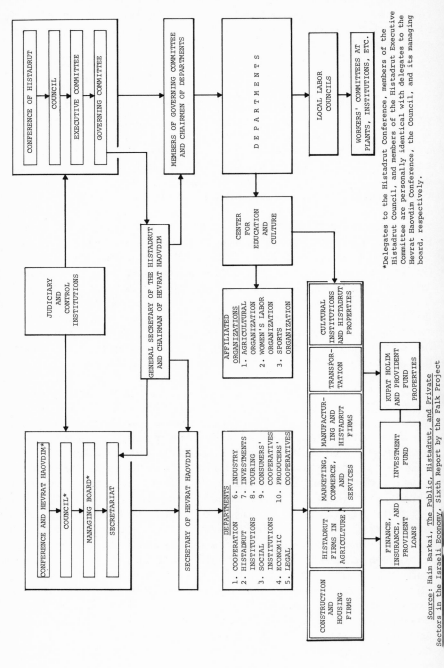

*Delegates to the Histadrut Conference, members of the
Histadrut Council, and members of the Histadrut Executive
Committee are personally identical with delegates to the
Hevrat Haovdim Conference, the Council, and its managing
board, respectively.

Source: Haim Barkai, The Public, Histadrut, and Private
Sectors in the Israeli Economy, Sixth Report by the Falk Project

Hamashbir Hamerkazi

The most important Histadrut company in the field of trade and commerce is the Hamashbir Hamerkazi.[7] Founded in 1921, it became the central wholesale organization for all cooperative undertakings of the Histadrut. It provides supplies for about one third of the Israeli population. Its customers are the agricultural settlements, both kibbutzim and moshavim, consumer cooperatives in towns and villages, government institutions, schools, and other public institutions. In fact, 28 per cent of its sales in 1964 were to government and public institutions.

Hamashbir Hamerkazi has eighteen departments dealing with groceries, animal fodder, building materials, clothing and shoes, grains, chemicals, agricultural machinery, stationery, tools, household goods, etc. It performs four main functions: (1) a supplier for cooperative settlements, government, and public institutions, (2) importer of goods, (3) producer of supplies that are sold to its own members and customers, and (4) a marketer and exporter of goods produced in its own plants and in plants belonging to its members and customers, including the industrial plants in the kibbutzim and plants in the regional centers serving moshavim.

As of 1964, Hamashbir operated sixteen plants employing 1,730 workers. They included an oil products factory, two flour mills, a textile factory, a paper products and printing plant, two fodder mills, a repair shop and small tractor assembly works, an electric incubator works, two modern bakeries, a foundry, a plant for rubber products, a sugar factory, and two food-packing plants. In addition, it has partial ownership of a Portland cement works, a fertilizer and chemicals plant, and a steel pipes plant.

On the consumer cooperative side, Hamashbir in 1964 serviced 1,200 retail shops of the four hundred Hamashbir consumer societies, all of which were members of the parent society. The societies are also members of the Consumers' Cooperative Union which, together with the Hamashbir, encourages the growth of

new societies and the establishment of modern shops
and supermarkets. Through its subsidiary, Hamashbir
Lazarchan, it operates a network of department stores
established jointly by the Hamashbir Hamerkazi and
the local consumer cooperative societies.

Hamashbir Hamerkazi has ten financial and commercial subsidiaries operated for a wide variety of
purposes: (1) general exports and imports, (2) grain
and cereal harvesting, (3) seed growing, (4) groundnuts and cotton marketing, (5) importation of sugar,
rice, and dried fruit, (6) fuel marketing, (7) ware-
housing and customs clearance, (8) supplying vessels
anchored in Israel ports, (9) finances and investments, and (10) as already indicated, department
stores. It also operates six funds for financing an
institution for consumer cooperative societies; promoting the building of new shops and warehouses for
cooperative retail societies; and improving and
equipping dining halls in collective settlements,
producers' cooperatives, clothing stores, and village
and kibbutz industries. It has exclusive selling
rights in Israel for the products of many important
industrial concerns throughout the world.

The total sales of the Hamashbir Hamerkazi in
1964 were IL 441 million, IL 260 million for the cooperative wholesale society, IL 80 million for its
commercial subsidiaries, and IL 101 million for its
industrial subsidiaries.

On the organizational side, Hamashbir Hamerkazi
was until 1921 a cooperative society based on individual membership. In 1929, it was reorganized along
the British Manchester model as a society based on
the membership of local cooperative societies. Its
national conference of member cooperatives is held
about every three years. This congress elects a
council of seventy that meets about every three months
and a supervisory commission that adjudicates disputes
between members and management. The council elects
from its own membership a board of directors of twenty
that meets monthly. The board elects an executive
committee of ten members that are paid full-time employees of the organization. The board represents the

different groups of member societies in accordance
with their purchases from the organizations. In 1965,
there were five from the national kibbutz organizations, three from the Moshav Movement, and two from
consumer organizations.

In the cooperative agricultural sector Hamashbir is more important to the kibbutzim than the moshavim. This is due to the large amount of purchases
by moshav members from other facilities in the cities
and regional towns. It also reflects the influence
of the regional purchasing associations, who regard
the Hamashbir Hamerkazi as one of a number of possible
sources of wholesale supplies for the immigrant settlements.

Hamashbir tried to promote consumer cooperatives
in the moshav olim through a subsidiary Hamashbir
L'Oleh operated jointly by the Hamashbir Hamerkazi
and the Union of Consumer Cooperative Societies. They
received loans from the settlement authority to help
the settlers establish consumer cooperatives. This
effort was not a great success, and the regional purchasing associations have taken over this work.

There has been considerable criticism of the
Hamashbir Hamerkazi for its inefficiency, high costs
and prices, and nepotism. To a degree this is caused
by the fact that its central distribution facilities
in Tel-Aviv have been antiquated and inadequate. New
facilities are being planned. In common with Tnuva,
affiliation with the Histadrut presents problems of
the clash of labor and society member interest. To
this must be added the problem of frequent changes in
its board of directors and executive committee and
inclusion in high posts of older people with a political rather than economic orientation. The organization has grown too large to keep in touch with the
problems of its local societies, particularly the
needs of the immigrant settlers in the moshav olim.
This in part accounts for the growth in number and
scope of activities of the regional purchasing associations. The postwar growth of competing organizations acts as a factor to improve the economic
efficiency of marketing organizations servicing the
agricultural sector.

Tnuva

Tnuva is the most important of the Histadrut
organizations serving the cooperative agricultural
sector.[8] It is an offshoot of the Hamashbir Hamerkazi, established by the parent organization in 1926
for the marketing of all agricultural products except
grains and fodder. Until recently all agricultural
settlements attached to the Histadrut were obliged
to market through Tnuva. This rule has been relaxed,
and now the settlements have free choice whether or
not to market through the organization. As of 1965,
fifteen moshavim chose not to market through Tnuva.
In addition to the settlements attached to the Histadrut, practically all the villages attached to the
religious labor movements, a considerable number of
villages attached to the Liberal Party, various agricultural schools and training farms, and some
middle-class moshavim market through Tnuva. If a
settlement chooses to market through Tnuva it agrees
to market all of its agricultural products through
the organization for a year. Fines are levied for
infraction of this agreement.

Tnuva is operated on a commodity and regional
basis. There are six branch managers for milk, fruit,
vegetables, poultry, miscellaneous products, and services. The miscellaneous products include wine,
cheese, fish, flowers and nursery products, and preserved foods. The services include the supply of
boxes and specialized packages to the settlements,
transportation, and technical assistance to the settlements in the development of marketing facilities.
The organization is divided into five management
areas: Jerusalem, Haifa, Galilee, Tel-Aviv, and the
Southern area. There are seven regional directors.
Haifa and Tel-Aviv have two directors, and the other
regions, one. Each area has its own management committee.

The actual marketing operations involve close
cooperation between the regional and branch organizations. Each region sends daily information based on
surveys of the settlements to Tnuva Central at Tel-
Aviv on quantities of products available for marketing

The regions receive orders from the branch heads
where to deliver supplies.   Surpluses are handled by
Tnuva Central at Tel-Aviv.

The actual methods of marketing vary by commodities.   All vegetables, except potatoes and unions,
and most fruits are graded and sorted at the village
or rural center.   They are sold by auction at the
various wholesale markets throughout the country.
Milk and dairy products are processed in a chain of
dairies located near consuming centers.   Broilers
are delivered to Tnuva either live or dressed and
are weighed at the cold storage plants.   Beef animals
are generally sold on the hoof.   Tnuva Center gives
the live weights to butchers who supply offers.   The
highest bidder is given a note to collect at the settlement, and he makes his own transport arrangements.
As previously indicated, however, livestock slaughter-
ing plants operated by the regional purchasing associations and regional councils are becoming increasingly
important.

The proceeds received by Tnuva are paid back to
the settlements in accordance with market prices less
commissions to cover handling and overhead charges
and settlement shares in Tnuva Central.   The commissions vary considerably by product, and are changed
annually.   The settlement shares are used for financing new facilities such as packing, processing, and
canning plants.   A recent innovation is turning part
of the membership taxes into a revolving fund to be
paid back to farmers after a certain number of years.

The main policies of Tnuva have been to market
farm products at a fair price to producers to have
fresh produce available to consumers throughout the
country.   It has, therefore, been interested in the
expansion and improvement of marketing facilities
that would give farmers a fair share of the consumers'
retail prices, and in expanding consumption in efficient retail outlets.

Responsible for marketing about 70 per cent of
the agricultural produce in the country, it controls
an extensive amount of marketing facilities and owns

shares through capital investment in other industrial
and commercial firms. As of 1964, it had 110 wholesale warehouses in twenty-eight cities and towns for
a full line of agricultural produce, a chain of modern dairies for processing and marketing bottled
milk, butter, cream, cultivated milk products, and
various kinds of soft cheeses; a factory for producing hard cheeses; refrigeration facilities for fish
at Haifa harbor and cold stores for wholesale marketing of fish distributed throughout the country; a
honey packing plant; fifteen egg grading stations; a
chain of ripening and cold storage facilities for
bananas and other fresh fruits; a large factory for
the manufacture of citrus fruit by-products, concen-
trates, juices, and for canning vegetables for export
and domestic consumption; a plant for producing alco-
hol from citrus peels, molasses, and grapes; and
eight large packing materials storehouses for all
types of products. It also controls an insurance
firm.

In addition, Tnuva participates in many partnerships in enterprises related to agriculture. The
most important as of 1965 were (1) a company for the
export of fresh produce other than citrus, (2) a
sugar factory, (3) a groundnuts and cotton marketing
company, (4) a national citrus marketing company,
(5) five wholesale markets in the principal population centers in the country, (6) a large winery, (7)
two large cold storage plants, and (8) a factory for
egg trays.

The size and importance of Tnuva may be gauged
by the fact that its volume of business in 1963 was
IL 448 million, of which IL 410 million were sales
from its own facilities and IL 38 million represented
the organization's share from its partnership corporations. In 1964, Tnuva employed 3,670 workers in
its industrial plants, mainly dairies, and in its
wholesale warehouses and offices. It also paid 950
people on a commission basis for distribution of
products to retail shops.

As for organization, its supreme authority is
its congress or general assembly held about every

three years. Each settlement sends one to three
delegates, depending on the number of its family
units. The congress elects a council of a hundred
members that meets four times a year. The council
elects a board of directors that consists of thirty-
four members representing the national settlement
organization, both kibbutzim and moshavim, in proportion to their representation in the general assembly.
The board meets monthly, making decisions on such
important matters as the annual investment program,
raising of share capital, the annual budgets of each
department, commission charges, etc.

The council also elects the secretariat of
Tnuva, consisting of fifteen representatives of the
settlement organizations in proportion to their representation in the general assembly. Five of the
fifteen are representatives of the Moshav Movement.
The fifteen members of the secretariat are the general manager, treasurer, the six branch managers,
and the seven regional directors. On leave from
their respective settlements, they are full-time paid
employees of Tnuva. The secretariat meets weekly.
It makes decisions on price policy, national marketing problems, handles finances, implements the investment program, is responsible for transportation
arrangements, and represents the organization before
the government and various other bodies.

In addition, there is a central control committee of eight persons representing the settlement organizations on policy and operational matters. It
also investigates complaints by the settlements.

There is no doubt that Tnuva has played a major
role in the growth of cooperative settlement in
Israel. Its work has been more effective with the
kibbutzim because of their more centralized controls
than with the moshavim. Nevertheless Tnuva has worked
hard with the moshav olim changing practices to meet
the needs of the new settlements, for example, the
creation of Nov. It has developed a large and important program in educating new settlements in first-
stage marketing practices and has advanced credits
for the organization of adequate facilities.

Yet, as in the case of the Hamashbir Hamerkazi, there is considerable criticism of Tnuva, claims of inefficiency, nepotism, excess interference from the Histadrut, and the estrangement of the organization from the actual needs of the settlements. These criticisms are widespread and are heard even in the older and more successful moshavim. This has resulted in the relaxation of the rule of compulsory deliveries to Tnuva and the growth of regional marketing and processing organizations.

Data in the Ministry of Agriculture indicate that the proportion of consumers' expenditures received by farmers in Israel is high in comparison to economically advanced countries in Europe. This in itself is not proof that Tnuva is efficient, since the studies do not isolate the specific influences of important independent variables: the short distances to market in Israel, the large amount of first-stage marketing activities in the village, and the quantity and quality of the marketing services carried out by Tnuva itself. The fact that Tnuva is a national nonprofit cooperative organization is hardly sufficient explanation for low marketing margins. As in the case of the Hamashbir Hamerkazi, there is a realization in Tnuva of the need for increased efficiency. The increased competition and use of other marketing agencies should be of benefit both to Tnuva and the farmers.

Tnuva has had an important influence on overall agricultural policy, helping guarantee food deliveries and the success of rationing during the early years of shortages after statehood. It also plays an important role in the production and marketing boards in the national planning of food supplies and in the implementation of this planning in providing marketing and processing facilities, both for national needs and exports.

Other Organizations

There are a number of other important Histadrut agencies serving agriculture. Two that are conducted jointly with other institutions deserve at least

passing attention. One is the water company, Mekorot.
While the planning of water development is the responsibility of a national water-planning authority,
the implementation of these plans on a national scale
is executed by Mekorot. The organization was founded
in 1937 as a joint initiative of the Histadrut and
the Jewish Agency. After independence the State became a third partner, buying one third of the company
shares. Mekorot is the principal water supply company in Israel. Under the present national agricultural and water plans Mekorot will be responsible for
70 per cent of the total water supply.[9]

Yachin-Hakal is an important agricultural development organization for agricultural workers who
do not wish to join cooperative settlements. It represents an amalgamation of two organizations, Yachin
Ltd., founded by Nir Shitufi in 1928, and Hakal Ltd.,
a partnership company of the Histadrut and the Jewish
Agency founded in 1949. Yachin-Hakal cultivates by
contract large tracts of plantations and market gardens. It regularly employs over five thousand workers. It also conducts marketing operations for
citrus. It and Tnuva Export are responsible for almost half of the citrus export trade of the country.
Yachin-Hakal also operates a citrus canning plant.[10]

SETTLEMENT ORGANIZATIONS

Practically all the settlements in the cooperative sector, both moshavim and kibbutzim, are members
of national settlement organizations.[11] This is a
result of the historical development of the country.
Before statehood settlements with similar economic,
social, and political philosophies banded together
for mutual aid and for representational purposes with
the settlement authority, Histadrut, and other public
agencies. Because of the political organization of
the country after statehood and the lack of geographical constituencies, national settlement organizations
were attached to political parties to achieve political ends. The settlers, however, have complete freedom to vote for the party of their choice, which often
is different from the party to which the settlement
is affiliated.

The affiliation of moshavim to settlement organizations is indicated in Table 22. By far the
most important of the national organizations is the
Moshav Movement attached to the Mapai, the leading
political party in the country. It includes over
60 per cent of the moshav settlers. Next in importance are the organizations attached to the national
religious parties, Hapoel Hamizrachi, Paole Agudat
Israel, and Agudat Israel. These organizations include about 20 per cent of the settlers. The remaining organizations represent the spectrum of the
Israel political parties. Haoved Hazioni and Herut
are attached to various groupings of the Liberal Party. Haichud Hachaklai and the Farmers' Federation
represent the middle-class moshavim and are generally
attached to the Liberal Party. Mapam represents the
independent socialist Marxist party.

TABLE 22

Moshavim Classified by Organizational
Affiliation, 1967[a]

Organizational Affiliation	Number of Settlements	Population
Moshav Movement	211	74,569
Hapoel Hamizrachi	55	23,425
Haichud Hachaklai	32	9,799
Haoved Hazioni	13	4,049
Paole Agudat Israel and Agudat Israel	9	2,543
Herut	8	1,550
Farmers' Federation	6	1,578
Mapam	2	392
No affiliation	9	3,347
Total	345	121,252

[a]Year end, 1967.

Source: Statistical Abstract of Israel, 1968, p. 26.

The Moshav Movement is relatively stronger in the veteran prewar villages. The religious settlement organizations have become more important since statehood since the majority of the immigrants from the Moslem countries were of traditional orthodox religious background. These organizations include but 10 per cent of the settlers in veteran villages as compared to 25 per cent of the poststate villages.

The following review of the activities of the national settlement organizations is limited mainly to the most important one, the Moshav Movement. It was founded in 1926, only five years after the establishment of the first moshav. Its main functions are (1) mutual assistance in economic and financial matters, (2) initiation and implementation of common enterprises, (3) educational and instructional activities in agricultural and general moshav problems, (4) youth activities, (5) general educational, social, and cultural activities, (6) legal and administrative activities involving guidance of disputes and control of moshav activities, and (7) representation of member villages in their contacts with national institutions and the government.

The Moshav Movement has established a number of financial institutions to supplement the activities of the national institutions, Ministry of Agriculture, and commercial banks. It thus provides additional credit, helps member moshavim refinance debts, and acts as a guarantor for member settlements. These activities are of particular help to the newer moshavim who need financial aid on easier terms than the established settlements.

Its principal financial institutions are (1) the Keren Moshavim (moshav fund) established in 1930, (2) Ein Hei, a cooperative credit society established in 1960, (3) Keren Tagmulim (savings fund) established in 1960, and (4) the Moshavim Mortgage Bank Ltd. established in 1963. A summary of the financial statistics of these organizations is presented in Table 23.

The Moshav Fund has been an important mutual aid activity and financial arm of the Moshav Movement.

TABLE 23

Credit Activities of Financial Institutions of Moshav Movement, 1968

Organization	Number of Member Villages	Own Capital	Deposits and Accounts	Balance of Credit	Investment Reserve Funds	Credit Guarantees
			(Thousand Israel Pounds)			
Keren Moshavim	200	3,700	10,500	12,500	1,700	8,000
Ein Hei Credit Cooperative	140	2,750	20,000	16,000	500	5,000
Keren Tagmulim	80	---	13,000	1,000	12,000	---
Moshavim Mortgage Bank Ltd.	110	1,200	2,200	3,400	---	---
Total	---	7,650	45,700	32,900	14,200	13,000

Source: Moshav Movement.

In 1968, its deposits were IL 10.5 million, and it was responsible for IL 8.0 million in credit guarantees. Its method of operation is that of a cooperative credit union, with creditors buying shares and debtors obtaining loans. This fund has been important in establishing the regional purchasing associations; Mattam, an organization for acquiring and servicing settlements with agricultural equipment; Dromit, a regional slaughter plant in the Negev; and in supporting the establishment of new villages for second generation moshav youth.

Ein Hei is a cooperative credit society with certain banking activity rights. The villages hold 50 per cent of its shares, the Moshav Movement and allied institutions, 48 per cent, and other groups, 2 per cent. As a cooperative bank it holds the deposits of members, guarantees their safety and accrued interest, and channels liquid assets for settlement mutual aid.

The purpose of Keren Tagmulim is to encourage thrift and cooperative savings by moshav members. Because of the government policy to encourage savings the members who use this facility obtain substantial income tax benefits. The investors at age sixty-five receive the sums saved plus interest. The capital of the fund is used for the good of all the settlements attached to the Moshav Movement.

The Keren Moshavim had invested a substantial sum of money for mortgage funds for building purposes in which the Ministry of Housing has taken an active part. In 1963, this type of investment was made the responsibility of the Moshavim Mortgage Bank Ltd.

The Moshav Movement also conducts a small life insurance operation. Members pay an annual premium of IL 20 for a policy of IL 5,000. Participants are accepted up to seventy years of age with no physical examinations needed.

The principal economic organizations of the Moshav Movement are Mattam Ltd., that functions as central supply organization, a mutual insurance

company, and a trust company. A summary of the per-
tinent statistics of these three organizations is
shown in Table 24. This table indicates total sales
in 1968 of IL 25.5 million and guaranteed credits of
IL 14.8 million.

TABLE 24

Business Institutions of the Moshav Movement,
1968

Organization	Own Capital	Total Sales (Thousand Israeli Pounds)	Credits Guaranteed
Mattam, Ltd.	900	21,000	9,500
Mutual Insurance	140	4,000[a]	5,300
Trust Company	32	500[b]	--
Total	1,072	25,500	14,800

[a]Premiums paid.
[b]Commission for services.

Source: Moshav Movement.

A major contribution of the Moshav Movement to
the economic services of its member settlements has
been in the organization and operation of the regional purchasing associations. It is now concentrating
considerable attention on the expansion of moshav
industry, particularly to help the moshav olim. It
is interested in expanding the following types of
industries: (1) home cottage industries, (2) small
group industries within the moshav, (3) moshav-owned
industry, and (4) regional industry that involves the
partnership of two or more villages. The Moshav
Movement, for the most part in association with regional organizations, has been particularly active in

recent years in promoting and supporting regional industries that contribute to the efficiency of agricultural production, reduce prices of supplies, and
increase farm incomes. In the main these represent
plants supplying inputs and services and food processing plants.

The principal regional industries include the
following: (1) three feed-processing plants, (2) two
oil-extraction plants, (3) a large ice cream plant,
(4) a large meat- and leather-processing plant, (5)
a central cooperative office for transport services,
and (6) partnership in a large cotton gin at Kiryat
Gat in Lakhish. Some smaller workshops have been
established in cooperation with Village Industries
Ltd., many of which are in the mountainous areas of
Galilee and Judea.

The Moshav Movement has an extensive educational
program. It has supplied the general instructors for
the moshav olim. It has also supported improved educational facilities in the new villages by contributing to the maintenance of a normal school for training
teachers for the village schools. It has organized
seminars and study groups and has cooperated closely
with the settlement authority and government extension
services and research institutions. It conducts in-
service courses for teachers in the older villages.
It supports agricultural schools and publishes one of
the more important agricultural journals in the country.

To meet the needs of the new immigrants from
traditional religious cultures the Moshav Movement
established a Department of Religious Affairs to supply the villages with copies of the Torah, religious
textbooks, and volumes for moral guidance.

The youth activities of the Moshav Movement are
channeled through the organization Hanoar Haoved
(working youth). The program includes many kinds of
social and educational activities: village, regional,
and national competitions; scouting; and vocational,
citizenship, and cultural courses.

The Moshav Movement has worked with Histadrut
bodies in the field of culture and to further cooperative ideology, mainly in common institutions for
education and information, and in publishing period-
icals, books, and other materials.

The Moshav Movement has important legal and
administrative duties in its member villages. It
sends its representatives to all village general assemblies to see that the moshavim live up to the obligations of their constitutions and the rules of
the settlement organization. It plays an important
role in settling disputes in the village as a second
degree legal appellant organization from decisions at
the village level. These functions were delegated
to it by the Nir Shitufi of the Histadrut. Based on
the decisions of its judiciary committee, the Moshav
Movement has published a legal handbook on various
aspects of moshav life for reference and guidance of
the moshav and its members.

Since the establishment of the State, it has
been more difficult for the Moshav Movement to maintain its position with the moshav olim as well as the
moshav ovdim. This explains its strong efforts to
pass the controversial cooperative law that would
endow the organization with legal status to maintain
its position vis-a-vis its affiliated villages. The
political reason for support of the law has been the
desire of the organization to maintain its relative
position in regard to the moshav sector with the active support of the Mapai party. There has been
strong opposition to the law and the new proposed
inheritance law even in the established moshavim.
This is but a manifestation of a change in moshav
values and the current desire for more freedom from
the Histadrut and its institutions and the parent
settlement organizations and their political attach-
ments.

In regard to representational contacts with the
government and settlement institutions, the Moshav
Movement performs for its villages what Nir Shitufi
in the Histadrut does for the cooperative agricultural

sector as a whole. Since the Mapai party has an
important position in the Histadrut, in the Jewish
Agency, and in the State, such representation has
been effective. There have been complaints of fav-
oritism to the Moshav Movement because of its strong
political position.

A function, very important in the past, but
which the Moshav Movement continues on a smaller scale
at present, is the formation of settlement groups for
new moshavim. It conducts informational and propaganda activities on settlement opportunities in Israel
to Jews throughout the diaspora and has a department
of foreign affairs that, among other matters, is concerned with settlement.

On the organization side, the Moshav Movement
is similar to the other institutions supporting settlement activities. Its national congress is held
every four years and is attended by delegates elected
by the constituent moshavim. The congress elects a
council and a secretariat, who manage the organization's business in the interim period. Its expenditures are based on a budget approved by its council.
Its income is derived from taxation of member moshavim
and revenues from its various economic institutions.

The Moshav Movement has a permanent staff who
work full time at headquarters in Tel-Aviv as well as
a number of people selected from the moshavim who
work on a part-time basis. The work at headquarters
is divided into the following departments: agriculture, absorption, education, youth, religion, judicial,
tax, health, foreign affairs, and community affairs.
In addition it has a special department for the moshav
shitufi. At headquarters there have been about thirty
employees on full-time duty in the various departments,
twenty employees from the moshavim on part-time duty,
mainly youth work, and fifty full-time employees concerned with the subsidiary financial agencies.

The Napoel Hamizrachi follows the lead of the
Moshav Movement in supplying similar services to affiliated villages. As to be expected, there is a much
greater emphasis on religious activities. Even though

there were few religious moshavim before the establishment of the State, it has done a good job in organizing and servicing new settlements with its
limited experienced personnel. Like the Moshav Movement, it has been responsible for selecting general
instructors for its member villages. Although the
religious parties are not members of the Histadrut,
the moshavim attached to the religious parties use
its services. They buy and market through Hamashbir
Hamerkazi and Tnuva and are members of its health
services, Kupat Holim.

The middle-class moshavim are also organized in
national settlement organizations. They are attached
to national buying and marketing institutions, Haspaka
and Tenne, smaller-scale replicas of the larger Histadrut organizations. Like Tnuva, Tenne not only markets fresh produce but also has processing and canning
plants. In 1964, its volume of sales reached IL 30
million. The village, however, can use whatever organization it wishes. Many, in fact, market through
Tnuva. As already indicated, the settlers also have
complete freedom of choice to participate in the Histadrut health plan.

MINISTRY OF AGRICULTURE

With the operation of the autonomous national
institutions in every phase of agricultural planning
and settlement, the increase in importance of the
regional institutions spawned by the national institutions, and with the land and water authorities completely autonomous, the role of the Ministry of
Agriculture, particularly in the postwar cooperative
settlements, has been substantially a residual one.

The Ministry of Agriculture is important,
nevertheless, particularly in agricultural planning,
research, extension, and credit. The role of the
State in planning has been described in detail, as
well as the activities of the Extension Service. The
importance of agricultural research in the development of the moshav has also been emphasized.

As for the provision of agricultural credit, about two thirds of the institutional loans to agriculture, about IL 650 million by the end of 1961, were for agricultural settlement, issued primarily by the settlement authority. From the periof of statehood through the end of 1961, about one sixth of the institutional credit for agriculture, IL 160 million, consisted of development loans from the Government Development Budget that have been financed by taxation and long-term loans in the country and abroad.[12] The main agency for making development loans is the Agricultural Bank of Israel, a government bank attached to the Ministry of Agriculture operating without branches or intermediaries. These loans represent an important source of long-term credits. A typical loan from development funds is given for a period of ten to twelve years at a rate of interest of 6.5 per cent. Cattle and machinery mortages and pledges of marketing agencies are used as securities.

Development loans have been an important source of funds to veteran moshavim. Poststate moshavim have also been able to use such funds to complement the investment program of the settlement authority when they reach the final stage of development.

The Ministry of Agriculture has not been pleased with the importance of the autonomous institutions in agricultural policy and settlement and would like to assume some of the responsibilities of these institutions.* Actually, this is happening. General Dayan, as Minister of Agriculture in the early sixties, succeeded in the consolidation of planning

---

*This is but part of the larger power struggle between the State and the Jewish Agency and Histadrut that has assumed particularly important political dimensions in recent years and has resulted in reorganizations and policy changes in the latter two agencies. General Dayan has been a leader of the political faction to increase the power of the State vis-a-vis the autonomous agencies.

and extension activities with the Jewish Agency. With
a limited program of new agricultural settlement and
the attainment of economic independence by many of
the poststate settlements and their release from the
guided development of the settlement authority, the
Ministry of Agriculture will achieve a consolidation
of further power.

REGIONAL ORGANIZATIONS

The functions of the regional purchasing organizations and the regional councils have been described
in detail in Chapter 6. They have assumed increasing
importance. The amount of share capital increased
fivefold from 1958 through 1962.[13] In the latter year
total sales to members amounted to IL 925 million and
total credits, IL 339 million. This fast growth has
continued in recent years. The development of the
regional purchasing associations has been encouraged
by the national institutions, particularly the settlement organizations and the settlement authority, as
institutional support for the moshav (and the kibbutz
as well) in line with its development needs, even
though the growth has affected national institutions
adversely, particularly Hamashbir Hamerkazi and also
Tnuva.

The regional purchasing associations and the
economic activities of the regional councils have developed as a result of the needs of the moshav, particularly the moshav olim. To a degree this has
reflected inefficiencies in the national service organizations, particularly high costs and political
party influences. This does not mean to imply that
the regional organizations are free of politics. They
are also organized along political lines. For example, there is one purchasing organization for all the
Hapoel Hamizrachi villages. It would be far more
economic if the religious villages belonged to the
same purchasing organization as their neighboring non-
religious villages. Regional councils similarly have
political overtones, and they generally consist of
villages that are attached to the same settlement organization.

INSTITUTIONAL SETTING OF MOSHAV AS A FACTOR
IN ITS SUCCESS

The role of the autonomous institutions in the
development of agricultural settlement in Israel and
the government cooperation with them is certainly
unique. Although to a certain degree they are competitive with one another, by pooling their resources
they are constantly creating special organizations as
needed. Thus they have given the cooperative agricultural sector extensive flexibility in organizational
support. The way these institutions, the government,
and even private enterprise can evolve new organizations is truly remarkable and would make a fascinating
study in development administration.

This does not mean to indicate that the national institutions are beyond criticism, particularly
the Histadrut and affiliated organizations and the
Jewish Agency. Criticism of these organizations by
the State and the press is rampant.* Nor does it
mean to imply that these organizations are necessarily
the best of models for agricultural development in
other countries. Nevertheless they have played an
outstanding role in cooperative agricultural settlement and development in Israel.

The sphere of the public sector in the development of the Israel economy has been large. In the

_____

*For example, the <u>Jerusalem Post Weekly</u> of
June 17, 1966, reports that Finance Minister Sapir,
addressing the National Religious Party Executive,
said, "At least two thousand of the four thousand
officials employed at the Jewish Agency are super-
fluous, and if they were transferred to other jobs
the Jewish Agency's work would become even more efficient." This concerns primarily central headquarters. A reorganization of the Jewish Agency
approved in late 1966 drastically cut the number of
employees. The creation of the new Absorption Ministry in 1968 should result in further reorganization.

period of 1950 to 1958, government financing of
capital formation in terms of total gross capital
formation ranged from 57 to 80 per cent.[14] The large
disparity between the government's share in investment and its share in the national product is explained by the fact that the State made available
large amounts of its investment funds to the Histadrut
and to private corporations in the form of loans. The
government through its relation with the Histadrut
was able to control the wage structure of the entire
economy when inflationary forces were rampant. The
Histadrut was a powerful institution with tremendous
political influence. It was there to be used by the
State in its massive development program that had to
be executed quickly for the ingathering and integration of exiles that was largely administered by the
Jewish Agency.

The importance of the role of the public sector
and the State can at best be only partially explained
by the domination of the government by the labor
Mapai party and its political allies. Other important
factors have been: (1) the Zionist doctrine of the
role of the State, (2) the limited resources of the
country, and (3) the country's security problem. Adoption of the Zionist principle of unrestricted immigration necessitated widespread public controls of
the economy to increase the capacity of the country
to absorb the immigrants. Poverty of resources acted
as a brake to private investments and made it necessary for the State to obtain foreign public and nonprofit funds. The country's security problem
necessitated the orientation of the economy in accordance with defense needs as well as economic considerations. This required a high degree of intervention
and planning in the economy that would have been
undertaken by any Israeli government. In no sector
of the economy has this been more true than in agriculture. Security considerations reinforced social
goals and political ideology in the absorption of
immigrants and the development of the cooperative
agricultural sector, that accounted for the high level
of participation by the autonomous institutions and
the State.

NOTES

1. From the files of Jewish Agency.

2. The Agricultural Settlement Department, Reprints from Reports for the Period April, 1960-March, 1964, submitted to the 26th Zionist Congress, Jerusalem, December, 1964 (Jerusalem: Jewish Agency, 1964), p. 35.

3. Nadav Safran, Israel Today: A Profile (New York: Foreign Policy Association Headline Series 170, 1965), pp. 52-53. This compares to Haim Barkai's estimate of 41.8 per cent of the net domestic product in 1959 in his study The Public, Histadrut, and Private Sectors in the Israel Economy (Jerusalem: Falk Foundation for Economic Research in Israel, Sixth Report, 1964), p. 33.

4. Jerusalem Post, June 10, 1966, p. 8.

5. Haim Darin-Drabkin, "The Structure of the Agricultural Cooperative Movement" (paper presented to the International Symposium, The Role of Cooperatives in Rural Development, Tel-Aviv, March, 1965), p. 18. (Mimeographed.)

6. Yehuda Chorin, Agricultural Labor Movement in Israel (Tel-Aviv: Agricultural Workers' Organization in Israel, 1961), p. 14.

7. All statistical material from files of the Hamashbir Hamerkazi and interviews with its officials.

8. The basic sources for this section were the files of Tnuva and interviews with Tnuva officials.

9. Noah Malkosh, Cooperation in Israel (Tel-Aviv: Histadrut, 1963), p. 47.

10. Ibid., p. 45.

11. Unless otherwise noted the basic sources of this section are the files of the settlement organizations and interviews with organization officials

12. Gershon Kaddar, "The Influence of the Cooperative Set-up of Agricultural Settlement on the Agricultural Credit System in Israel," p. 7.

13. From the files of Moshav Movement.

14. Don Patinkin, <u>The Israel Economy the First Decade</u> (Jerusalem: The Falk Project for Economic Research in Israel, 1960), pp. 86-87.

8

MEASUREMENTS OF SUCCESS

Preliminary to the analysis of the exportability of the moshav model, it would be well to judge the extent to which the moshav has been a success in its native habitat. The conclusions of the analyses of the development of the moshav ovdim and moshav olim are that both types can be considered a success. The conclusion concerning the moshav olim, the model for export, is still tentative, since many poststate moshavim have either not reached economic independence or achieved it only very recently.

It has been emphasized that the success of the moshav cannot be judged by economic criteria alone. From the point of view of the State, social, security, and political criteria have been as important as economic criteria in the establishment and maintenance of the moshav. From the point of view of the settlers, these other criteria are also very important. In its early stages of development, while the moshav is struggling to reach economic maturity, social considerations may be more important than economic ones in maintaining group solidarity. Unless the moshav is very close to a city with special employment and/or marketing conditions, the settler will only remain as a permanent member, and the children will only choose to become moshav members, at least under conditions of reasonably full employment, if the amenities of the moshav match those of the city.

One of the better indicators of the success of the moshav is the degree of turnover, the statistics

233

on the number of settlers leaving the village. For
the poststate moshavim as a whole the number of settlers leaving the village, expressed in terms of the
total number of inhabitants in the village in the
previous year, dropped from 12 per cent in 1956 to
about 2 per cent in 1964.[1] In the years earlier than
1956, especially in the 1949-51 crash period of settlement, this percentage was very much higher. In
the Jerusalem district, one of the most difficult
areas of settlement, turnover has dropped from about
22 per cent in 1956 to 2 per cent in 1964.[2] These
figures do not prove that the people remaining in the
village are all successful farmers. There is a considerable and probably growing amount of part-time
farming, and some families derive almost all their
income from nonagricultural sources. These figures
indicate the growing trend to stability in the village and, along with income statistics, substantiate
the success of the village.

Personnel turnover in the early years of the
moshav was high, even in the moshavim established under comprehensive regional planning where the settlers
were fairly well screened. In the Lakhish region
10 to 15 per cent of the settlers left immediately
after arriving at the village to join their relatives
in other parts of the country.[3] It was not difficult
to find other families to take their place. In a
fairly successful Kurdish moshav olim chosen for special study the turnover ratio was 9 per cent in the
first year of settlement and since then has gone down
to practically zero.[4] The estimate of 5 to 10 per
cent of unused moshav units is probably a minimal operational figure, since these units are being held
for the children of the settlers.

By strictly economic criteria cost-benefit
ratios in the agricultural sector should be compared
to those of other sectors. It was not possible to
engage in such an exercise in this study. It does
not follow that if the benefit ratio is lower in agriculture than in other sectors that these other sectors should be expanded at the expense of agriculture
The importance of noneconomic criteria for agricultural settlement has been emphasized. It is highly

doubtful in the case of Israel that settling the entire country and decentralization of its population
structure could have been accomplished on other than
the basis of expanded agricultural settlement or the
combined agricultural-industrial base in the context
of comprehensive regional planning.

The drive for decentralization of the population has been reasonably successful. The percentage
of the total population in the three principal cities,
Tel-Aviv, Haifa, and Jerusalem, dropped from 52.1 per
cent in 1948 to 31.1 per cent in 1967.* The fall in
per cent of the total Jewish population of the country in these three city districts, which include their
environs, was slightly greater in the same period.
The percentage of the country's total Jewish population in its Southern District rose 10.3 points in this
period, from 0.9 per cent to 11.2 per cent.[5]

It is still useful to compare the net product
of the gainfully employed persons in agriculture with
the other sectors. One such study of the Histadrut
sector of the economy was made for 1959. As may be
seen from Table 25, the net product from agriculture
was lower in that year than from the other sectors
of the economy controlled by the Histadrut. The figure for the agricultural cooperative group, the
moshavim in column 4, was very low because of the
relatively poor position of the new moshavim. The
figure for agriculture for the collective settlement
group, the kibbutzim in column 5, was also low because of the influence of the poststate kibbutzim,
and compares badly with the net-product figure from
manufacturing in the kibbutzim that represents well-
organized enterprises in the veteran kibbutzim. The
figure for agriculture in the Histadrut companies
group, column 2, is for hired labor. The table indicates lower productivity in the moshavim than for
the kibbutzim or hired labor.

The conclusions of this study follow:

---

*Includes East Jerusalem in 1967.

The low productivity in the cooperative
settlements group is a source of difficulty not only in the short run but even
more so in the long run. The large gap
between labor productivity in agriculture
and in manufacturing revealed by our data
makes it questionable whether the implied
differences in the standard of living between the cooperative settlements group
on the one hand and the collective settlements group and other forms of economic
organization on the other hand can be
bridged simply by providing additional resources for agricultural production to
cooperative settlements. Yet if the solution to the standard of living problem
in the moshav calls for a more heterogeneous industrial structure, to be
achieved by a shift into manufacturing
similar to the process taking place in the
collective settlement group, difficulties
related to the social structure of this
type of settlement have to be faced. These
are due to the basic tenet of cooperative
settlement ideology, which calls for identity of the production unit with the family. This condition was satisfied by
means of the family farm as long as agriculture was the only type of production.
Whether it can be satisfied when manufacturing becomes an alternative or complementary type of industry in moshavim is
open to doubt.[6]

These pessimistic conclusions have been belied
by time. Providing more inputs and more carefully
supervised management has definitely increased the
net output of the moshavim so that their relative
position in productivity has improved in comparison
to the other sectors. The improvements in agricultural productivity since 1959 have been notable and
are still continuing. While the average income of
farm operators in the country as a whole is still
below that of the average income of the gainfully
employed in the whole economy, the increase in farm

Net Product per Gainfully Employed Person by Economic Group in Histadrut Sector, 1959

	Total[a] Histadrut Sector	Histadrut Companies Group (Israeli	Producers' Cooperative Group Pounds)	Cooperative Settlement Group	Collective Settlement Group
1. All branches	4,279[a]	5,075	7,388	2,360	3,102 3,713[b]
2. Agriculture, forestry, and fishing	2,343	2,756	—	2,060	2,566
3. Mining, quarrying, and manufacturing	5,797	6,030	5,946	—	5,463
4. Construction	4,438	4,438	—	—	—
5. Transport and communications	8,381	—	8,381	—	—
6. Banking and finance	9,259	9,259	—	—	—
7. Trade and other services	3,564	5,526	4,000	—	2,424
8. Histadrut administration	4,412	—	—	—	—
9. Nonprofit institutions	6,337	—	—	—	—

[a]Includes items 8 and 9 not included in group averages.

[b]Value added per employed worker in agriculture and manufacturing only.

Source: Haim Barkai, The Public, Histadrut, and Private Sectors in the Israeli Economy, Sixth Report by the Falk Project for Economic Research in Israel (Jerusalem, 1964), p. 56.

income from 1959 to 1967 was higher than that of the
average labor income in the economy as a whole.[7]
The author completely overlooked the flexibility of
the moshav structure and possibilities for industrialization by the regional purchasing associations, regional councils, and through comprehensive regional
planning.

CRITICAL SUCCESS FACTORS

The next step in the analysis of the success
of the moshav is the isolation of the critical success factors, both exogenous and endogenous, their
examination as to the degree of particularity to
Israel conditions, and whether they can be operational or substitutable in other developmental environments. This is basic to the general analysis of the
exportability of the moshav for the agricultural development of other countries and the specific case
analyses of the adaptability of the moshav in two
countries.

Exogenous

As to the exogenous critical success factors,
first is the high quality of leadership. For the
most part, the leaders in the development of the
moshav olim were the original volunteer prestate
settlers, both from the kibbutzim and moshavim, and
some extremely competent career public servants from
the national institutions and the State, particularly the Settlement Department of the Jewish Agency.
This quality of leadership in Israel was not limited
to the agricultural sector but extended to the economy as a whole, enabling a country with the most limited of resources to become a developed country withi
a decade.

The second of the success factors lies in the
nature of the institutions supporting the cooperative
agricultural sector. The development of neither the
moshav nor the kibbutz would have been possible without them. These institutions reflect the quality of
leadership of the cooperative agricultural sector.

The third factor is the unifying bond of Zionist ideology, the maintenance at all costs of the
Jewish national State. Yet, despite national support
of this ideology, criticism of the World Zionist
Organization is rampant, and political party disputa-
tions and cleavages are legion. The nationalism and
patriotism, nurtured by the ideology of a Jewish
homeland and strengthened by the historical course of
events, has welcomed the influx of immigrants, the
ingathering of the Jews from the diaspora. It has
supported their settlement in the moshav olim, even
though this has meant economic sacrifices by the
farmers in the older settlements. The new lands gained
when the State was established could have been given
to the existing moshavim and kibbutzim. Instead private interests were subjugated to national needs, and
the older settlements contributed to the development
of the new.

The fourth factor is the quality of the government. Although the political development of the
country has lagged behind its social and economic development, in comparative terms, in respect to developing countries, it is high indeed. A significant
proportion of the political leadership in the country,
including the present and past prime ministers and a
number of cabinet officers, have come from the agricultural sector. General Dayan is one of the most
illustrious products of the moshav. Political leadership in Israel in the early years of statehood has
been, to a large degree, synonymous with cooperative
agricultural leadership.

The fifth factor is the prestige and relative
position of the cooperative agricultural sector in
the economy. This reflects the continuing influence
of agricultural fundamentalism in the country as supported by its institutions, particularly the Histadrut and the Jewish Agency, and the influence of these
institutions on the politics of the country. Although
Israel is an industrial country, its agriculture has
not been neglected and has been given financial support, in spite of the rise in demand for financing of
the other sectors and an increase in general sentiment
for the deemphasis of cooperative agriculture and its

values. The agricultural sector has maintained its position and influence even though there has been a change in social values in the moshavim that has affected their organizational structure.

The sixth critical success factor has been the development of a specialized role for the moshav within the cooperative agricultural sector. It is particularly adapted to labor-intensive types of culture and complements the capital-intensive kibbutz with its more extensive type of agriculture.

The seventh factor is the financial support of the cooperative agriculture sector by Jews throughout the diaspora through the World Zionist Organization and the Jewish National Fund. It is a strange sociological phenomenon that in the Jewish communities in the cities of the United States and the British Commonwealth much of the social life revolves around the activities of fund raising for Israel or transfer of money from Jewish capitalists to Jewish socialists that pleases both sides. While the sums thus collected have been high, they have never been high enough for the settlement budgets of the Jewish Agency. Difficulties in financing and delays in obtaining basic investment budgets have been among the principal factors for the fact that a longer period than originally planned has been needed by settlements in reaching economic maturity.

The eighth critical success factor has been the national agricultural policy that has favored cooperative agricultural settlement and has effectively integrated macro agricultural planning at the national level with micro planning at the settlement level. The aim of this planning as noted has been to provide the settlers with income opportunities equivalent to those of trained urban labor in the cities.

Despite the fact that national economic planning has lagged behind agricultural sectorial planning, Israel has evolved in a remarkably short period into an industrial, prosperous, developed economy. The domestic level of demand for food and fiber is high and is important in contributing to the prosperity of

the cooperative agricultural sector. The moshav has
to compete for its labor supply with the other sectors of the economy. If conditions are less favorable
in the moshav than elsewhere, the settler will leave.
Therefore, favorable economic conditions constitute
the ninth critical success factor by acting as a constant prod to the institutions supporting settlement
to be efficient.

A tenth factor promoting the success of the ag-
gricultural cooperative sector has been the land-
tenure system. Most important are the nationalization
of land and the security of long-term 49-year leases
with low rents and inheritance rights. The tenure
system has also prevented land speculation.

An eleventh factor that has been particularly
emphasized has been the national economic, social,
and political goals that have favored the development
of the moshav as compared to other agricultural structures. The moshav has been an important instrument
for increasing agricultural production, assimilating
new immigrants, and settling the entire country as
well as developing successful, commercial, intensive
family-sized farms.

A twelfth factor is the relatively small size
of the country that has facilitated agricultural planning and the implementation of planning on a national
scale.

A thirteenth factor is that Israel, on statehood,
inherited a road and railroad-transportation network
from the British. This was of some importance in agricultural marketing. It was not a major success
factor since the transportation network was barely
adequate for the phenomenal growth of the country after statehood. It was, however, a facilitating factor.

Endogenous

The first of the principal endogenous factors
is the flexibility of the moshav as an institution
and the use of this flexibility by the institutions

concerned with settlement in molding the moshav olim
to the needs of the poststate settlers.

The second is the institutionalization of the
family farm in a structure operationally consistent
with the economic, social, and political goals of the
country. Officials of the Agricultural Center stated
that if the moshav had not already been in existence,
something like it would have had to be created as the
instrument of absorption of the poststate immigrants
into the agricultural sector.

A third factor is the inherent nature of the
moshav as an institution for integrating individualism in a cooperative pattern. This was of particular
importance in the absorption of immigrants from traditional societies into a Western type of agriculture.

A fourth one is the character and motivation
of the settlers. Undoubtedly the unusually high motivation of the farmers was an important factor contributing to the success of the moshav ovdim. The
cultural backgrounds of the majority of the settlers
of the moshav olim, however, were quite similar to
those in many underdeveloped countries. The problems
in Israel of developing modern farmers from settlers
of traditional cultures represents the general problem faced by developing nations throughout the world.
There are those who believe that the Jews are different; and, therefore, what works in Israel is not applicable to other developing countries. This thesis,
in fact, is belied by what is happening in the adaption of moshav principles in other countries.

UNIQUENESS OF SUCCESS FACTORS TO ISRAEL

To what degree are the critical success factors
unique to Israel? Certainly the national bond of the
ideology of the Jewish State is unique to Israel.
Many would categorize the quality of leadership and
the nature of the institutions supporting the agricultural sector as highly particular to Israel. Leadership includes not just top-level but middle-level
staff and settlement advisors. Granted that the

quality of personnel in Israel at all levels has indeed been unusually good, does it follow that this
high a level is an absolute necessity for the application of moshav principles for the agricultural development of other countries? Probably not. Some of
the development literature has made a fetish of administration as the limiting factor in development
planning and implementation without any real substantive analysis of the matter in terms of developmental
problems and accomplishments. Were such analyses
made, they would probably disclose a degree of administrative competence of the level of that of Western
Europe or the United States but on a scale large
enough to match the immensity of the countries' problems. It seems that neither the lack of administrative competence nor the complexity of the basic
administrative needs are limiting factors to the application of the moshav principles in Latin America,
the Near East, or the Far East. Sufficient evidence
is at hand that administrative competence for the
support of the moshav in countries in these regions
can be developed, provided there is a minimum pool of
trained personnel.

The nature of the institutions in Israel supporting the cooperative agricultural sector must be
considered indigenous unique phenomena of Israeli history. It does not follow that it is necessary to copy
these institutions exactly for the development of the
moshav in other countries. The moshav can be developed and administered by institutions and/or cabinet
agencies already in existence or by a new agency
created specifically for cooperative settlement.

The condition of full employment has also, to
some measure, been particular to Israel. In most developing countries there is usually a serious problem
of unemployment in the cities and disguised unemployment in the countryside. Consequently there would be
little of Israeli type pressure to the moshav administrators. The settlers would have few alternative
economic opoortunities. In other developing countries
the moshav may be used as an instrument for absorbing
disguised unemployment as well as to increase agricultural productivity and production.

The very small size of the country may also be
a factor rather particular to Israel. Because of the
cost of setting up cooperative settlements, large
countries may have to limit their efforts to selected
regions. The small size of the country has facilitate
setting up a rational transportation system.

None of the other exogenous success factors is
completely particular to Israel. Many countries have
the minimum level of political stability for experi-
menting with the moshav. Many are interested in promoting agricultural cooperation. Unfortunately many
have used, to their dismay, and are continuing to use
Western models that are completely inapplicable. The
story of agricultural cooperation in developing countries, based on these models, has generally been a
story of failure. It is is quite disheartening to see
the United States, the Food and Agriculture Organization of the United Nations, and the International
Labor Office promoting agricultural cooperatives that
often have little or no chance of success. In other
countries, as in Israel, family-type moshav farms
could complement the existing agricultural structure.

Establishing a moshav system on a large scale
would involve substantial expenditures of public
funds. The moshav system, however, in other countries
need not be as comprehensive or as expensive as in
Israel. As already indicated, in most countries the
moshav would be limited to certain regions of the
country. It also might include fewer functions than
in Israel, particularly municipal functions. Financial obligations are also not of overriding importance
for the few privileged developing countries with favorable trade balances, a number of countries in the
Near East and Venezuela, for example. Granted that
costs of adopting the moshav as an instrument of agricultural development, settlement, and/or reform
would be expensive, in all cases the moshav should
be analyzed as compared to other possible alternatives
in the allocation of financial priorities. Such an
analysis may (or may not) reveal that funds used on
other development projects could be diverted to the
moshav. Loans by international banks would also be
available. They are now used in a number of countries
for cooperative agricultural settlements.

As for agricultural planning, most countries now have it to some degree, and there is even a growing interest in peasant agriculture as compared to private large-scale commercial agriculture. Few countries openly favor a cooperative sector as strong as in Israel. But many countries are willing to develop a cooperative sector based on family-type farms.

National economic planning is quite the fashion in all developing countries, at least the phase of inviting foreign experts to write up plans and then filing them for future reference. Also there is an increasing realization of the importance of the agricultural sector in economic development, and confidence in the extreme priority given to industrial development in the various year plans is now on the wane. Many countries realize that the supply inelasticity in the agricultural sectors is a principal limiting factor to their economic development and are naturally interested in how this institutional block may be removed. The application of moshav principles might possibly be a way.

Land has been nationalized in most of the politically centralized socialized countries. There is a certain amount of public ownership in agricultural resettlement projects in a number of European countries, Holland and Italy, for example. The resettlement projects in these two countries incorporate many moshav features. In Poland and Yugoslavia there has been a substantial return from nationalized collective farms to small-scale peasant holdings. One cannot say that moshav principles are being applied in these countries. The systems are rather those of controlled benevolent backwardness. The wide-scale use of the nationalization of land for promoting cooperative villages of family farms probably may not be common outside of Israel and is unlikely to be used in many countries for political reasons.

The national goals--economic, social, and political--that have favored the moshav in Israel are not unique to that country. Many countries would like to break the agricultural supply bottleneck, and some are beginning to realize that investment in peasant

family-sized farms may be a method of doing this.
They are genuinely interested in improving the social
amenities of the peasants and in the diffusion of
political power. The ends of land reform that have
been widely adopted throughout the world are social
and political as well as economic. The political
ends, however, frequently become more important in
practice than the social and economic ones.

Many countries have given the implementation
of national transportation systems high priority as
basic infrastructure for national economic development. This would support the moshav as well as other
improved agricultural structures.

Evaluation of the critical endogenous factors
necessitates some further definitions or specifications. The organization and operation of the moshav
in Israel have been described and analyzed in considerable detail. What is exported, however, if the
moshav is at all adaptable to other developmental
environments, is not a physical or operational model
but the basic principles, the doctrine of the moshav
from which the actual models for the countries concerned will be developed. The basic principles are
(1) comprehensive, coordinated, and integrated agricultural planning, (2) planning and implementation
at the village level that includes everybody in the
village, and (3) settlements based on family farms.

If the basic principles of the moshav are
adaptable to other countries, there is enough flexibility in the moshav structure to meet, within limits,
the different development environments. Thus the
first three of the endogenous success factors of the
moshav are not unique to Israel, since they are primarily concerned with its structural flexibility in
meeting (1) the needs of the settlers, (2) economic,
social, and political goals of the country, and (3)
integration of individualism within a cooperative
structure.

The leaders of the moshav in Israel have demonstrated the flexibility of the institution in its
adaptation to the needs of the new poststate immigrant

from traditional cultures, not unlike those existing
in other developing countries. The economic goals of
increasing agricultural production and productivity
within a structure of family-type farms, the political
goals of diffusing the pattern of the political power
structure by incorporating the peasants within it and
of settling new areas of the country, and the social
goal of providing amenities to farmers to improve
their social status are not at all particular to Israel. Therefore, the possible role of the moshav in
integrating individualism in a cooperative pattern
would also be similar in other countries. At the
same time, it is realized that there may be institutional blocks in the path of the critical endogenous
factors in other countries that may make success more
difficult than in Israel and that, in some cases,
they may be insurmountable.

The differences in character and motivation between the poststate settlers in Israel and peasants
in other countries needs elaboration. In most respects the poststate Oriental immigrants to Israel
were little different, except for religion, from the
non-Jewish inhabitants of the countries from which
they came. At best they may gave been slightly more
literate. The rate of illiteracy of poststate male
immigrants from Asian countries was 22.5 per cent,
and of females, 57.8 per cent.[8] This figure is for
immigrants as a whole. The illiteracy rate of the
immigrants that were sent to the moshav was higher,
as the educated immigrants were absorbed and trained
for more specialized work in town.

There may be two important factors, however, as
far as the poststate agricultural settlers are concerned, that could differentiate the Israeli situation
from others. One was the fact that the majority of
the settlers knew nothing about agriculture and could
learn agricultural processes with an open mind. The
other was the shock effect of their immigration into
a new country with a new culture that made them more
susceptible to accept innovations and change. There
is a similar shock effect, however, in large-scale
resettlement projects in other countries involving
the transfer of many people over long distances to

new parts of a country that are completely different from their native habitat.

DIFFICULTIES IN DEVELOPMENT OF MOSHAV

It should be emphasized that the development of the moshav in Israel has not been easy. Over and above the financial, organizational, economic, and sociological obstacles of developing merchants and craftsmen from traditional societies into modern farmers, there have been a number of other difficulties. The principal ones have been (1) saturation of the domestic market as a limiting factor to the development of farmers' incomes, and the need to develop products for export to new markets, (2) the Arab blockade that affects the development of export markets and obtaining inputs at lowest prices, (3) the limitation of water supplies, (4) the constant peril of Arab marauders in border settlements, and (5) the economic prosperity that has increased the competition for a limited labor supply from the industrial and services sector. In the light of all the difficulties the success of the moshav olim is indeed remarkable and is a tribute to the endeavors of the people and institutions concerned. In comparison with other countries, many of these difficulties are, in fact, unique to Israel.

NOTES

1. Based on data from files of Settlement Department of Jewish Agency.

2. Ibid.

3. Benjamin Kaplan, "Lakhish Settlement Project" (paper presented to Study Group on Problems of Individual and Group Settlement, Tel-Aviv, April-May, 1956), p. 3. (Mimeographed.)

4. From files of Settlement Department, Lakhish district office.

5. *Statistical Abstract of Israel, 1968*, pp. 21, 30, 31.

6. Ibid., p. 60.

7. See Table 7.

8. Statistics for Jewish population aged 14 and above, as of June, 1957. This understates the degree of illiteracy as many had achieved literacy after immigration. From Patinkin, *op. cit.*, p. 27.

CHAPTER **9** APPLICABILITY OF MOSHAV
PRINCIPLES FOR
AGRICULTURAL DEVELOPMENT
OF OTHER COUNTRIES

MOSHAV PRINCIPLES

What can we learn from the development of the
moshav as an institution and from its success in Israel for the agricultural development of other countries? In the preceding chapter the point was made
that it was not a physical model that is transferred
to other countries but rather the principles of the
moshav that can be used in a flexible manner, in accordance with conditions in the countries concerned.
These principles were enumerated as (1) comprehensive
coordinated, and integrated agricultural planning,
(2) planning and implementation at the village level
including everyone in the settlement, and (3) settlements based on family-sized farms. A corollary to
these principles is that cooperatives are used insofar as possible.

As far as the latter is concerned, Israel authorities are not dogmatic on the matter of cooperation. In practice this has meant, in the case of the
moshav olim, that the principal cooperatives are generally precooperatives at the village level and secondary cooperatives at the regional and national
levels, with the regional cooperatives growing in importance relative to the national. Although cooperation per se was a basic value and goal in itself to
the early pioneers of the second and third aliyas,
and cooperative orthodoxy has, to a degree, been institutionalized (particularly in the Histadrut agencies), cooperation is generally regarded as a means
to economic, social, and political ends, the

attainment of viable rural villages with high-level
social amenities diffused throughout the country.
Rather than occupying the lowest rung of the social
ladder, cooperative agricultural communities have
contributed a very high share of leadership in the
country. It is anticipated that the new immigrant
villages will also provide leadership and preserve
the values of rural life that rank high in the ideology of the State.

The principles of the moshav need further
elaboration. Comprehensive agricultural planning
means that all services are available to the farmer
at the village level for all his farming needs: planning his production program; credit for obtaining
specified inputs; supplying these inputs in the
amounts and at the times needed; all the production
services to put the production program into effect
such as irrigation, drainage, pruning, etc.; and
marketing services, including first-stage marketing
facilities at the village or rural center. Marketing
services also include cooperative plants for manufacturing inputs and processing outputs so that the
farmer may obtain his inputs at lower prices and better returns on his outputs.

Coordinated planning signifies that all the
activities of agricultural planning that provide the
full line of services to the farmer are coordinated
at the various administrative levels: local, regional, and national. This means the horizontal coordination at these levels among all the institutions
and ministries concerned with the moshav. This is
of particular importance in comprehensive regional
planning for the moshav olim.

In addition, coordinated agricultural planning
signifies the harmonization of local planning at the
settlement level with macro planning at the regional
and national levels, the vertical coordination of
planning. Macro agricultural planning, as already
indicated, is comprehensive in scope, and includes
production planning and controls, supply of credit,
price and marketing controls, promotion of exports,
import regulations, national water and conservation

programs, and promotion of industries for servicing
agriculture.

Integrated planning means that implementation
is an integral part of the planning process and that
the principal purpose of planning is its implementation at the village and farm levels. To this end,
the economic planners of the settlement agency have
worked out of the regional offices as members of
interdisciplinary teams to implement plans at the
village level and assist the settlers at the farm
level. In addition, they also supply basic data and
assist the authorities in the Agriculture and
Settlement-Planning and Development Center on the
making of the plans and the implementational support
at the national level. There is thus a well functioning mechanism for feedback to help in the integration
of planning and its implementation.

Coordinated, comprehensive, and integrated
planning in Israel signifies a push rather than a
pull theory of administration. Individual farmers
in the West can obtain agricultural services if they
wish and make their own arrangements to do so. The
farmer in the guided moshav olim obtains services
without asking. He is supposed to follow a specified
production program, adopt recommended practices, and
buy and market according to plan. There is a certain
amount of leakage, and not all farmers have followed
the rules. The successful farmers generally have.
A handful of successful farmers in the village has a
considerable demonstration effect to keep the other
villagers in line.

On a village basis means that the village with
all its farms, rather than the individual farmer, is
the center of planning. There are compelling social,
economic, and political reasons that the village
rather than scattered individual farmers be the locus
of development planning. In the first place, the
social and cultural necessities of rural life must
be planned on a village basis in which all can participate. Unlike Western Europe and North America,
farmers in developing countries commonly prefer to
live near one another in a village. This can be a

facilitating factor for the improvement of mutual
aid and solidarity for the enhancement of rural life.

On the economic side, including all the farmers in the village confers advantages of scale to
small-sized family farms. It makes possible more,
better, and cheaper services. Although there is an
egalitarian basis to the moshav, there is a fairly
wide spread in incomes among moshav farmers. Important causal factors are the size of family and the
amount of income from outside work. Nevertheless
moshav organization with everyone having a plot of
the same size and an equal amount of irrigation water
prevents extreme differences in income, protects
farmers from predatory activities of neighbors, and
the emergence of kulaks in the village.

Equally important are the political advantages
of the moshav emphasis on the village as the center
of development. Village organization for self-
government is central to the moshav, even under the
regional council system. The moshav is a way to in-
troduce principles of self determination at the village level and to diffuse the national power structure
to a village basis.

As to the third principle, the family-type farm
may be the most efficient for many types of culture
and the most adaptable to the development milieu.
Experiments in collective farming have generally not
been a success, mainly because membership controlled
(democratic) collective farming, as exemplified in
the kibbutz in Israel, requires a highly educated and
dedicated membership. Lacking such membership, management is supplied from the outside, as in the Russian
model, by a government agency which often tends to be
autocratic in nature. The result is that the peasants
lack any feeling of pride or participation in a common enterprise, and productivity falls. The structure
of the moshav allows for a combination of individualism and cooperation, the aims of which can be trans-
mitted to peasants in traditional cultures.

INSTITUTIONAL PACKAGE FOR DEVELOPMENT

Beginnings have been made in the literature on the implementation of agricultural development that recognizes the importance of a coordinated or so-called "package" approach.[1] Some of the literature, however, represents barely more than a laundry list approach of the services needed to get agriculture moving. The moshav offers a framework for an institutionalized package approach to agricultural development.

The need for a coordinated technological package approach has been rationalized. The development of new types of modern agriculture in underdeveloped countries, particularly in the tropics, requires a coordinated approach of development of new plant species with the adaptation of fertilizer and water requirements and suitable types of culture. While it seems obvious that a single-solution technical approach would be doomed to failure, this has been the approach commonly used in bilateral and multilateral aid programs. For example, it has been the rationale behind large-scale fertilizer programs (the FAO fertilizer program of the Freedom from Hunger Campaign, for example), irrigation programs (the big dam approach to development as sponsored by United States aid and international agencies), and agricultural resource programs (the Rockefeller program in Colombia, for example, for the development of new crop varieties with little or no investigation on the economic aspects of the uses of these varieties and their response to different water and fertilizer requirements). The technological package approach, as opposed to the single solution approach, and how it has worked in the Ford Foundation program in India has been developed by Dr. Sherman Johnson.[2]

To be operational, the technological package, however, necessitates an institutional package. The first requirement is farm production-planning assistance. To put the plan into effect credit is needed to obtain the necessary perquisites and to tide the farmer over until the returns from the sales of his output are received. Obtaining the perquisites

necessitates organizational support to check that
they are based on agricultural program needs and to
see that the correct amounts and types are delivered
at the right time. To insure that the production
plans are actually put into practice necessitates
the provision of production services such as spraying, irrigation, drainage, etc. and extension services to assist the farmer in production practices.
Marketing has to be integrated with credit to recover
the loans, and organizational support is needed so
that the produce is marketed to best advantagge. This
may require first-stage marketing facilities at the
village and the establishment of food-processing
plants.

The moshav provides this multi-purpose institutional structure that also includes the social and
municipal needs of the settlers. Single purpose
programs are still common in economic aid to developing countries. Examples include supervised credit
programs based on the single-farm approach without
further institutional support, grandiose marketing
facilities programs that completely overlook inelas-
ticities in supply response, United States type of
extension services that may be inapplicable to peasant
agriculture, and the support of Western European and
United States models of single purpose agricultural
cooperatives that have no sound basis in the development milieu.

The responsiveness of farmers in underdeveloped
countries to price changes still remains a widely
debated subject. Recent studies in West Pakistan and
Colombia based on analyses of statistical evidence
provide interesting case studies. Falcon found that
in West Pakistan there were significant acreage re-
sponses to changes in relative prices, particularly
for cash crops, such as cotton, and even for food
crops. There was little responsiveness, however, in
the allocation of nonland factors, because of practical difficulties. The policy implications of his
study are that while it is possible to shift the composition of agricultural output by changing relative
agricultural prices, unless there is a basic reform
in the provision of services and facilities to farmers,

high prices alone can have little effect in raising
yields per acre. He maintains that West Pakistan's
difficulties appear to be less a matter of farmer
motivation and more of a problem of reducing uncertainty and improving the organization of agricultural
services.[3]

Research on the development of agriculture in
the Cauca Valley, Colombia for the 1955-62 period
support Falcon's observations as to farmers' response
to price. The agricultural structure in the Cauca
Valley is very different from that in West Pakistan.
It is based mainly on large tracts farmed on a short-
term rental basis. There was a tremendous variability
of production in the principal commercial crops, not
only from one year to another but also from one season
to another within the year. This was largely the result of frequent and capricious changes in the profitability of the various crops because of changes in
government price controls in response to the pressures
of competing commodity groups. Price policy in Colombia was not based on rational macro planning but on
the power position of the various producer groups.
So-called commercial farming in the Cauca Valley is
mainly a matter of speculation, of making a killing
within a short period. It has a similar position
with the middle class as speculation in the securities market in the United States. Commercial agricultural production is carried out to a large degree
on rented lands and by hired labor and resident hired
managers. The social amenities of rural towns are
poor to negligible.

The land owners live in the cities or in the
United States or Europe. The farmers not only shift
easily from one crop to another, but also in and out
of agriculture. Farm services are sporadic and poor.
This represents suitcase farming at its worst, a low
productivity, low investment, high price type of farming. Agricultural production in this most fertile area
in the country has had little relation to dietary need
To obtain necessary supplies, food-processing industries have had to go into farming themselves and/or
develop contractual arrangements with farmers that included guaranteed prices and some service provisions.[4]

The response of farmers to price incentives in developing countries still needs additional research to reach definitive conclusions.[5] This response has to be studied for different types of agricultural structures. It is evident, however, that the limitations to the improvement of agricultural productivity in these countries are largely institutional in nature. In the periods under review total per capita agricultural production in both Pakistan and Colombia was stationary.[6] Consumption levels in these countries are low, and both are on an import food basis. In the case of Colombia the conditions prevail not because of the lack of quality resources or a high population-land ratio but rather because of agricultural and political structural difficulties.

The conclusion follows that there is a great need in underdeveloped countries of a package institutional approach to agricultural development to supplement and make effective the technological-package approach. The moshav combines the technological and institutional elements in one package. In some instances it is possible that this may be too large and complicated a package for application to other countries. The type of institutional package and its organizational support may differ from country to country. It is quite clear, however, that the implementation of this institutional package cannot be left to chance. Adam Smith's invisible hand will not supply it. It has to be specifically planned and implemented as part of an overall agricultural development program.

ROLE OF THE AGRICULTURAL SECTOR IN ECONOMIC DEVELOPMENT

This is not an attempt to present a comprehensive treatise on this complex subject. There is a plethora of literature on the strategic role of the agricultural sector in general economic development: that is, it should have a high priority, low priority, and of course, the middle way of balanced agricultural-industrial development.

The concerns of this study are much more pragmatic: that in general the agricultural sector has
acted as a brake to economic development and what the
application of moshav principles may do to ameliorate
this condition. In many countries agricultural production is lagging behind the growth in population.
Furthermore there has been sound research to indicate
that not only is there no reason to expect a reduction
in absolute numbers of the agricultural population in
the reasonably near future, but, in fact, that there
will be a continued increase for some time to come.[7]
Myrdal estimates that the employment creating effect
of industrialization will be small to negative and
that the greater part of the labor force increase,
between 2 to 4 per cent per year, will remain outside
industry, mainly in agriculture.[8]

It follows, then, that with these increases in
the agricultural labor force, unless fundamental
changes are made in the structure of agriculture the
result will be increasing misery for poor peasants.
Agricultural policy should, therefore, be based on a
new, labor-intensive approach. This type of agriculture would require both new technology and a new institutional structure. The agricultural revolution
in the United States came quite late and was helped
by a rapid decrease in the agricultural labor force
and the absorption of the surplus labor force into
the other growing sectors of the economy. This condition does not generally obtain in underdeveloped
countries.

It is important to note that this structural
change to intensive agriculture is not a step backward to subsistence agriculture or agricultural prim-
itivism. It represents a definitive step forward to
a new type of commercial agriculture. This transition is aided by the fact that in underdeveloped
countries the productivity of land is at present extremely low. It is reasonable to assume that great
increases in labor inputs and labor efficiency can
result in significant increases in productivity.

On the institutional side there is considerable
danger in the emphasis on industrialization as the

remedy for the ailment of underdevelopment. It serves the vested interests of those who are unwilling to consider adequately the serious problems in the agricultural sector. Emphasizing the take-off and the self-sustaining growth of industrialization, the political leaders and the industrial elite cover up the failure to change the economic and social order of the villages and to raise the productivity of agricultural land and labor.

FAO has calculated that about one half of the world's population is suffering from hunger, malnutrition, or both. This half lives almost entirely in the underdeveloped countries, to a large degree in the agricultural sector. FAO also estimates that to provide a reasonable level of nutrition for all the people in the world, food supplies must be doubled by 1980 and tripled by 2000.[9]

Most of this increase in production must take place in the underdeveloped countries. These countries cannot rely on the continuation of subsidized food imports from the United States. Failure to reach higher goals of production could imply a world calamity. Thus there is a pressing need for substantive institutional change to support a new structure of a more intensive type of agriculture for agricultural development in the poor countries of the world. The possibility of the application of moshav principles in this respect merits examination.

TRANSFERABILITY OF MOSHAV: GENERALIZED APPROACH

Professor J. K. Galbraith has made an interesting classificdtion of underdeveloped countries, mainly for purposes of United States development aid policy.[10] This classification is very suitable as a generalized framework for the analysis of the transferability of moshav principles for the agricultural development of these countries.

His three principal classifications are (1) the sub-Sahara African model, (2) the Latin American model, and (3) the South Asia model. While these models as a matter of convenience are given geographic designations, the particular countries designated by the model are not necessarily limited to the geographic area, nor are all the countries in each geographic area included in the model classification.

Model 1 countries represent the most primitive of the underdeveloped countries. Besides the countries in sub-Sahara Africa (excluding Ghana) this model includes countries in Oceania such as Samoa, countries in Central America such as Haiti, and countries in the Near East such as Yemen. These countries are the anthropologists' delight where they study the effects of cultural change. The principal barrier to development in model 1 countries is the absence of a minimum cultural base, and the key to progress is the widening of the cultural base. The minimum cultural base refers specifically to the absence of an educated elite, particularly to take on the administrative tasks of a stable government.

In model 2 countries the principal barrier to advance is the social structure, and the basic necessity for progress is the improvement of the social structure by the disestablishment of the nonfunctional groups. As to the countries included, Mexico and Costa Rica do not conform to this model, while a number of countries in the Near East do: Syria, Iraq, and Iran. In these countries, many of which are proud of their history and their ancient or European heritages, the absence of trained and educated people is not the basic barrier to development. The social structure grants a favored position to a privileged few through such means as ownership of large blocks of land, a "comprador" or trading role in the port or capital cities, government employment, position in the armed forces, or as clergy in the state-supported church. Income and political power derived from these positions are not proportionate to economic services rendered. In the agricultural sector, instead of deriving their incomes from small areas farmed efficiently, absentee owners obtain their revenues from large areas farmed inefficiently. The rural worker earns the right to cultivate a small plot of land by service to the estate on which he resides, or he lives

on a "minifundia," a very small plot of about three
acres or less. In either case he has no economic
incentive to farm efficiently. Control and position
in the other sectors of the economy are equally nonfunctional. Because of the inequities in income distribution and low productivity the amount of income
in relation to its claimants is low. This results
in endemic inflation in many of these countries.

In model 3 countries the principal barrier to
development is the bad proportioning of the factors of
production. This classification, which includes but
few countries, India, Pakistan, and possibly Indonesia,
conforms to the generalized standard model of the development economists who relate economic development
to massive capital investments, big push theories, and
the take-off to industrialization and modernization.

The moshav as an institution for agricultural
development may have a role in all these models. In
model 1 countries a few moshavim may be established
as model demonstration agricultural villages to widen
the cultural base in the agricultural sector. Their
demonstration effects can be passed on to farmers for
the modernization of agriculture. This is, in fact,
what Israeli experts are doing with some success in
a number of countries in Africa: the Central African
Republic, Senegal, and Dahomey, for example. The
role of the moshav is thus limited and is not a factor for major development of commercial agriculture.

More ambitious attempts in adopting moshav
principles for larger settlement schemes in Western
and Eastern Nigeria are running into considerable
difficulties because of the lack of cultural base,
the low levels of agricultural technology and project
administration.[11] The moshav projects in these two
countries are the only instances of large-scale application of moshav principles outside the official
Israeli-aid channels.

One of the basic instruments for rectifying or
attempting to rectify the agricultural institutional
structure of model 2 countries is land reform. Unfortunately the history of land reform, particularly

in Latin America, is a history of failure because of
the lack of implementation of these reforms.[12] Reform often means no more than parcelation of land,
and that frequently on a small scale, sometimes with
little or no attempt to continue even those services
that had previously been supplied by the landlords.
The application of moshav principles can definitely
help in the implementation of land-reform programs.
In fact, its use in Venezuela and Iran will be analyzed as special cases. It is probably in model 2
countries that the moshav may have the most to offer
as a peaceful solution to structural reform in the
agricultural sector.

The application of the moshav principles is
limited in India and Pakistan, the two principal model
3 countries, because of the constraint of the land/
population ratios and the very small size of holdings.
Both countries have studied the moshav model and are
making limited application of moshav principles in
their community-development programs. There is, of
course, a minimum limit to the size of holding, beyond
which the economics of moshav organization will not
yield viable farms and communities. What the minimum
size is needs to be determined in the light of new
possible technologies.

In the actual transfer of moshav principles,
the Israelis are very careful not to stress their
national model or even use the term moshav. This is
good policy and good politics. They have agricultural experts or teams of agricultural developers in
many countries throughout the world. These experts
try to apply moshav principles, if warranted, in a
flexible manner in accordance with local needs.

MOSHAV AND OTHER FORMS OF FARM ORGANIZATION

The moshav represents but one of a number of
possible institutional structures for use in the development of the agricultural sector in underdeveloped countries, particularly in the context of land
reform and rural resettlement. On the economic side
this involves a comparison of the efficiency of

different types of economic structures. Political
and social considerations, however, are also important in the choice of alternative farm structures.

The moshav in Israel must compete with alternative forms of farm organization, principally the
kibbutz and private farms. Although it competes with
these alternatives, it also complements them, since
it has advantages in the production of certain products.

The situation could be similar in practically
all developing countries. The advantages and disad-
vantages of the moshav type of organization will have
to be compared with other types for specific projects
and for specified areas in the countries. In addition, the moshav would compete with and complement
other organizational forms in the national agricultural structure.

Schickele has adopted a two-classification
typology, large-scale versus family-type farming, as
the principal alternative structures for agrarian reform in developing countries.[13] While this is a
highly simplified classification, it is a workable
one for analytical purposes. Large-scale farming
means centrally operated farms in which the farmers
are reduced to the role of employed workers. This
term subsumes private plantations, collective farms,
and other large-scale farms. Family-type farming
represents farm units where most of the labor is provided by members of the farm family, where little
hired wage labor is used and where the head of the
family is both farm operator and worker. The term
includes tenants of various kinds as well as owner
operators.

There are many types of farms included in each
of these two classifications. The basic differences
in these broad categories are in the farmers' managerial functions, their attitudes toward the land,
and their motivations and incentives to produce.

Centrally managed large-scale farms and family
farms may be under either public or private ownership.

Farmers may be laborers paid by the hour, or according to some other unit measure of work output, or they may be tenant farmers operating under a wide variety of different tenure arrangements. These arrangements may include rental contracts ranging from one-year to long-term contracts. The renter may be a large-scale commercial operator using hired labor or small operators whose units are centrally managed by the owner. Similarly there are a large variety of share cropping arrangements on both the large and family-sized farms. In addition, large-scale farming can subsume family-sized farms that are privately owned, rented, or leased on a share arrangement, but are managed, either the entire farm or part of it, as parts of a centrally operated estate.

The social organization of farmers in both categories includes a wide variety of forms. The farmers may live on the large farms or their own family-sized farms, in compact villages on or off the farms, or may be dispersed in houses in the nearest village or town. They may or may not have a small plot of their own for subsistence and possibly for sales of surpluses to markets. Where farmers live in villages they may or may not be provided with basic social services: schools, first-aid clinics, and recreation facilities. If not, the farmers may do without these services, or they may depend on a nearby town for them.

The proponents of large-scale farming maintain that it is more efficient, more profitable, and more practical than a system of small family farms. Only a relatively small number of managers need to be trained in scientific farming as compared to thousands or millions of widely dispersed farmers in family units. Large-scale farms can be more effectively mechanized and obtain capital and credit at better terms. Because of their larger outputs they can more easily obtain quality control and higher returns through more efficient marketing. Macro planning can be more effectively coordinated with micro planning with large units as compared to family farms.

The proponents of family-type farms maintain that since internal economies of scale are more

limited in agriculture than in industry, family-type
farming can successfully compete with large-scale
farming. In the first place, family farm operators
can be more easily motivated. Small family farms
can also achieve economies of scale in obtaining capital and credit and in purchasing inputs and marketing outputs through cooperative and state programs.
The existence of a large, underemployed, farm labor
force, at present and probably for some time in the
future, acts as a brake to the economic use of large
farm machinery and large-scale farm mechanization.
On the other hand, tractors and specialized machinery
that are economically practical for family-type farms
can be made available through cooperative, private,
or public service programs. Farmers can be trained
to adopt improved production methods by various educational programs and advisory and extension services
molded to their needs. Finally, family-sized farms
provide not only adequate incomes but also a way of
life that results in rural communities characterized
by a stability of very positive political and social
as well as economic value to developing countries.

The advantage of centrally managed large-scale
farms have particular attraction to governments in
the Far and Near East and Africa, especially those
governments where socialist ideology is strong. The
particular structure as well as the legal basis of
ownership and operation is largely experimental.
Large collectives or state farms seem to be the most
popular models, but with substantial modifications
on the Russian prototypes. Land ownership may be
invested in the State, a public corporation, or a
cooperative. Government participation is central,
retaining some control over general standards of culture, land use, tenure, employment, wages and other
incomes of the farmers, and allocation of individual
usufructuary rights to part of the land. Major points
at issue in the development of particular structures
are membership eligibility, security of occupancy and
employment, wage scales classified by skills, bonuses
and penalties for individual or crew performances,
incomes partly in money and partly in kind, supervisory responsibility, and the particulars of the function and organization of management.

The experience in large-scale farming in Southeast Asia and Africa has been limited to more or less
monocultural plantations originally established by
Europeans under colonial regimes. The large holdings
of individual landlords were often not centrally operated estates but were divided into family-type
tenant farms. The bad economic and social conditions
of farm workers on private plantations have little
appeal for emulation by the newly independent regimes
This explains why many planners were seriously affected by the literature and short, well-conducted
tours in Russia and continental China. As a matter
of fact, there is little systematic research availabl
on the adaptability of collective or centrally manage
large farms in Russia or China for constructive use i
developing countries in modernizing and improving the
social and economic conditions in agriculture. The
relatively poor performance of the agricultural sector in the USSR and the setbacks in China after the
seemingly early successes of the great leap forward
have dampened the enthusiasm of many proponents of
collective farming.

The organization of large-scale agriculture in
the USSR and China is primarily motivated by politica
rather than economic considerations. In the USSR the
agricultural sector has had a low priority because of
the relatively favorable man/land ratio. Increases
in efficiency were not of paramount importance as lon
as sufficient basic foodstuffs could be obtained by
forced deliveries at cheap prices for distribution to
industrial workers in the cities. Only after success
ive years of bad harvests that necessitated large imports of basic grains from the capitalist West, has
a higher priority been given in recent years to the
agricultural sector, with more emphasis on improved
efficiency, increased use of fertilizers, and price
incentives.

Yet, where governments have land available for
establishing new settlements, many still lean towards
forms of large-scale mechanized farming, as in Indonesia, Ghana, Algeria, and other countries in Asia,
Africa, and even Latin America. The Indian governmen
promotes "cooperative" farming through voluntary acti

by rerenting land to villages and applying ceilings
to individual holdings. There is still no widespread
interest by farmers to band together voluntarily into
collective farming units. On the contrary, where
political considerations have permitted, decollecti-
vization has occurred, as in Yugoslavia and Poland,
because of farmers' insistent preference for even very
small family-type farms.

Part of the difficulty underlying the predilec-
tion for centrally managed large-scale farms is the
association of increases in efficiency in large-scale
agriculture comparable to those in large-scale industry. There are many substantive basic differences
between industry and agriculture, the most important
of which are due to the fact that agriculture depends
on biological processes that make it much less susceptible to division of labor, large-scale organization, and impersonal management methods than is the
case in industry. The possibility of specialization
that determines the extent of the division of labor
is limited in agriculture because of the wide variety
of tasks dictated by seasonal requirements. Managerial
difficulties are greater in large-scale farming than
in industry because the workers are spread over larger
areas as compared to factory workers, and their performance cannot be regulated and supervised by controlling the rate of flow of materials on an assembly
line. The dominance of biological processes in agricultural production makes the role of individual incentives and motivation much greater and more
critically important than in industry.

The issue of large-scale farming in Latin
America differs from that in Asia and Africa in that
large-scale farms under private ownership of nationals is much more prevalent. It is the aim of government policies in most of the countries of the
region that agricultural and possibly social progress
can be achieved by gradual internal reforms, such as
the education of the hacienda owner and his major
domo, minimum wage and housing laws for farm workers,
taxation according to land use capabilities, and
other measures. In addition, many countries have
land reform laws whose side effects promote progress

along the lines of such reforms. The possible effects of these gradualistic reform measures seem
questionable in the light of the problems of political stability, the needs and aspirations of farm
families, and growing needs for food and fiber of
the countries concerned.

From the point of view of economics, the large
farm-family-farm controversy would seem to relate to
economies of scale and resource productivity relation-
ships. While there has been a considerable amount
of research in these problems by agricultural economists as they concern agricultural development in the
United States, only beginnings have been made in research, and little has been done in the relation of
such research to the context of development planning
and, in particular, institutional planning for agricultural development in underdeveloped countries.
The research that has been done stresses the need for
further research using more case methods and investigations.

In his research on the relation of size of farm
to economic development, Kanel has worked in the
framework of (1) larger-than-family farms; (2) adequate family farms, that is farms with enough land
to employ family labor and the indivisable units of
capital efficiently; and (3) inadequate family farms
that do not have enough land.[14]

The problem in the economics of scale is whether
family farms in developing countries can be as efficient as larger-than-family farms in the combination
of other resources with the labor supply of the farm
family. Kanel has been concerned with (1) the unit
costs of farm production on family and larger farms,
(2) problems in providing basic services such as extension, credit, marketing facilities to farms of
different sizes, and (3) differences in entrepreneurial attitudes and behavior on farms of different
sizes.

The economic decision on the use of labor is
different on small and large farms. On small farms
the basic economic decision is how to obtain the most

income or food production from family labor and other
family-owned resources. Use of labor on the farm is
not limited by the factor market cost of labor. Market wages become relevant as opportunity costs only
if off-farm employment is readily available at the
prevailing wage. The efficiency of small farms,
therefore, cannot be judged by measurements of cost
that are based on prevailing wages if off-farm employment is not available at these wages, a condition that
frequently exists in developing countries.

The intensive organization of small farms is
desirable from the national point of view in the case
of countries with heavy pressure of population. Where
the size of the population relative to other resources
is such that full employment is achieved with marginal
productivity at less than subsistence, and the factor
markets maintain wages at subsistence, then farms
hiring labor will not be able to obtain all the labor
they need under prevailing wages. The more intensive
organization of family farms, then, offers income to
those who do not find wage employment and helps maintain wages in the labor market.

Substitution of machinery capital for labor in
agriculture is of less importance in developing than
in developed countries. The substitution of capital
inputs that primarily increase yields and have little
effect on labor requirements per acre of land can,
however, be very important. These capital inputs include seed of improved varieties, fertilizer, insecticides, etc. The use of these inputs usually
represents not only a change in factor proportions
within a given production function, but also the introduction of new technologies that represent a shift
in the production function. The profitable use of
these inputs is characteristically highly interdepen-
dent. The use of fertilizer is more profitable with
new varieties of crops bred to give a greater response
to fertilizer. Water requirements and protection
from plant disease is more critical for the higher
yielding fertilized varieties.

Most of these yield-increasing new inputs are
highly divisible and, therefore, can be used profitably

on both large and small farms. The development of
these new inputs and the technology for using them
depends on state, cooperative, and private efforts
in research and extension, manufacture, and distribution of the inputs, reinforced by credit, production, and marketing services. Large farms cannot
perform most of these functions. Introduction of
these new inputs, thus, does not affect the competitive efficiency of farms of different sizes.

In terms of economies of scale, Kanel finds
that in developing countries there is no overwhelm-
ing advantage to any particular size of farm, and
the advantage is more likely with the small farm in
most types of farming. Bachman and Christensen maintain that statistical evidence indicates that economic progress in agriculture is possible under a
wide variety of farm size conditions and that other
factors are more critical.[15]

The major task for development purposes is not
economizing among known alternatives but providing
farmers with new alternatives. The concern should the
be whether a particular size of farm is more conduciv
to better management that seeks out new practices and
adopts and utilizes them. Although, historically, bet
ter management and greater use of new technology have
more often been found on larger than on smaller farms
in underdeveloped countries the majority of larger
farms still are operated under inactive and tradition
management. The issue of size of farm should then be
considered in a different framework than that of conventional analysis on the economies of scale.

First, entrepreneurial activity in modernizing
agriculture, whether on large-scale or family farms,
has to depend on efforts by other nonfarm entities
in organizing and operating research, extension,
supplies of inputs, credit, improved marketing facilities, etc. Second, it is known that older, less
educated, poorer farmers on smaller farms are generally later adaptors than other farmers. Size of
farm enters because operators of these farms are dis-
advantaged in access to education and credit and are
less likely to be leaders in the social structure of

the community. The example of Israel shows that
this is not an inherent consequence of size of farm.
It indicates that where farm people are educated and
are well served by government, cooperative, and private agencies, farmers on all sizes of farms can
adopt new practices. There need be no dichotomy between a more progressive sector of larger farms and
a traditional sector of small farms making little
contribution to increases in agricultural production.

Finally, in those cases where it is proposed
to increase the size of farm by instituting an adaptation of the collective farm (the Russian or Chinese
model) or even a state farm with hired labor, the
issue must be raised whether scarce managerial resources are best used in direct control of day to
day production decisions or in extension, credit, and
other agricultural services that assist farmers in
making their own production decisions. Long[16] and
Schickele support the second approach.

There may also be a time dimension in the organizational choice for agricultural development.
It is possible that in the short run of some three
to five years, the large-scale farming approach, particularly if applied to a limited number of projects
supported by highly qualified managers and technicians, could show faster adaptation to modern practices. The advantages of large-scale farming, where
better machines and seeds and more fertilizers may
be immediately ordered, may offset the workers' lack
of incentives to carry through all the various improved practices for obtaining optimum results. In
the longer run, and covering larger regions of the
country, the family farming approach supported by
basic services such as extension, credit, and cooperatives might well perform better. The stronger incentives to farmers are more likely to develop native
managerial skills and responsibilities so that they
may operate their farms to better advantage in their
own interests.

The arguments for family-sized farms seem to
be based on a moshav type structure, the adoption of
moshav principles, or the development of other

institutional models similar to the moshav. One must
differentiate between the moshav principles and variations thereof and alternative, somewhat similar
models. The case for family farms emphasizes the
supporting services so that these farms may attain
the economies of scale and adequate incomes. If
family-sized farms are to be an economic success,
particularly in land-reform programs, a minimum package of supporting services (extension, credit, and
marketing, for example) are needed. If these services are not provided, if the aims of the land reform
are only political, the peasants may be no better
off economically, possibly even worse off, than before the reform. At best they may have title to a
small lot of land, but nothing else, and no replacement for the services previously supplied by the
landlords. These services were expensive, but often
they were the only ones readily available to the
farmers. Without the supporting services farmers
may have to give up their land, and new concentration
of ownership may arise.

Similarly there is a need for basic supporting
services in new land-settlement schemes, more so than
in areas already densely populated. Also, if these
services are not supplied by a government, a cooperative, or some public entity, they may not be provided at all. Without the provision of supporting
services, resettlement projects may also be just
temporary political expedients with little benefits
to the farmers involved.

Most of the adaptation of the moshav model to
local conditions in other developing countries would
involve the application of the first of the moshav
principles, comprehensive, coordinated, and integrate
agricultural planning. It might omit the political
activities of municipal government. Social goals
may be more restricted, for example, not to include
local schools or recreational activities that may be
provided by the church or one of the units of government. The structure of the local cooperative may
also not be as complex as in Israel. The national
institutional support probably would not be as extensive as in Israel and in the early stages of

development would not include industrial plants for
the manufacture of inputs and processing plants for
outputs. The national agricultural situation may
not necessitate a close coordination of macro planning at the regional level with micro planning at the
farm level. The national food supply situation may
be such that for most commodities there may be no
problem of markets for whatever is produced.

The second principal of planning and implementation at the village level, including everybody in
the village, may be adapted to local conditions. The
moshav may include all the farmers in the village,
but not necessarily all the economic activities. Some
local marketing and processing activities may be carried out by the State and other public bodies or even
by private enterprise. The village would still be
the locus of planning and implementation, not just
selected individual farms as in the United States
sponsored, supervised credit programs.

While the collective or state farms are important prototypes of centrally managed large-scale
farming and the moshav with supporting cooperatives
and public services a prototype of family-sized farming, there are other possible institutional models.
One is the combination of large-scale and family-type
farming as exemplified by the Gezira scheme in Sudan.
After forty years of operation it includes over a
million acres of irrigated land and over twenty-five
thousand tenant farmers. The farm families produce
cotton under large-scale farming conditions with
central management and supervision but produce other
crops and animal products under family-type farming
conditions. The scheme represents the most progressive farming system in the Sudan and is the main
source of the country's export earnings and government revenue.[17]

The decision on the adoption of an institutional arrangement that will promote agricultural progress is a key issue in the agricultural policy of
developing countries. The decision between large-
scale centrally managed farms, particularly variants
of large-scale collective farming, and family size

units will probably be made more on political than
economic grounds. Both the adoption of large-scale
and family-sized farms will involve a substantial
amount of public administration and coercion. The
newly developing countries are overwhelmingly agrarian. The government will have to rely more and more
upon majority support of the people at large, including those in the countryside. The fact that most
peasants have a strong preference for family-type
farming is well known. The difference in potential
productive efficiency between the two systems may
then be secondary in the institutional choice.

NOTES

1. Arthur T. Mosher, Getting Agriculture
Moving (New York: Praeger, 1966); Sherman E. Johnso
"Combining Knowledge, Incentive, and Means to Accel-
erate Agricultural Development in Economic Developmen
of Agriculture," in Economic Development of Agricul-
ture (Ames, Iowa: Iowa State University Press, 1965)
pp. 209-23; John W. Mellor, "Production Problems and
Issues in Agricultural Development," Journal of Farm
Economics, XLVII (December, 1966), pp. 1195-1209;
P. G. H. Barter, "The Implementation of Agricultural
Plans," Lectures on Agricultural Planning Delivered
at the FAO Near East Regional Training Center on
Agricultural Development Planning, Food and Agricul-
ture Organization of the United Nations Planning
Studies No. 3 (Rome: FAO, 1963), pp. 172-80; Max
F. Millikan and David Hapgood, No Easy Harvest
(Boston: Little, Brown and Co., 1967); and The 1967
and 1968 FAO State of Food and Agriculture, pp.
114-17, and 111-13 are examples.

2. Johnson, op. cit.

3. Walter P. Falcon, "Farmers' Response to
Price in a Subsistence Economy: The Case of West
Pakistan," American Economic Review, LIV (May, 1964)
pp. 580-91.

4. Jesus Humberto Colmenares "Analisis de la
Produccion Agricola en el Departmento del Valle"

"Analysis of the Agricultural Production in the Department of Valle" (senior thesis, Universidad del
Valle, Cali, Colombia, 1964).

5. A summary of recent work in this field is
contained in Raj Krishna "Agricultural Price Policy
and Economic Department," Agricultural Development
and Economic Growth, eds. Herman M. Southworth and
Bruce F. Johnston (Ithaca, N.Y.: Cornell University
Press, 1967), pp. 497-540.

6. 1968 FAO State of Food and Agriculture,
pp. 150-51.

7. Folke Dovring, "The Share of Agriculture
in a Growing Population," FAO Monthly Bulletin of
Agricultural Economics and Statistics, VIII (August-
September, 1959), pp. 1-11.

8. Gunnar Myrdal, "The United Nations Agriculture, and the World Economic Revolution," Journal of
Farm Economics, XLVII (November, 1965), p. 895.

9. Food and Agriculture Organization of the
United Nations, Third World Food Survey, Freedom
From Hunger Campaign, Basic Study 11 (Rome: FAO,
1963), pp. 9-10.

10. Galbraith, op. cit.

11. Carl Eicher, "Israeli Innovations" (paper
delivered to Seminar on Adopting Agricultural Cooperatives and Quasi-Cooperatives to the Market Structures and Conditions of Underdeveloped Areas (Lex-
ington, Ky.: University of Kentucky, April, 1967.

12. Ernest Feder, "Land Reform Under the
Alliance for Progress," Journal of Farm Economics,
XLVII (August, 1965), pp. 652-68.

13. Rainer Schickele, "Land Economics Research
for World Agricultural Development," eds., Joseph
Ackerman, Marion Clawson, and Marshall Harris (Balti-
more, Md.: Johns Hopkins Press, 1962), p. 102.

14. Don Kanel, "Size of Farm and Economic Development," Land Tenure Center Reprint 31 (Madison, Wisc.: University of Wisconsin, 1967).

15. K. L. Bachman and E. P. Christensen, "The Economics of Farm Size," Agricultural Development and Economic Growth, eds. Herman M. Southworth and Bruce F. Johnston (Ithaca, N.Y.: Cornell University Press, 1967).

16. Ervin J. Long, "The Economic Basis of Land Reform in Underdeveloped Economies," Land Economies, XXXVII (May, 1961), pp. 113-23.

17. Arthur Geitskell, Gezira, A Story of Development in the Sudan (London: Faber and Faber, 1959).

CHAPTER **10** CASE OF VENEZUELA

Venezuela and Iran represent the principal country cases where moshav principles are being applied with the assistance of Israeli consultants for agricultural development. In both countries the application of the moshav principles is in the context of the implementation of national land-reform programs.

As the moshav projects in both countries are relatively new, conclusions regarding their success or permanence can, at best, be only tentative. However, an appraisal of the experiences of the early years in these two country cases is still valuable for the analysis of the problems in the application of moshav principles in countries other than Israel, for the examination of the potentialities of the moshav in these countries in accordance with the critical success factors developed in Chapter 8, and as a guide in the possible application of moshav principles in other developing countries.

SUMMARY BACKGROUND INFORMATION

Venezuela represents the anomaly of the country with the highest per capita national income in Latin America, $800-$900,* with one of the most underdeveloped agricultural sectors in the region. It is probably the most prosperous of the less-developed countries in the world. Its gross national product

---

*This is a liberal estimate of per capita personal income in 1966-67.

277

tripled in the short period from 1945 to 1960 as it
developed into the world's third most important
petroleum producing nation.[1] The rapid growth of
the economy dependent on oil exports was accompanied
by a highly uneven distribution of wealth and a very
low level of incomes in rural areas. Estimates of
the average farm family income in 1965 ranged from
$200 to $400.

Venezuela is in northern South America facing
the Carribean Sea. It includes an area equivalent
to 352,170 square miles (about the size of the United
Kingdom, France, the Low Countries, and Switzerland)
with an estimated population in 1967 of 9.3 million
people. About half the country, most of the area
south of the Orinoco River, is unpopulated. Agriculture is generally limited to the region lying north
of the Orinoco, including the Andean highland region
in the west and north of the country and its bordering central plains.

According to the national census of 1961, arable
land and land in permanent crops represented but 3
per cent of the total area of the country, while 19
per cent was in permanent meadows and pastures, of
which only 16 per cent represented cultivated or improved pastures. That is, in 1961, only 22 per cent
of the land in the country was used for agriculture,
3 per cent for crops, and 19 per cent for cattle
raising, the latter for the most part on unimproved
pasture.

With the economy primarily dependent on the exports of petroleum products, exploited mainly by
foreign interests, agricultural resources remain underdeveloped and agricultural productivity, very low.
Despite a favorable land/population ration, about
one-quarter of the country's food needs are imported.
Although there may not be as much first-class agricultural land as in some other Latin American countries, more than adequate resources are available for
the development of an efficient agricultural sector
that could supply most of the country's food and fiber
needs and provide reasonable returns to producers.

The industrial origin of the gross national product in Venezuela in 1965 was as follows:

	Per Cent
Industry	42
Agriculture	7
Construction	2
Transportation and communication	4
Commerce and finance	15
Other	30
Total	100

Although the agricultural sector is the most important source of employment in the country, utilizing one third of the total labor force, it accounts for only about 7 per cent of the country's gross national product. On the other hand, the petroleum industry that employs only 2 per cent of the national labor force has been responsible for almost 30 per cent of the gross national product. As petroleum is responsible for almost three quarters of the industrial activity and about 90 per cent of the value of the country's exports, the national economy is quite unbalanced. Although Venezuela enjoys an enviable balance of payments position, prosperity is limited but to a favored few.

The depressed condition of agriculture has caused a rapid movement to urban centers. Industry has not been able to absorb the migrants. Unemployment is conservatively estimated to be at least 15 per cent of the total labor force, probably higher. Meanwhile population is increasing at an annual rate of possibly as high as 4 per cent.

National nutritional levels are low. Per capita food consumption in the 1960-67 period is estimated at less than 2,300 calories per year. Per capita protein intake is also relatively low.

Venezuela, as most other Latin American countries, has had a turbulent political history. The

installation of a liberal democratic regime in 1959,
after a long period of repressive dictatorship, has
had a decided effect on economic priorities for development that have favored the agricultural sector.
Emphasis has been placed on a planned development of
the economy, diversification and expansion of its
economic base, increased controls and participation
by the government and national interests in the petroleum industry, and the development of agricultural production promoted by public policies including
a national land-reform program. The new agricultural policies have had positive results. Per capita
agricultural production that had remained stationary
in the decade of the 1950's increased more than 20
per cent from 1960 through 1966.*

Efforts by the new democratic regime in improving educational facilities have also been quite effective. The rate of illiteracy has decreased from
57 per cent in 1958 to about 25 per cent in 1966.
The illiteracy rate in rural areas is much higher
than the national average. Improvements in rural
areas, however, have also been made. Education is
free, and attendance in elementary school is compulsory. Actual attendance, however, is estimated at
no more than 50 per cent.

ECONOMIC AND AGRICULTURAL PLANNING

The fall of the Jiminez dictatorship in 1958
heralded a new era for planned economic development
in Venezuela and basic structural reforms in the
economy.[2] Economic development planning is in the
framework of national four-year plans. The four-
year plan for 1963-66 provided for diversification
of the economy, an annual increase of 8 per cent in
the gross national product, an expansion of industrial production by 14 per cent, and a reduction of
unemployment by 4.5 per cent. The plan aimed at an

---

*Preliminary figures for 1967 indicate a con-
tinuation of this increase.

8 per cent annual growth of output in the agricultural sector, to be achieved by increases in productivity through provision of additional credits, increases
in mechanization and irrigation, and improved marketing outlets. It called for self-sufficiency by 1966
in rice, potatoes, sesame, tobacco, and eggs. This
had been accomplished by 1964 for rice and sesame.

One of the basic aims of agricultural policy is
to encourage higher national production of all agricultural commodities, except wheat, barley, and oats,
and to reach national self-suffieicney as soon as
possible. The government has enacted numerous programs to attain these goals including import protection, support prices, subsidies, production credits,
development plans, and the continuation and improvement of its land-reform plan. Import protection is
achieved mainly through quantitative restrictions in
the form of import licenses. In addition, imports
are restricted and domestic production encouraged by
tie-in purchase requirements for many commodities.
Import licenses are granted only after stipulated
quantities of domestic production have been purchased.
Producer prices and marketing outlets are guaranteed
for many basic commodities. These commodities are
purchased at fixed prices by the national agricultural bank or processors. Subsidies are paid on coffee
and cocoa exports when world prices fall below a certain level and on milk for domestic consumption.

LAND REFORM PROGRAM

Land reform, after passage of the reform law
in March, 1960, has been the State's most important
concern in the agricultural sector.* Its principal
immediate economic aims are to correct the inequi-
table land-tenancy system and to stimulate agricultural production. Its longer range economic purpose
is to elevate the peasant farmer to an efficient

---

*Called in Spanish _reforma_ _agraria_. This is
translated as land reform.

producer so as to increase farm incomes consistent
with the economic development of the country as a
whole. The program is comprehensive in nature, providing for large-scale technical assistance in extension, credits, marketing, and infrastructure
including the construction of roads, houses, and farm
buildings. The purposes of the program are social
and political as well as economic. The former consists of improving the social amenities of the peasants by providing them with education, housing,
health, and recreation. The latter includes diffusion of the political power to give peasants the
rights guaranteed them by law.

The fundamental objectives of the land reform
law were clearly delineated by President Betancourt
in signing the legislation as:

> The transformation of the agrarian
> structure of the country and the in-
> corporation of its rural population
> in the economic, social, and politi-
> cal development of the nation through
> the substitution of the latifundia
> system by a just system of proprietor-
> ship, tenancy, and cultivation of the
> soil based on its equitable distribu-
> tion, the adequate organization of
> credit and integral assistance to farm-
> ers so that the land will constitute
> for those that work it a base for their
> fundamental economic stability for
> their continuous social welfare, and to
> guarantee their liberty and dignity.[3]

The National Agrarian Institute (IAN), the
agency entrusted with the implementation of the land
reform law, envisioned its implementation in three
stages. The first was giving land to the landless
to stop the migration to the cities. The second was
to provide the economic requisites and social amenities to farmers on the land. The third was to make
the farmer an active factor in the economic development of the country, both as a producer and consumer
of economic goods, through intensive development of

small- and medium-sized farms, using cooperative
methods.

The need for land reform was the grinding poverty and insecurity of tenure of the peasants. In
addition, there was a lack of an efficient agricultural commercial sector to meet the country's food
needs. The 1950 national agricultural census showed
that while only 2.9 per cent of the agricultural
holdings were in units of one thousand hectares and
above, these holdings included 82.6 per cent of all
the agricultural land in the country. That is,
farmers on 97.1 per cent of the holdings controlled
but 17.4 per cent of the agricultural land.[4] A sample survey of the Ministry of Agriculture in 1956
indicated that less than one quarter of the farmers
had clear titles to their lands. About one quarter
were renters and sharecroppers, and about one half
worked public and semi-public lands without title.[5]
The Ministry of Development in 1960 estimated that
there were 218,121 peasant families in the country
with insufficient (less than two hectares) or no land.[6]

The main criterion for the incorporation of
public and private lands in the land-reform pool for
distribution to peasants is whether the lands perform
their social function. This is interpreted to reflect intensity of land use and contractual arrangements with the peasant cultivators. Private farms
and estates were considered as not performing their
social function if the owner did not cultivate his
land, did not personally assume management and financial responsibilities for working it, did not work
his land in accordance to its proper function (for
example, used good crop land for livestock grazing),
or did not comply with the legal rules on the use
of labor and cadastral registration. The peasants
form local associations and apply for specific tracts
through the local unit of the National Peasant Federation. The law stipulates that applicants for parcels must work the land personally and must be older
than eighteen years. The minimum limit for the individual plot is five hectares; the maximum for an
irrigated plot is fifteen hectares and for an unirrigated plot, 150 hectares. After the settlement is

organized, farmers form a general assembly with an
administrative committee to represent the interests
of the settlers.

A summary review of the accomplishments of the
land-reform program in the light of its needs, problems, and objectives is presented to aid in the evaluation of the application of moshav principles in the
implementation of this reform.

Peasant resettlement was started almost immediately after the overthrow of the dictatorship in
1958, before the official passage of the law in 1960.
The land reform agency was already in existence and
supervised the movement of peasants in 1959 back to
the public lands from which they were removed by the
previous regime and to the expropriated lands of the
high officials of the previous dictatorship.

The situation in Venezuela was such that it was
relatively easy to pass the Land Reform Law and put
it into effect immediately. There was national consensus for passing the law and agreement that the mal-
structure and low productivity of the agricultural
sector was one of the country's most urgent problems
that needed immediate corrective action. The old
dictatorship favored industry, particularly petroleum
and lavish public works. The peasants, as well as
labor and students, needed to see immediate benefits
from parliamentary democracy to stop the inroads of
Communism that was supported by Cuban agents. There
was a substantial amount of public land that mini-
mized the need for expropriation of private land, and
there were ample sources of revenue for high payments
to private landowners who lost their lands. There
were legal and legislative precedents for the 1960
legislation, the previous laws of 1945 and 1948 that
were sabotaged by the previous dictatorship. In addition, there was a lack of rural elite and of a
well-organized conservative party. Petroleum and
commercial ventures completely overshadowed agriculture. The interests of the small landed-gentry group
were well provided for by high land payments and liberal exemptions. The institutional framework for
administering the law was already in existence, the

government agencies, and the farmers' and workers' federations. Implementation of the law meant more responsibility for these agencies and their administrators.

The performance of IAN in terms of number of settlers, families settled, and area distributed to farmers is indicated in Table 26. It shows that the three big years for the distribution of lands were 1959, the year before the passage of the law, 1960, the first year the law went into operation, and 1965. The number of settlements organized from 1961 through 1964 declined considerably. In 1963, there was a sharp cut in the IAN budget that was not restored until 1965. More than the lands distributed were from the public domain, and a substantial amount of the work of IAN was in organizing settlements for farmers already on these lands. At the end of 1964, only 20 per cent of the land-reform program had been completed in accordance with the 1963-66 four-year plan goals. About 20,000 families were resettled in 1963 and 1964, in comparison to the 50,000 families that were planned for each year. In 1964, there was an administrative reorganization of IAN, and the tempo of the program increased in 1965. This tempo, however, was not maintained in 1966 and 1967.

The first years of the reform were devoted mainly to the physical distribution of lands to the peasants. After 1963, the emphasis shifted to the consolidation of settlements that had been established, the beginnings of micro planning on farms and settlements, and large regional projects. Through 1965 the program may have reached about half of the peasants with insufficient land, mainly the squatters on public lands and the cash renters. By 1967, according to IAN, about 90 per cent of the requests for land had been met.

The budget of IAN for the years 1959 through 1964 has been as follows:

Million Bolivares*

1959	110.1
1960	160.6
1961	179.7
1962	139.3
1963	107.8
1964	150.8

Total   848.3

About one quarter of the budget in 1959 and 1960 was
spent on the purchase of lands. Consolidation expenditures, amounts spent on roads, buildings, houses,
irrigation, drainage, land preparation, technical
studies, etc. as percentages of total expenditures
for the years 1959 through 1964 were as follows: 43,
30, 46, 49, 14, and 15. The proportion of the budget for other expenditures, mainly administration,
have been high, never less than 30 per cent and in
1963 and 1964, above 70 per cent.[7]

The purpose of this review is not a criticism
of IAN. It had a big job to do in a hurry and in its
early years concentrated on giving land to the peasants. In many instances its planning of settlements
was bad, for example, dividing a tract mechanically
into units of equal size, completely disregarding all
topograhical and drainage features and differences in
productivity. Money wasted on land purchases has
been high, in some cases for nonexisting land. Its
statistics of accomplishment may well be inflated.
One government official who follows the program carefully claimed that the number of settlements incorporated in the program in 1965 was overstated by two
hundred. Another study indicates that the IAN official figures on the number of families settled is
overstated by about 40 per cent. This is a result of
the fact that different members of the same family

---

*The budget which was actually spent increased
from about 150 million bolivares in 1965 to about 180
million bolivares in 1967, according to IAN estimates.

TABLE 26

Venezuela: Results of Land-Reform Program, 1949-67

| Year | Number Families Settled | Number Settlements | Area Affected (Hectares) | | |
			Total	Private Lands	Public Lands
1959	5,874	53	460,769	185,309	275,460
1960	25,221	308	900,823	460,034	440,789
1961	11,074	147	180,892	115,027	65,865
1962	14,603	135	261,492	214,314	47,178
1963	9,656	60	171,003	29,375	141,628
1964	10,250	--	202,864	106,654	96,210
1965	36,443	--	784,250	383,709	400,541
1966	16,852	--	445,457	134,998	310,459
1967	14,100	--	380,000	102,895	277,105

Source: IAN.

make solicitations for and are awarded separate
tracts of land.

There are substantive amounts of expenditures
by other agencies working with IAN on the land-reform
program. One of these is the National Agricultural
Bank. The amounts of money loaned in short-term
credits by the bank to peasants in the program have
been as follows:

Million Bolivares[8]

1959	56.9
1960	75.5
1961	70.9
1962	83.3
1963	78.0
1964	111.0
Total	475.6

The rate of repayment has been poor, and in 1964 it
was somewhat less than one third.[9]

The majority of the settlements in the reform
represent small-scale individual holdings, particularly in the early years of the program. Of 699
settlements in 1963, the average holding in 115 was
under the legal limit of five hectares. In about
half the settlements the average holding was under
ten hectares.[10]

About 10 per cent of the settlements were collective farms, and a few other settlements included
a mixture of collective farming and small individual
holdings. The figures were as follows:

Number of Settlements[11]

Private farms	620
Collective farms	68
Mixed private and collective farms	11
Total	699

The collective farms represent mainly coffee and cocoa plantations or farms with large central installations, such as dairies, operated as a single unit. Decision-making for the collectives is by governmental officials operating from the capital and regional headquarters. The settlers are paid money wages according to duties performed as advances on yearly profits. As the farms have not been generally profitable, the advances represent wages, and the settlers are actually just paid workers. While these farms have generally not shown profits, production has increased.

It is too early to judge the results of the Venezuelan agrarian-reform program. There have been many mistakes of commission and omission. It has, however, been more than just politically inspired. Mistakes have been corrected, improved methods of implementation have been adopted, and substantive economic assistance has been obtained. A group making comparative studies of agrarian reform in Venezuela with Mexico and Bolivia concluded that as of early 1964 the supplementary programs of agricultural extension and community development were more extensive in Venezuela than in the other two countries. They were also impressed with the self-critical attitudes that permeated the discussion of reform among the employees and officials of the various agencies concerned with its execution.[12] The improvement in the implementation of reform since 1965 has been particularly striking.

Agricultural production in Venezuela has increased sharply since 1959. Much of this has been caused by government policies that have encouraged a more efficient commercial sector. The peasants in the agrarian-reform settlements, however, have made a substantial contribution to this increase in production. It was estimated that in 1964 reform settlements may have accounted for possibly 10 per cent of the value of total agricultural production. For 1967, the estimate rose to about 30 per cent. Reform settlements are now major producers of national staple foods such as rice, maize, and yucca.

INSTITUTIONAL ORGANIZATION FOR LAND REFORM

The institutional support of land reform is primarily the responsibility of a number of autonomous government agencies. Except for IAN these agencies have other functions besides those pertaining to land reform. Coordination of the work of these agencies is thus essential for the smooth functioning of the reform program, both in the planning and implementation phases and in the application of moshav principles to make the reform effective. In addition to governmental agencies, the interests of the peasants are represented by their national federation, Federación Campesina de Venezuela (FCV). A summary of the role of these agencies follows:

The National Agrarian Institute, IAN, is the official settlement agency responsible for carrying out the land-reform legislation. It obtains the lands for settlement, establishes the villages including all the physical planning, and is responsible for community development, including aid in the supplying of the physical requisites needed for agricultural development. One of its major programs in this respect has been supplying agricultural machinery, particularly tractors. It operated machine tractor stations in the provinces for a number of years.

The National Agricultural and Livestock Bank (BAP) is the national credit and marketing agency. It supplies the peasants short-term credits on a commodity basis using specific norms per hectare. The credit is given in installments, its provision dependent on execution of certain farm practices. It is also the official marketing agency responsible for purchasing basic commodities at fixed government prices. Its activities in the reform program are but a part of its many functions. It is responsible for extending credit to commercial farmers as well as peasants. Through 1962 this was a larger program than the peasant credit program. The promotion of commercial agriculture is still an important part of its duties. Its price and marketing functions are basic to the entire agricultural economy as well as to land reform.

The Ministry of Public Works (MOP) is the agency responsible for irrigation and infrastructure such as roads. Important regional-reform projects are based on the construction of dams for supplying irrigation waters. MOP thus has an active role not only in the support of reform, but also in the administration of its most important projects.

The Ministry of Agriculture and Livestock (MAC) is primarily concerned with agricultural research, extension, and the agro-planning functions of land reform. In addition, it is responsible for the commodity boards that conduct the special commodity programs for the development of national production.

Another supporting agency is the Ministry of Sanitation and Social Assistance (SAS). This agency has been primarily responsible for the construction of homes and health and sanitation facilities in the village.

The Presidential Office for Coordination and Planning (CORDIPLAN) is the budget, economic planning, and coordinating agency in the Executive Department. It is responsible for issuing the four-year plans and for coordinating the programs and projects for their implementation. The chief of its agricultural sector is responsible for the national agricultural plan. There is a national committee for land reform that includes the chief of the agricultural section of CORDIPLAN, top officials of the government agencies concerned with the reform program, and the head of the FCV. This committee is charged with planning the program and reviewing its implementation. Their plans are reviewed by the President and his cabinet. This coordinating committee has similar committees in each of the provinces that provide for coordination and communication, both vertical and horizontal. There are similar coordinating committees for specific programs such as irrigation, marketing, etc.

The large regional-reform projects are operated similarly by a coordinating committee. The one at Majaguas, the largest project in the country, includes the local chiefs of sections of IAN, BAP, MAC, MOP,

a representative of the FCV, and the chief project
coordinator, in this case a representative of MOP,
who is designated by the government entities as head
of the project and supervisor of the work of their
cooperative personnel.

An alternative organization would be an independent autonomous regional authority. Because of
the heritage of dictatorship such an organization is
not considered practical in Venezuela. Although
there are difficulties of coordination at the project
level, and direct communication by the officials of
the independent agencies with their superiors in the
capital is common, this type of organization is the
best that can be accomplished under Venezuelan conditions.

There have been frequent changes in the heads
of the important government agencies, IAN, BAP, and
MAC, concerned with land reform. In a 1962 solici-
tation by the FCV of the local syndicates on their
principal problems, of the 873 comments on the administration of the reform program 786 were concerned
with BAP. Of these 544 were specific complaints on
the timing, size of loans, and inefficiencies of the
organization, while 242 cited the need for new credit
activities. BAP is vulnerable to criticism in both
its credit and marketing activities and has not been
able to absorb efficiently all the new activities
necessitated by the reform program. The other eighty-
seven comments were complaints against IAN.[13] Like
IAN, however, the work of BAP in the implementation
of land reform has improved considerably in recent
years.

The role of CORDIPLAN in the coordination of
the planning and implementation of agricultural policy, including land reform, has been quite commendable
Its agricultural section has had strong leadership.
It has worked hard for the effective implementation
of the reform program and has also been responsible
for the invitation of the Israeli experts to apply
moshav principles in this respect.

The institutional support of the FCV merits
elaboration. Its roots predate agrarian reform. It

has been in the vanguard of the struggle of democratic
forces against dictatorship in Venezuela. It is the
most important unit of the National Labor Federation,
comprising about three quarters of the national membership. About 85 per cent of its operating budget
of $200,000 is from a subsidy of the Ministry of La-
bor, as the possibility of raising internal funds is
limited because of the very low income level of its
campesino members.[14]

Local government in rural areas in Venezuela
is restricted by the national constitution. In addition, the revenue base from which to perform politically effective local government is very small. Rural
leadership in the FCV, by forging an alliance with
the major political parties has been the instrument
in obtaining municipal type services such as roads,
sewage systems, potable water, schools, and dispen-
saries. It has also been the instrument through
which the campesinos' interests are represented in
the planning and administration of land reform. In
this connection the FCV has two representatives on
the five-man board of directors of IAN. It is on the
board of directors of BAP, the National Planning
Board, the commodity boards of MAC, and is represented in other entities concerned with land reform.[15]

In the early years of the reform program the
FCV concentrated largely on organizing the peasants
in requesting land and in providing leadership to the
village assemblies. It still performs these functions,
and, in addition, is becoming more active in the consolidation phase of reform and in assisting in the
technical phases of its implementation. It has been
concerned with the establishment and operation of vocational schools where campesinos can receive courses
in basic agriculture, land reform, and syndicate formation. Four schools were in operation in 1965. A
total of ten were planned, each to give five two-
month courses to classes of fifty for a total of 2,500
graduates a year. The peasant is taught modern farming operations and how to improve his standard of living. He is encouraged and expected as a possible
future leader to share his knowledge with the other
members of his community.[16]

The FCV holds promise in the economic implementation of land reform, particularly as the leaders
become convinced of its importance and learn the
technical aspects. Institutionally it corresponds
to the Agricultural Center of the Histadrut in Israel,
and, in fact, has started to assume some of the same
economic functions. In addition to the peasant
schools, it has organized a unit for the importation
of agricultural tractors that are assigned to FCV
local leaders in the settlements. The fees for the
use of the tractors by other farmers are returned as
purchase payments. The FCV is interested in the establishment of credit and consumer cooperatives in
the villages. Plans are being made for an agricultural purchasing organization for farmers' perquisites
in which it will hold shares. It has established a
rice processing plant in a large land-reform settlement that markets its output through the Rockefeller
supermarket chain. It is also working on the establishment of a net of farmers' markets. The FCV may
evolve into a political institution with important
economic functions and objectives.

The FCV also plays the role of the national
settlement agencies in Israel attached to the political parties, the Moshav Movement and others. It
thus strengthens the position of the campesinos in
the political parties and the dedication of the parties to agrarian reform. Interparty cooperation has
been quite good. The FCV leadership is competent and
reasonably well educated, with long periods of service
to the labor and campesino movements.

ISRAELI TECHNICAL ASSISTANCE: CIARA

The Israeli bilateral technical-assistance
program, involving the application of moshav principles in the implementation of land reform, originated
from the work of Mr. Itzhak Abt, one of the economic
planners of the Lakhish region who arrived in Venezuela in 1961. He worked out, with the assistance of
a number of technicians from the agencies supporting
reform, a comprehensive agricultural development and
settlement plan for the Majaguas area in the State of

Portuguesa in the western part of the country. The
plan included the details for the parcelation of
nineteen thousand of the total thirty thousand hectares that were to be irrigated from a large dam,
whose construction had begun in 1958 and was nearing
completion. The dam and irrigation network had been
built by the government with no specific planning on
how the water was to be used for the development of
the sourrounding area. Abt applied the principles
of moshav regional planning used in Lakhish, working
out the plans for the settlements, service centers,
and all the details of the individual family farms
including cropping patterns, labor utilization, and
complete income and expense budgets for a long-time
period. He persuaded the Venezuelan officials that
the large investments already made in the dam and
irrigation networks should be written off, as their
opportunity costs without the detailed settlement
plans were zero. Even without these fixed charges
the costs-benefits ratio was only .75. The ratio
was conservative, as the input-output coefficients
were based on local data that did not fully reflect
the possibilities of improved practices. CORDIPLAN
approved Abt's plan as the basis for developing
Majaguas as a regional pilot project for land reform
and as a way to rationalize and recover the large
infrastructure expenditures already made.

A Venezuelan team representing all the official
agencies concerned with land reform was dispatched to
Israel in late 1962 for a six-week intensive study
of settlement planning and implementation in all its
various aspects, concentrating on the poststate
moshav. Each member of the team was given individual
attention to enable specialization in the various aspects of settlement.

CORDIPLAN made a contract with Israel to support an Israeli team of five members to assist in
settlement work. This team included specialists in
physical planning, farm credit, agro-economic planning, irrigation, and institutional planning. The
latter acted as head of the team. The group arrived
in Venezuela in February, 1963. Their headquarters
and base of operation was, until June, 1966, an

integral part of CORDIPLAN, called the Center for
Training and Applied Research in Agrarian Reform
(CIARA).

CIARA has been the principal institution responsible for the improvement of the implementation
of land reform in Venezuela. It has accomplished this
through its program of work in training courses, applied research, and advisory work with emphasis on
future planning along a broad spectrum of project activities. This has included agro-economic, socio-
economic, and physical planning. The agro-economic
has centered mainly on village and farm production
planning and supervised credit programs on a village
basis. The socio-economic has been principally concerned with the institutional organization of the
village cooperative societies and their role in credit, buying, selling, industrial, and other economic
activities as well as in helping provide for the
social amenities and organizations of the settlement.
Physical planning has been mainly concerned with
rural architecture, the layout of the settlements
and farms and their buildings, and with irrigation.

CIARA has been particularly successful as a
catalytic agency working with the principal entities
concerned with land reform--government entities such
as IAN, BAP, MAC, and BOP, and with the FCV and
others. This has resulted in improvement of coordination and efficiency at all levels and planning future activities along more effective pragmatic lines.

The Israeli team was mainly concerned, at
first, with the integral planning and implementation
of these plans with the Venezuelan officials at its
center and in the field. In fact, the name of the
center before it was changed to CIARA in 1965, was
the Center for Integral Planning of Peasant Settlements. The principal method to effect this approach
has been a thirteen-week course entitled Integral
Planning of Peasant Settlements. The chief aims of
the course are (1) to develop the concept of comprehensive planning, (2) to train in planning methodol-
ogy, (3) to form interdisciplinary teams for

settlement planning, (4) to elaborate specific development projects, and (5) to apply the integral
planning-implementation concept.

The courses have combined both theory, field
work, and the planning of specific projects that
would be implemented by the participants. Basic
planning theory was developed in the early weeks.
The application of the theory was then examined in
a week of field work. The group was then divided
according to fields of specialization: physical,
agro-economic, credit, and institutional planning,
and was offered theory in these specialized fields.
Then, based on the collection of basic data in the
field, the participants worked out the details of
the specific projects that they themselves would
later administer in the field. In the latter weeks
of the course the groups were united to review the
projects as a whole. The students were then assigned
to the projects by their ministries, with an agreement that they remain on the project for two years.

By 1965, CIARA had offered four integrated
planning courses that were attended by ninety-seven
government professionals concerned with settlement
work, including three from the land-reform agency
in Colombia. Five projects were already being implemented by course graduates. These represented
different types of projects and settlements where
the integrated approach was to be applied. Two were
supervised credit programs of villages that had already been established. Two were large regional
settlement programs. The last was the development
of a new settlement to be operated on a communal
basis in its early years and then to be divided into
family farms after an irrigation system was installed.

Majaguas, the largest regional project, was
the first to be inaugurated with Israeli technical
assistance. But because of its size and the necessity of building a large physical infrastructure, it
will take many years to show results and appraise its
effectiveness. The Israeli experts wanted to adopt
a representative project that would show quick results

with no additional investment. Therefore, in 1964, a supervised credit program was put into effect in El Cortijo.

El Cortijo was an older settlement in the state of Arragua of one hundred and ten families on four hundred hectares of dry farming, with the average size of holding from three to five hectares, based mainly on the cultivation of maize. The agricultural experience of the settlement had been bad. In 1963, only 38 per cent of the credit extended by BAP had been recovered In 1964, the first year of the operation of the credit program, 90 per cent of the credits were recovered. In 1965, practically all the credit was recovered and average family farm incomes had reached 3,000 bolivares. By 1968, average incomes were estimated at about 4,000 bolivares, and irrigation was being installed. This would make possible higher yields and increased diversification of crops. With irrigation, income goals of 8,000 to 10,000 bolivares are expected in a few years.

Based on the success of El Cortijo, a supervised credit program was started in 1964 in the settlement of El Amparo. This has gone well also, and average net family incomes of 4,000 bolivares were achieved within two years. El Amparo has become one of a group of eleven settlements in the state of Cojedes, in the north-central part of the country, in which a regional approach to settlement development is being tried.

The early success of CIARA prompted the Venezuelan authorities to give it a permanent legal status. This was accomplished in June, 1966, when CIARA became a semi-autonomous public agency. Its top directive council consists of the head of the Agricultural Section of CORDIPLAN, the President of IAN, the Director General of MAC, and the Director of Irrigation of MOP. The council chooses its president, in 1968 the President of IAN. All these agencies contribute money and/or personnel to CIARA. In addition, CIARA obtains funds from national and international agencies for work in its fields of competence in connection with land reform. Its total operational budget from

all sources in 1967 and 1968 averaged about $350,000
average level. The executive secretary of CIARA, a
young and highly competent person, has been with the
Center since its beginning in 1963. This is also the
case with his deputy. Both, as well as the manager
of the Majaguas project, were in the original group
of Venezuelans that went to Israel in 1962.

The effects of the activities of CIARA on land
reform from 1965 to 1968 has been remarkable. The
advance has been in all fields of endeavor and represents both a broadening and deepening in its activities. The staff has increased from six in 1965 to
thirty-four in 1968, twenty-four professionals and
ten clerks.

The integral planning of settlements and the
course for the training of officials concerned have
continued. As of 1968, sixteen projects including
many additional settlements were being implemented
or about to be implemented. This included two groupings of individual projects in regional development
schemes as well as two of the early regional projects
where the settlements are administered as one large
project. The basic course (the eighth was offered
in 1968) is now given at a higher level and is primarily for university graduates, with exceptions for
those who have done well in the field or in other
CIARA courses. Courses are now attended by students
from other countries in Latin America. IAN offers
sixteen to eighteen scholarships annually to such
foreign students. Project supervisors and their
principal assistants are still trained to work out
the project they will administer. Students from all
parts of the country are sent to the courses, and
they return to work on projects in their home areas
that they know well.

The scope and types of courses have widened
considerably. All are operational in character and
project oriented. The physical planning courses are
of particular concern to IAN and MOP. Five such
courses have been offered with excellent results.
Now rural architects and irrigation technicians have
to obtain a CIARA course certificate to be eligible

for their work. This had cut down agency waste and
increased job effectiveness.

Special courses in the use of credit, at all
levels, have been similarly successful. This has increased the efficiency of the officials of BAP and
MAC and the village credit associations and enabled
the directed credit program to expand to 134 villages
in 1968. Credit courses have been offered to village
technicians, regional BAP bank managers, and to high
officials of BAP. BAP performance has improved considerably, and ineffective field men are now dismissed

New types of courses are also being offered at
the campesino level. In 1968, there were three such
courses. One was for regional directors of the FCV
to improve their effectiveness in land-reform activities. Another was for the directors of the village
credit associations to improve the operation of these
associations and the control of their own affairs by
the campesinos. This may be a practical way to coun-
teract traditional paternalism. A third course was
offered to the sons of campesinos in village administration, particularly the administration of credit
unions.

Other advanced courses and seminars in such
matters as credit and economic evaluation of projects
were offered to high officials of the supporting institutions. This has resulted in better coordination,
increased interest and job effectiveness, and a lower
rate of turnover of these officials.

CIARA also participates in training courses
conducted by other organizations such as the OAS for
rural teachers and for home demonstration agents in
the context of community development. This is to
promote better teamwork in the social organization
of land-reform villages.

The research program of CIARA is also of a
pragmatic, operational type. It includes calculations of the costs of production and rates of returns
on different types of model farms, the development of
livestock farms for Majaguas and other projects, and

an evaluation of the supervised credit program for both an economic and social point of view, a study of farm operation and management at Majaguas, and agro-industrial possibilities for the regional group-ing of settlements in Cojedes.

The advisory and planning work is mainly con-cerned with possible future developments. Planning in land-reform settlements is conceived in three stages. The first is the preinvestment stage. This is represented by village supervised-credit projects like El Cortijo. It involves making village and farm plans for a year, obtaining credits, and supervision of operations for recuperation of credits. Large in-creases in incomes in such projects can be achieved within a very short time. But without further in-vestments these increases level out at about 4,000 bolivares per family.

The second stage is one of consolidation in-volving increases in investments and incomes. This may involve the introduction of irrigation, a wider choice in farm enterprises, the purchase of commer-cial inputs such as fertilizer and pesticides, and the introduction of products that are not under the jurisdiction of BAP, for which marketing outlets have to be planned and provided. Also included at this stage may be the more effective use of farm machinery. Most of the work of CIARA and much of the work of supporting institutions is in this consolidation phase.

The third stage is called the contribution stage, where the land-reform projects and farms ac-tually become real commercial farms. They will then produce substantial surpluses and net farm family in-comes of 8,000 bolivares or more, consistent with the project goals of achieving farm incomes of a level of 80 per cent of urban-worker incomes.* This stage

---

*The Israeli estimate of net farm family in-comes in 1965 was $400 (1,800 bolivares), and family incomes of employed urban workers at about $2,200 (10,000 bolivares).

calls for new institutions, many of a cooperative
nature not previously existing in Venezuela. For example, the forward planning may involve the establishment of regional purchasing organizations along
the Israeli model for the purchase of inputs and the
processing and marketing of outputs; regional agro-
industrial corporations for farm-supported industry;
the promotion of specialized farm exports and cooperative farm enterprises for special crops; consumer
cooperatives; and regional bookkeeping associations.
This stage is just beginning in Venezuela, and Israeli
experts and others are involved in such technical assistance. This stage may be harder to achieve than
the other two, since the necessary institutions have
to be established and adapted to the local situation.
Substantial investments must be made and additional
personnel with administrative skills developed.

With the progress in the implementation of land
reform the role of the Israeli experts in CIARA has
changed. The original team has returned to Israel
after four years in Venezuela. The new experts are
specialists working in different specialized fields
such as the development of intensive livestock farms
and new industrial and marketing possibilities. While
the original Israeli experts worked behind the scenes
in close cooperation with the national officials, the
early CIARA program was Israeli inspired. Now, while
Israeli technical assistance is still important, the
nationals have effectively assimilated this assistance
into a truly Venezuelan program.

The supervised credit program deserves further
elaboration. The new Israeli credit expert now works
in IAN, the operational agency, rather than CIARA.
His responsibilities, however, are primarily of a
consultive nature. The program was expanded with the
training of the village and regional technicians.
The credit expert has introduced norms and procedures
for the yearly credit and production programs. He
has been influential in planning the credit and short-
term production programs in advance on a yearly basis
thus enabling more credit to be obtained at better
terms from BAP and the purchase of perquisites, particularly fertilizers and pesticides, at lower prices

since the orders can be made well in advance. The
coordination of yearly production and credit planning
are done more efficiently now at the village level,
with all forms and transactions on an individual basis through the village council. In some cases there
is even differentiation of production plans on different farms. Recuperation of loans remains high.
In 1966, it was 88.27 per cent of all credits extended.[17] It is estimated that the 1968 program will
reach 134 settlements, will amount to over thirty-one
million bolivares, and that the average net farm
family income of the villages in the program will be
4,108 bolivares.[18] While these are official IAN statistics and may be on the optimistic side, they check
reasonably well with an independent study of land reform in Venezuela.

EVALUATION OF APPLICATION OF MOSHAV PRINCIPLES

An evaluation of the Israeli technical-
assistance program in Venezuela based on the experience since 1961 shows clearly that the application
of moshav principles has been an important factor in
the implementation of land reform. The three basic
moshav principles have been applied on a settlement
basis for established villages and for new villages
and on a regional basis for large projects and smaller related individual projects in a regional context.
The emphasis is on the micro planning of agricultural
production and in the implementation of this planning.
The implementation has included scheduling production
operations, supplying the means of production through
credit management, and control of marketing. Processing facilities for additional inputs and outputs and
the development of additional cooperative facilities
is included in future planning. A program has started
on the development of the settlement councils and
their role in implementing the progress of the social
and cultural amenities in the settlements.

The analysis of moshav principles in terms of
the critical success factors is basic. First the
exogenous factors.

1. Quality of leadership. When the Israeli
program started in 1961, there was considerable skep-
ticism in Venezuela on what land reform could accom-
plish beyond the limited political goal of the
distribution of lands to peasants. There was considerable sentiment by the young professionals in the
reform program for the adoption of the Cuban collective and Cuban political institutions. The fact that
micro planning on a settlement and possibly a regional basis has been shown practicable has had a profound
effect on the personnel concerned with reform, demon-
strating that land reform could be practical and com-
patible with democratic procedures and institutions.

Excellent leadership has been trained for the
early projects where moshav principles have been applied. In addition, there has been strong support
at the executive level of the agencies concerned with
reform by those who have visited Israel and who have
taken interest in and have followed the work of CIARA.
Good leadership at the project level can increase
rapidly because of the multiplier effect of training
at CIARA and village projects. Trained technicians
from educational institutions are becoming increasingly available. Agricultural schools are becoming
increasingly aware of the possibilities in the development of peasant agriculture.

2. Quality of supporting institutions. In
general, the performance and stability of the supporting institutions that were quite faulty in the
earlier years of reform have improved greatly in recent years. The early successes of the new projects
have had a salutary effect on the agencies. All support the work of CIARA and the Israeli team. IAN is
expanding its work in the consolidation and economic
implementation of the settlements and in the application of moshav principles.

There has been a growth of interest and action
by the FCV in the economic implementation of reform.
There was resentment by the local FCV leader in the
early stages of the project at El Cortijo and appre-
hension that the success of the new program would en-
danger his own status. In fact, the project developed

new leaders who will be important in the growth of
the village. Problems involving the change of leadership may be important in projects at established
settlements. The FCV, however, recognizes this problem and strongly supports the Israeli technical assistance.

3. Nationalist ideology. Zionist ideology is
particular to Israel. However, national attempts for
the rehabilitation of the peasant and his integration
in the social, political, and economic life of the
country is the Venezuelan substitute for nationalist
ideology. These attempts are reasonably effective.

4. Government. The democratic regime and
parties have been strongly committed to agrarian reform. The quality of the top leaders has been good.
The government has provided stability for the development of the reform program, and, in turn, the growth
of political consciousness among peasants acts as a
stabilizing factor for the maintenance of democracy.

5. Cooperative agricultural sector. The village council is a precooperative, not a western type
cooperative. Cooperative values have popular support
in the country. The application of moshav principles
enhances the operational role of the settlement council and its possibilities in the economic development
of the village. While the agricultural sector has
not had much prestige or success since the development of the petroleum industry, the feasibility of
peasants attaining economic success through guided
cooperation has led to a goal and program that are
politically popular.

6. Specialized role of peasant agriculture.
Peasant agriculture in the reform program has concentrated on the production of basic staples in which
there have been deficits. Beginnings have been made
in the intensive production of high-value products.
The promotion of such products is particularly important in the newer projects and in regional planning.

7. Financial support. Venezuela is quite for-
tunate in this respect. National petroleum revenues

act as a substitute for the National Zionist Organization. Additional sources of revenue for irrigation and regional-development programs and for special projects have been available from the Inter-American Development Bank and the United States AID program.

Micro planning through supervised, specialized credit projects, as exemplified by the El Cortijo and El Emparo projects, is not costly. Project costs are considerably less than the supervised credit programs sponsored by AID on an individual farm basis, since one BAP technicial can serve a whole village instead of four or five families. Also, the uneven development of a favored few in the village has bad social results.

IAN estimated in 1965 that the costs of settlement per family in the regional projects was $40,000 in Majaguas and about $20,000 in Bocono.[19] The higher cost of the former was partly due to the lack of proper planning in the initial phases of the scheme. Costs have since risen above these amounts. These projects, however, have definitely not been written off as failures, as the settlement programs in both are still in the initial stages.

8. <u>Agricultural planning</u>. The planning framework for agricultural development has been helpful in the application of moshav principles. Land reform and the work of the various agencies in the implementation of reform as part of the larger scheme of macro planning for the agricultural sector as a whole The comprehensive plans of credit, price, and marketing supports and special commodity programs have been facilitating factors in supporting the application of moshav principles. While the coordination of micro and macro planning has hardly been perfect, the mosha approach offers possibilities of improved coordinatio in micro planning and implementation to achieve macro goals.

9. <u>General economic conditions</u>. Economic conditions have not been favorable for the absorption of peasant migrants in the city labor force. The moshav approach shows that realistic income and employment

goals can be achieved in the peasant villages and is
a practical way of equalizing economic opportunities
between the countryside and the city as well as increasing the production of food.

10. Land tenure. The Venezuelan reform program is based, in most projects, on individual ownership of the land. The government has been slow in
confirming titles. No arrangements have been made
as yet for payment of the land by the peasants. The
reform law has provisions against the sale of land
received by the peasants. There are cases, however,
where peasants have surrendered their parcels or share
crop them with management and credit supplied by private sources, as an example of share cropping in
reverse. These examples emphasize the need for effective implmentation as an integral part of land
reform.

11. Support of moshav. The moshav is not
favored over other alternative agricultural structures.
The government, however, is strongly committed to the
promotion of peasant welfare and the support of the
family farm. It has, therefore, supported the application of moshav principles for the implementation of
agricultural development. The application of moshav
principles has definitely assumed national, Venezuelan
characteristics.

12. Size of country. Because of the large size
of the country, implementation of land-reform projects by the moshav type of micro planning has to be
limited to a selected sample of regions and villages.
The number of people involved, however, can be quite
substantial.

Closely related to the size of the country is
the size of the market. Venezuela is still on a deficit food basis despite the rapid growth in private
commercial agriculture in recent years. The extent
of the national market, however, in the longer run,
may be somewhat limited, in that it could prevent
agricultural reform projects from reaching their
fullest potential. In view of present low consumption levels, the national market can expand with

increased industrial development. The importance of
increases in productivity in the peasant sector is
evident in competition with the present commercial
sector.

As far as the endogenous factors are concerned
the application of moshav principles has been made
in a flexible way consistent with settlement needs.
For example, the village supervised credit programs
are on a voluntary basis. The individual farmer is
free to elect whether or not to join. Development
of the community council has been consistent with its
ability to take on additional tasks. They have not
been loaded down with municipal functions that they
could not perform.

Rationalization of the peasant family farm in
Venezuela has been implemented in a manner consistent
with the economic, social, and political ideologies
of the country: the need for settling people on the
land because of the limited industrial absorption of
labor and high rate of unemployment in the cities,
decentralization of population and settlement of new
areas, decentralization of the political power structure by favoring peasants, and the need for implement
ing land reforms for meeting and overcoming the
imminent political threat of Communism.

As in Israel, the application of moshav principles is a method of integrating individualism in an
accepted cooperative community pattern. The economic
response of the peasants to improved institutional
arrangements has been remarkable. Before the Israeli
supervised credit plans were applied in El Cortijo
and El Ampero, BAP declared that over 60 per cent of
the farmers in the two projects concerned were not
credit worthy. Not only have the settlers become
good credit risks, but the application of moshav prin
ciples is transforming these villages into commercial
agricultural settlements in a relatively short period

As to the character of the settlers, El Cortijo
was a substandard agricultural village with a demographic pattern in which older persons predominated.
The settlement was purposely chosen to illustrate

dramatically what could be done quickly by effective
micro planning with people who were considered below
average. In El Cortijo it was not the character of
the settlers but the lack of implementation support
and proper planning and services that was the main
block to progress until the supervised credit program
was started in 1963.

On balance, the analysis in terms of the critical success factors seems favorable for the application of moshav principles in Venezuela. The supervised credit program can be definitely termed a
cess. The income goals of CIARA integral planned
projects may be high, the time needed to reach them
may have been underestimated, and, in some cases,
the amount of investment to attain the goals may also
have been underestimated. In all projects, however,
productivity and farm incomes have substantially increased. No project, not even the most difficult,
can yet be considered a failure. As in Israel, there
is considerable variance in achievement among the
farmers in the settlements. A number have already
achieved project goals ahead of time.

However, a substantial number of the land-
reform settlements will not reach their full potential.
There is still sufficient evidence to indicate that
the application of moshav principles to selected projects can change a substantial number of peasants who
had previously existed outside the economic mainstream
of the country into efficient agricultural producers
who will receive adequate remuneration for supplying
food that the country needs for development.

NOTES

1. The statistical data in this section, although originating from a variety of national sources,
were checked with CORDIPLAN, the national planning
and budgetary office.

2. All statistics from CORDIPLAN.

3. Venezuela, National Agrarian Institute,

The Venezuelan Agrarian Reform 1959-1963, p. 4.
(In Spanish.)

4. From files of Ministry of Agriculture.

5. Ibid.

6. "Rural Resettlement in Venezuela" (paper submitted by Secretary-General of IAN to Inter-regional Technical Meeting on Rural Resettlement, Ashkelon, Israel, 1965), p. 5. (Mimeographed.)

7. Based on tabulations of Inter-American Development Bank from materials in IAN reports. The exchange rate of the bolivar to the dollar was 4.5 in 1964, and in previous years, 3.35.

8. Venezuela, Agricultural and Livestock Bank, Annual Report, 1964, p. 103. (In Spanish.)

9. Ibid.

10. "Rural Resettlement in Venezuela," p. 7. IAN data indicate a substantive increase in size of holding from 1964 to 1967.

11. Ibid.

12. Dwight B. Neatle, Charles Erasmus, and Hans C. Buechler, "Land Reform and Social Revolution in Bolivia," Manuscript in Library of Land Tenure Center, University of Wisconsin. (Dittoed.)

13. John D. Powell, Preliminary Report on the Federation Campesina de Venezuela, Land Tenure Center (Madison, Wisc.: University of Wisconsin, 1964), p. 15.

14. Ibid., p. 20.

15. Ibid., p. 22.

16. Ibid., pp. 24-25.

17. Venezuela, National Agrarian Institute, Operational Plan of Supervised Credit 1968, p. 1B. (In Spanish.)

18.   *Ibid*., p. 1^F.

19.   "Rural Resettlement in Venezuela," *op. cit*., p. 7.

CHAPTER **11** CASE OF IRAN

The other country case on the application of
moshav principles for agricultural development is
that of Iran. This case is quite different from that
of Venezuela. The country is at a much lower stage
of development; this refers to both the economy as a
whole and the agricultural sector. The method of
application of moshav principles is also quite different in that the Israeli consultants are not only
responsible for the planning of a large regional agricultural development project, but also for its implementation.

SUMMARY BACKGROUND INFORMATION

Iran can be categorized in the Galbraithian
developmental classification as a low level model 2
country, economically, socially, and politically.[1]
Average per capita income is variously estimated as
from $130 to $150 per year. Rural population accounts for somewhat over 70 per cent of the total
population. Average net farm family income is probably at about the $200 level. The agricultural ex-
tension service estimates that about one half of the
rural families have family incomes of $100 or less.
Despite the importance of oil revenues that account
for 10 to 15 per cent of the GNP, it is only in very
recent years that the industrial has exceeded the
agricultural sector by a relatively small amount as
the major source of gross domestic product.

The Kingdom of Iran, which covers an area of
628,000 square miles and has a population of some
twenty-two million inhabitants, occupies the western
and larger half of the great Iranian plateau between

312

the Indus and Tigris Rivers in Southwestern Asia.
The area of the country is roughly equivalent to the
combined areas of Texas, New Mexico, Arizona, and
California, states whose topography and climate are
somewhat similar to that of Iran. It is a country
rich in oil and mineral resources and with a relatively favorable land population ratio.

About 10 per cent of the land is arable land
or in permanent crops. The amount of land in permanent pastures and meadows is very small. There are
about eighteen million hectares of forest land and
about thirty-three million hectares of unused but potentially productive land. The latter represents over
twice the amount of arable land. Although there is a
deficiency of water in most parts of the country,
somewhat less than half the crop land is irrigated.

Iran is barely self-sufficient in food at very
low consumption levels. Sugar, tea, and vegetable
oils are imported in large quantities. In years of
drought wheat imports are large. Per capita agricul-
production from 1956 through 1966 has been more or
less stable. Agricultural exports are of some importance to the economy. The principal exports are wool
carpets, dried fruits, nuts, resin and furs, cotton,
and rice.

Labor productivity in agriculture is very low,
and agricultural techniques are extremely primitive.
With known practicable techniques the potential exists for vastly higher yields. Improved seeds, fertilizers, and modern machinery are little used. The
facilities for credit, marketing, and irrigation are
very unsatisfactory. Grazing is unregulated, and
there is a desperate need of fodder for livestock.

About 70 per cent of the population is illiterate. Although primary education is compulsory and
free, there is a general lack of educational facilities. The government is now devoting considerable
energy to remedy this situation. A crash program for
the eradication of illiteracy was inaugurated by the
Shah in 1963. This program seems to have been successful. There is also a large program for the

training of national leaders. In the 1965/66 school
year there were about twenty thousand students study-
ing abroad, mostly in Germany and England.

Politically the country cannot be classified
as either democratic or totalitarian. Iran is a
constitutional monarchy that has had a constitution
since 1906, providing for an elected parliament
(Majlis), a senate of which half the members are appointed by the Shah, and a prime minister, also appointed by the Shah. Because of the high degree of
illiteracy and the proviso that a member of parliament need not be a resident of the district he represents, there is strong political control by the
Shah and a small clique of leading families. Research has indicated that 150 families with considerable influence and prestige in the country control
more than one third the members of the Majlis and
senate and about two thirds of the membership of the
cabinets.[2] Parliamentary government has not been
responsive to the needs of the people, nor is there
a stable electorate with a stake in the government.

Until the very recent land-reform program the
controlling elite was commonly associated with the
ownership of land. There have been no reliable statistical estimates of the size distribution of agricultural holdings. According to the land-reform
statistics, 10,418 of the 45,000 odd villages in the
country were bought for distribution to the peasants
in the first stage of the program that limited landlord holdings to just one village. One landlord
owned villages equal in area to the size of Switzerland.

Until the reform, over 90 per cent of the
farmers had been sharecroppers. Their harvests were
shared with the landlords according to the ownership
of the five basic items: land, water, seed, draft
snimals, and labor. Farmers, then, generally receive
but one to two fifths of their crop. Because of the
primitive agricultural practices, farmers have only
been able to farm very small plots adjacent to their
villages. The villages generally have none of the
basic social services. One scholar has concluded tha

historically the condition of the Iranian peasant has
worsened constantly from the eighteenth century to
the present.[3]

ECONOMIC AND AGRICULTURAL PLANNING

Agricultural planning in Iran is an integral
part of overall economic development planning and is
the function of the Plan Organization, an executive
agency of the government supported by oil revenues.
This organization has been responsible for two seven-
year development plans and for the five-and-a-half-
year development plan initiated in September, 1962.
The Plan Organization is also the budget agency for
the implementation of development planning and is
responsible for the allocation of funds for individual projects to the appropriate government department.   These plans included liberal participation by
foreign consultants.

The principal objectives of the recent economic
plan were (1) an increase of 6 per cent in the GNP,
which represented a continuation of the growth
achieved in the previous plan, (2) an increase in
employment opportunities, and (3) a more equitable
distribution of national income.   The principal objectives of the plan for the agricultural sector
were (1) to raise agricultural output with a goal of
self-sufficiency for most agricultural products, (2)
to increase farm income levels, mainly through increases in productivity accompanied by a rise in national demand, and (3) to improve the distribution
of agricultural income.

Conditions in the agricultural sector were
radically changed with the inauguration of the new
land-reform program in early 1962.   The land-reform
program that became the principal policy for the agricultural sector was not foreseen in the new agricultural plan that had already been prepared.   The
governmental agencies concerned with the agricultural
sector and the Plan Organization had to revise their
projects to accommodate themselves to the fulfill-
ment of the agricultural policy.

National agricultural planning has been a highly centralized process at the capital with practically
no field testing by the agencies actually responsible
for project implementation. This is particularly important since all field-operational functions connected with the third and current development plan were
transferred from the Plan Organization to the regular
government departments.

The Iranian government, while concerned about
agricultural development, traditionally has resorted
only sparingly to direct market intervention. Fixed
or support prices are used only on a modest scale for
a few basic crops, wheat and barley purchased by the
government, and for special commodities controlled by
the state monopolies: tea, sugar, tobacco, and silk
cocoons. Foreign trade is regulated through tariffs
and import and export licenses to protect domestic
production. Bilateral agreements are made for promoting agricultural exports and balancing foreign
trade.

LAND REFORM PROGRAM

Land reform in Iran goes back to a decree of
1949 for the distribution of crown land to peasant
sharecroppers.[4] This law began to be implemented in
1951. By 1962, crown lands including 1,670 villages
inhabited by nearly one million people were distribu-
uted. The land was sold to the cultivators at prices
below assessed values on the basis of twenty-five annual installments. Income from the sales of the
property went to the Bank of Development and Rural
Cooperatives that supplied credit and some services
to the farmers.

A law was passed in December, 1955, providing
for the sale of state-owned land to small farmers.
The government was slow in implementing this law.

A royal decree of January, 1962, became the
basic law for country-wide land reform, after an
earlier law passed in 1960 proved ineffective. Under
the terms of the new decree no landland could own

more than a single village. The surplus villages were
purchased by the Land Reform Organization, the agency
of the Ministry of Agriculture administering the reform, and distributed to the peasants. The value of
the lands was determined in accordance with former
tax payments and is to be paid by the government in
fifteen annual installments. The farmers receiving
the land are obliged to pay the State the purchase
price plus 10 per cent. The profits from land sales
are used as a development fund supporting reform.
The specific holdings of the farmers were the areas
cultivated at the time of the reform. This obviated the need for detailed surveys. The Ministry
of Agriculture retained the right to equalize and
reparcel holdings. A condition of land distribution
to the farmer was that he accept membership in the
cooperative association of the village.

The first stage of reform, limiting landlord
holdings to but one village, was completed in October,
1963. The law governing distribution of lands in the
remaining landlord villages was passed in January,
1963. It gave the landlords three possible options
for distribution of land to cultivators: (1) a
thirty-year lease to tenants on the basis of rentals
charged the previous three years, with provisions for
revision of rents every five years, (2) outright sale
of lands to the peasants by mutual agreement, and (3)
division of the lands between the cultivators and
owners according to the customary ratios of landlord-
peasant shares. The law contains a proviso that
where there were difficulties delaying land distribution the government could purchase villages for distribution to the peasants.

The distribution of lands in the villages still
owned by landlords, referred to as the second phase of
land reform, started in February, 1965. Maximum landlord holdings were limited in accordance with the use
of land and its location. Holdings farmed with mechanical equipments and also orchards, if the trees
were owned by the landlord, were exempt from distribution. The second phase also provided for long-term
ninety-nine year leases on a cash rental basis for
land in the public domain to cultivators in the same

village, with the possible revision of the rents every
five years.

The physical distribution of land to peasants
has progressed rapidly. As of September, 1965, lands
of 38,418 villages were distributed: 10,418 villages
in the first phase, and 28,000 in the second.[5] Over
350,000 peasant cultivators received land in the first
stage, and by September, 1965, 810,000 in the second.
The cost of the villages purchased in the first phase
was 6.5 billion rials, and the first installment paid
to the landlords in cash amounted to 1.1 billion
rials.*

A condition for a peasant to receive lands in
the reform program is membership in the village cooperative. The Central Organization of Rural Cooperation of the Ministry of Agriculture (CORC) is
responsible for the development and supervision of
these cooperatives. It took over the cooperative
functions from the Agricultural Credit Bank in August,
1963, with initial capital resources of one billion
rials extended it by the bank and supplemented by an
additional advance by the Plan Organization. The number of local societies in September, 1965, was 5,382
with membership of 750,000 farmers and a total capi-
talization of almost $8 million. By December, 1958,
about 8,000 societies had been formed.[6] The local
units have been established as rapidly as possible,
with an eventual goal of fifteen thousand cooperatives
servicing all the villages in the country.

The local cooperative society is essentially a
precooperative with compulsory membership. Management is in the hands of a board of three directors
and a managing director, all chosen by the members.
The cooperatives are primarily agricultural-credit
societies providing short-term credits for current
operations. Many, in addition, provide requisites
such as improved seeds, fertilizers, and insecticides
and also some consumer articles such as kerosene,

---

*The exchange rate was seventy-five rials to
the dollar.

state monopoly items such as sugar and tea, and cloth
at certain times of the year. The arrangements for
deliveries of these items by the societies are made
by CORC. The value of the farmer's share in his local
cooperative has been, on the average, between five
hundred and eight hundred rials, with two hundred the
minimum and two thousand the maximum. The specific
amounts are decided by the board of each society. The
average size of loan in 1965 was six to seven thous-
and rials; the maximum was ten thousand. The size of
the loan is determined by the local board in accordance to the size of the farmers' capital shares and
their needs. The local cooperative receives its
credits from its regional organization at 4 per cent
and charges the farmers 6 per cent. The regional
organization obtains its money at 3 per cent. All
loans are unsecured.

The local societies are organized in geographical unions that report to the central organization in
Teheran. There were thirty-four unions in September,
1965. Actually these unions were founded before the
locals, and, in limited cases, provide services that
the locals cannot perform. This includes marketing
of selected crops, principally to the armed services,
by a few unions, and a tractor and farm machinery
pool by another. One union plans to participate in
the construction of a sugar beet plant.

The services and functions of the local cooperative have been rather limited. Some additional
programs are planned, including accident insurance.
It is not intended that the local cooperatives operate
village wholesaling or retailing establishments for
farmers' needs. Their programs are restricted to
credit and the distribution of selected basic requisites to keep farmers in production through the land-
reform transition period.

Another basic necessity for maintaining agricultural production during the period of institutional
change is the development of an agricultural-extension
service to farmers. AID estimates that there were
about seven hundred extension agents in the country
in September, 1965. The government goal is to have at

least one agent for every seven to eight villages
reaching at least 80 per cent of the farmers. Even
with this standard there is a need to train more
than seven thousand extension agents in about ten
years. At present there are a number of crash programs in operation in cooperation with the national
armed services, the Extension and Development Corps,
and the Literacy Corps.

As in Venezuela, it is too early to make a
definitive appraisal of the land-reform program.
Preliminary observations may be made to indicate the
direction in which it is moving. This is important
in the appraisal of Israeli technical assistance.
The success of the land-reform program, that could
sweep away the feudal system from Iran, depends on
how soon the peasants can organize the management
of their small farms and the government establish
and execute the necessary supporting programs. Considering the small size of the holdings, about five
hectares, frequently less, and the state of the political, social, and administrative organization of
the country, the conditions for success are difficult.

The government, in its propaganda program, has
stated the economic and social aims of land reform
quite explicitly to improve the economic status of
farmers and to provide them with improved amenities.
It is still the consensus of many experts in Iran
that the aim of the land-reform program is primarily
political. The Shah has used it to steal the thunder
from opposition elements by proving more liberal and
farsighted than his political opponents. Two students
of economic planning in Iran have concluded that land
reform was a desperate step and an example of poor
planning. It was a reaction to a deteriorated situation where reform was so overdue that planned development was impossible.[7]

The physical distribution of land in the reform
program has indeed been accomplished very quickly,
particularly the second phase of the program. This
distribution has been much faster than the provision
of supporting services. There has been an insufficien

number and a lack of adequately trained people in
the CORC, in some cases even less than one supervisor for fifteen villages. The amounts of credit allotted have been too small for the production needs
of the farmer. As a result, many farmers have been
forced to make additional loans from private sources
at exorbitant rates of interest. At the same time,
because of administrative difficulties and the lack
of proper controls on the utilization of its funds,
CORC is unable to absorb all the money available to
it. For example, it received but 150 million of the
500 million rials budgeted for it in 1964 by the Plan
Organization.

     The village institutions, the cooperative soci-
ety and the council, have in their early years not
been functioning well. Lack of supervisory personnel
and the low literacy level of the members have been
contributory reasons. The function of the new village councils established in reform villages is the
collection of income taxes and their use for development and local services. These local institutions
were intended for the participation of the peasants
in community management. Partly in response to pressure from above, the villagers have elected traditional leaders to head their cooperative and council,
not because of the moral respect they command, but
because they are literate and can keep simple accounts.
The head of the village cooperative is not remunerated
for his extra duties and often accepts money for arranging a loan. Loans have not been tied in with
sound farm management plans or plans for the reorganization of the village economy. They have been,
therefore, often dissipated on personal consumption.

     The time lapse between the first and second
phases of the land reform caused landlord insecurity
and the withdrawal of investment funds from and dis-
continuance of services to their properties. They
did not maintain irrigation works, with the results
that the water dried up or was reduced. The peasants
could not repair the damage. Yet when leasing arrangements were made in the second phase of reform,
the rents requested were based on incomes when the
irrigation works were operative. Though the farmers

protested, they were forced by reform authorities to
sign such contracts. It is highly unlikely that
leasing conditions in the second phase of the reform,
often the only practical alternative for the peasant
to stay in farming, will equalize opportunities with
those of farmers benefited in the first stage of reform. They may not even represent an improvement to
their tenure arrangements in the pre-reform era.[8]

The peasants were not fully informed early in
the reform program of its purposes and operations.
Their reaction, therefore, was less than completely
enthusiastic. One study revealed that the peasants
in the program did not yet consider themselves landowners. They believed that the government was the
new landlord. The previous landlords continued to
collect their shares through bailiffs. Village councils, though formed, had not met. Development taxes
had not been collected, or, if collected, had not
been used for development. Peasants retained relations with former landlords who even helped them in
dealing with government organizations.[9]

It is impossible to evaluate the effects of
land reform on agricultural production for the entire
country. The good harvests in 1965 and 1966 were
caused primarily by favorable weather conditions.
Land payments by the farmers to the government are
often lower than the shares paid to the owners. Farmers have been able to expand production of vegetables,
forage crops, and fruits, products that were formerly
not permitted by landlords because of the difficulty
in checking production.

ISRAELI TECHNICAL ASSISTANCE

The Israeli technical-assistance project is to
plan and implement the agricultural development of
the Ghazvin area.[10] This area, east of Teheran,*

---

*The provincial capital of Ghazvin is 140 kilo-
meters east of Teheran.

includes some 378,000 hectares, and is a typical part
of the Central Iranian Plateau. The climate is semi-
arid, with an annual precipitation of eight to ten
inches. The total population of the region is 250,000
persons, of which 100,000 live in two towns. The
agricultural population as designated in the Land Reform Act is about 105,000 persons, some 22,280 families dispersed in 270 villages in the area. The
average village is quite small, containing less than
eighty families, with many containing less than forty
families. The area is well serviced by roads and
railroads to the capital and other parts of the country.

A disastrous earthquake hit the area and adjacent regions in September, 1962. Thousands of people
were killed, and a number of villages were totally
destroyed. The means of production were sharply reduced. Many sources of water were dried up, and draft
animals and flocks of sheep and goats were killed.
One third of the Ghazvin area was affected. The government decided to provide for more than immediate
relief and rehabilitation needs. It was interested
in the comprehensive planning of the agricultural development of the area so as to raise the level of
production and standard of living of its inhabitants.
This was motivated by the fact that the area was typical of the Iranian plateau as far as physical characteristics, population, standard of living, and type
of farming. Successful developmental experiments in
this area could serve as models for large regions in
other parts of the country.

The government asked Tahal, the water agency
of Israel, to act as the planning consultant. The
Tahal team started work early in 1963. It included
twenty-four specialists in the different branches
of regional development who worked with twenty-nine
Iranian specialists in corresponding fields. The
principal objectives of the team were

1. To carry out an overall reconaissance
    survey of the Ghazvin area as a basis
    for the initial planning of its develop-
    ment and for making recommendations for

later stages of planning and implementation and

2.   To plan the physical rehabilitation of
     the earthquake zone, including the de-
     tailed plans for the construction of new
     villages built in the summer of 1963.

It also investigated the possibilities for setting up demonstration plots for new crops in the
area, training peasants in improved agricultural
methods, and training Iranian technicians to implement development.

The detailed findings of the team were published
in August, 1963, by the Plan Organization as "The
Ghazvin Area Development Project Reconnaissance Report." Its principal recommendations were

1.   A substantial increase in irrigated land
     by drilling deep wells;

2.   Use of the additional water to modify
     the cropping pattern by changing from
     low value to high value crops, particu-
     larly industrial crops, vegetables, and
     fruit;

3.   The introduction of more efficient methods
     of irrigation and cultivation through
     mechanization, use of fertilizers, im-
     proved seeds, pesticides, etc.

The report also presented a working program for the
first two years of operation and recommended the
preparation of a master plan and feasibility report
for the development of the entire Ghazvin area based
on the experiences and additional data gathered in
the first two years.

The recommendations were approved by the Plan
Organization. It then made a contract with Tahal for
a permanent field team of Israeli consultants. This
field team commenced operations in March, 1964. By
1966, it included over forty specialists. The team

is assisted by the Tahal headquarters in Tel-Aviv
which sends additional experts as needed for brief
visits to the field. The agencies concerned with
regional development in Israel are consulted by Tahal, including the Settlement Department of the Jewish Agency, which has furnished many technical experts
including the team leader. Iranian specialists from
the Ministry of Agriculture and the Ministry of Water
and Power assist in the implementation of the project.
As of 1966, the Ghazvin Area Development Project comprised over five hundred persons. This number includes many nonprofessionals such as tractor operators, well operators, and mechanics. Volunteers of
the European equivalent of the Peace Corps have as-
in the implementation of projects at the village
level, living in the villages.

The work of the field team falls under four
main headings: agricultural implementation, extension, agricultural planning, and water planning. Agricultural implementation includes the operational
phases of the development projects and organizations
such as the tractor and machinery pool to service the
projects. The extension service includes agriculture
and home economics. Agricultural planning comprises
general planning for the master plan, detailed planning for current operations, and soil surveys and
analyses. Water planning involves planning for the
master plan, detailed irrigation planning for current
operations, and groundwater and well utilization.

The activities of the team have evolved within
the framework of the reconnaissance report and have
included working out a master plan and feasibility
report for the development of the entire Ghazvin area,
prepared in 1966, and the implementation of specific
developmental projects. In 1964, development implementation on peasant farms was limited to demonstration cases on selected farms where one hectare of
sugar beets was raised according to instructions.
With the implementation of the second phase of land
reform in the area in 1965, development plots were
selected and detailed planning was achieved for land
adjoining eleven villages. In addition, developmental
orchards were planted adjacent to three of these

villages. In 1966, the work was expanded to fifty-
five villages and in 1967 to ninety-two villages.

The principal aim of the project is to change
the existing traditional subsistence farming into a
modern, market-oriented, agricultural economy. The
cultivated area had in the past been mostly winter
wheat dependent on the small rainfall and the limited
water supply of an inefficient irrigation system.
The principal implementation projects are the development plots and orchards. They represent new fields
chosen among the fallow communal fields of the villages. They are irrigated from new deep wells by
modern techniques with optimum quantities of water
supplied at the optimum time. After tha land is
leveled and canals laid out, the new fields are divided into sectors in accordance with the number of
"bonehs." The boneh work group represents an indigenous labor organizational pattern originally organized for mutual assistance in irrigation and production. The number of farmers in each boneh varies and
averages about ten. Each boneh divides its land into
equal shares among its members. Working with bonehs
represents only a transitional phase. The project
intends to have farms for each family and work directly with them.

The crops raised on the plots are determined by
the agricultural planners. They include subsistence
grains, sugar beets, and other commercial and vegetable crops, some of which, chick peas and potatoes,
for example, were either little known or unknown in
the area. The agricultural development plan based on
market research is flexible to enable the adjustment
of existing and newly introduced crops. For example,
more intensive crops like vegetables will gradually
replace grains. The new crops introduced early in
the plan were relatively easy to grow. The sectors
were so arranged that the commodity plots are adjacent
to allow for the most economical use of practicable
machinery, such as tractors, and the most efficient
methods of cultivation and irrigation. Modern economical methods include utilization of improved seeds,
chemical fertilizers, pesticides, etc. Operations on
the development plots are supervised by technicians.

In 1965, the development plots included .3 hectares
of orchard and .5 hectares of field crops for each
family. These plots have since been enlarged in accordance with the master plan.

The new village fields are worked by the peasants in addition to their own private plots. The
deep wells that irrigate the new fields will gradually decrease the amount of water available from the
primitive wells used for the old private plots. In
ten years the major part of farmers' incomes will be
derived from the enlarged development plots and orchards. The orchards are maintained by project headquarters until they bear fruit, when they will be
transferred to the farmers themselves.

In addition to the development plots and orchards there are a number of other activities for the
improvement of agriculture in the area. They include
two experimental farms that raise many different crop
varieties. In addition to their demonstration and
experimental value, they provide improved seeds for
the development plots. A large tree nursery provides
the saplings for the orchards. There is a program
for pasture and sheep improvement to increase farmers'
income from livestock. It includes ameliorating
natural pasture, reseeding grasses, planting improved
shrubs, grazing control, sheep dipping, and artificial
insemination for increase of milk yields

The guidance and instruction program is aimed
at both the farmers and the Iranian project personnel.
To prepare the latter for assuming managerial responsibility professional courses are given for agronomists, agricultural technicians, orchard foremen, and
nursery technicians. Courses are also given for tractor drivers and well operators. Basic instruction
is offered farmers mainly through practical demonstration. Field days are organized for selected farmers.

The service organizations have been operated by
the project headquarters. The tractor-and agricul-
tural-equipment organization and well-operating organization were established in 1965, and the supply
and marketing and land-cultivation organizations in

1966. Other organizations, such as credit institutions, are being planned. The machinery pool includes tractors, crawlers, motor graders, and land
leveling equipment, some of which were built in Iran
for the first time under the supervision of Israeli
experts. The supply and marketing organization is
responsible for the purchase of inputs and the sale
of farm commodities. To aid in the introduction of
new crops, it has the authority to pay guaranteed
prices.

The limiting factor to agricultural development
is the availability of water. The agricultural development plan, therefore, is based on the master
plan for water development that is conceived in three
stages. The first is to 1971 and the second from
1971 to 1976. The first is based mainly on the more
intensive utilization of available groundwater, principally for the new development fields and orchards.
It is the period of conversion from existing subsistence agriculture into modern guided farming. The
early years of this period are the critical ones when
the new lands allotted to the villages will be producing alongside with the old. Yields in the old
fields may rise as the result of using modern techniques, thus adding to farmers' incomes. This facil-
itates the difficult task of transferring activities
from the old to the new lands.

The second stage is aimed at further increase
in production through an augmented water supply derived from two sources: more efficiently utilized
surface flows and a temporary overdraft of groundwater to be replaced later by diversion of water from
the Taleghan River to the north of Ghazvin. The
Taleghan River diversion is a major irrigation project serviced by Japanese consultants. As the availability of the latter source of water is not absolutely
certain, alternative plans have been worked out based
merely on additional surface flows.

Plans for the first two developmental stages
have been elaborated in considerable detail with specific crop and income goals based on two different
productivity assumptions: a conservative yield

estimate and a more liberal one as a result of improved cultural practices. Specific types of farms in the new fields have been worked out for all the zones in the area. The crop goals were based on studies of market demand, including the examination of relevant elasticities and income population projections.

The third stage of development would bring about the optimum use of all available water resources, including external sources such as the Taleghan River.

The estimate of net family income from subsistence farming in the area as of 1965 was about $178. It is calculated that net incomes will double by 1971 at the end of the first development stage. This seems a conservative estimate and does not include returns from investments in the new orchards. It is further estimated that farm incomes could approximately triple by 1976, even without overpumping. With overpumping, more land will be cultivated, and income is expected to more than triple. These estimates also do not include the returns from investment in new orchards that would add at least more than $100 of net income.

With overpumping, it is anticipated that each farm by 1976 would cultivate intensively an area of four hectares including half a hectare of orchard. In addition, it would breed a flock of ten ewes. Each farm would use an average of 26,000 cubic meters of water supplied at proper times of crop demand. This compares to over two hectares of inefficiently irrigated land in 1964.

It is difficult to assess the validity of these goals. Actual progress in 1965 and 1966 went according to plan. Yields have been good. Over $100 was added to family incomes from the new fields in the villages participating in the 1965 program.

The master plan also provides for the building of processing and cold storage plants. The processing facilities include a fruit canning and drying

plant, a vegetable dehydrating facility, a dairy,
and possibly a wool spinning plant.

Three rural centers patterned on the Israel
model to provide the area with social, economic, and
administrative service have also been planned. The
Plan Organization has been interested in financing
at least one center.

The Ghazvin project is conceived to be self-
financing. Initially, it has been financed by relatively small administrative budgets from the parent
ministries: Agriculture, Water and Power, and a development budget provided by the Plan Organization.
All services such as the tractor and machinery pool
and supply and marketing organizations are self-
supporting. It is assumed that money for investment
projects can be obtained on the basis of feasibility
reports, and calculations made in the master plan include the cost of loans. Different estimates of the
cost of the project vary from $40 to $60 million.
Total costs per family, however calculated, are considerably below settlement costs in Israel and the
Majaguas project in Venezuela.

There have been problems of the administrative
coordination of the personnel and activities of the
two parent ministries. The Israeli consultants have
recommended the creation of an autonomous Ghazvin
Development Authority with policy and program review
provided by a High Council, consisting of the Ministers of Agriculture, Water and Power, the Director
General of Plan Organization, and additional ministers
as required. They have also recommended the establishment of regional offices in the development area
with specified executive duties. This would reduce
the number of headquarters personnel, increase the
amount of work in the field, and help the eventual
transfer of project activities to Iranian personnel.
The government has agreed in principle to the establishment of an independent authority, except that
water supply activities would continue under the
jurisdiction of the Ministry of Water and Power.

EVALUATION OF THE APPLICATION OF MOSHAV PRINCIPLES

Comparison with Venezuela

There are important differences in the Israeli operation in Iran from that in Venezuela that are basic in the analysis of the application of moshav principles.

In the first place, the projects in Venezuela are primarily resettlement operations, the establishment of new settlements, or the reorganization of relatively new settlements. The peasants have voluntarily chosen to settle in the new villages. The peasant leaders are in a position of political power, have fought for agrarian reform, and represent the interests of the peasants. The reform program has the support of a cadre of national technicians and administrators who identify with the program and are sincerely attempting to implement it.

The purpose of the Israeli project in Iran is the modernization of agriculture in a large area where the peasants have been living and working for centuries under feudalistic conditions. Neither the national land-reform program nor the Ghazvin Development Project was of their doing. Both were imposed from above. The peasants suspect the intentions of both the Shah and his representatives as well as the foreign experts.

In addition, all the Israeli efforts in Iran are concentrated on one very large regional project. The differences in the nature and size of of the project and in the level of country development as compared to Venezuela result in two basic difficulties: (1) greater institutional impediments in the implementation of the development project, and (2) the necessity of a larger Israeli field team in the development area to deal with a wider scope of activities.

To a degree, the larger Israeli team in Iran is a reflection of the lack of sufficiently trained

national personnel and government services in the
agricultural sector. The larger team is also needed
because of the size of the project and because Israeli
experts have the responsibility of not only working
out the grand design, but to execute its implementation. The Israeli field team is not large in relation to its responsibility and the scope of the
project. The addition of implementation to planning
and advisory responsibilties, concentration on a very
large regional project, and greater institutional
obstacles to development make the Iran operation more
difficult than that in Venezuela.

Implementation responsibility of so large an
operation makes project organization more important.
The relation of the Israeli consultants with the
Iranian personnel has appeared to be good. The Israelis work with national counterparts in dealing with
the farmers. The Iranian nationals have been rather
slow, however, in the early years, in displaying
initiative in higher level project responsibilities.
The director of the activities of the Iranian personnel attached to the Ministry of Agriculture is in
Teheran, and makes only occasional visits to Ghazvin.
His deputy is in residence in Ghazvin, primarily occupied with representational activities. The Iranian
field professionals support the project as a practical
development effort that results in increased production and the improvement of the economic status of
the peasant. They have regarded the project, however,
as an Israeli operation. The rationale for an independent Ghazvin Development Authority is not only to
tighten the organizational structure and increase its
efficiency, but to bring about more effective responsibility and participation by national officials.

The Israel team adopted two guiding principles,
agreed to by the national authorities, for the project: (1) to deal only with peasants and not with
landlords, and (2) to aim at equality of incomes for
the farmers. There are institutional blocks that
prevent the realization of the latter principle. In
addition to the over 22,000 farm families with land
and water rights there are about 8,000 rural families
without such rights in the area. Because of legal

difficulties the latter cannot be included as bene-
ficiaries of the project. This leads to greater
inequalities in the village and represents an important exception to the moshav principal of including
all the families in village development.

The Israeli authorities utilize archaic national institutions, the boneh work group for example,
if they help project development. Each village must
approve the adoption of development fields and orchards. Obtaining the initial approval of the village in early years was difficult. The peasants
would have preferred the extra water allocation for
their regular farms. Adopting development plots on
fallow communal land was necessitated by the limited
water resources and to avoid complications with landlords. It was easier to obtain village approval and
organize the work on the new fields through the boneh
groups. Project technicians functioned as foremen
on the new irrigated fields and the boneh headmen
as team leaders. Actually the existence of boneh
groups had become quite insecure. In some villages
they were organized anew to obtain project advantages,
even though it was known that it would be difficult
to retain harmonious relations within the group. A
number of the boneh groups working on the village
developmental plots in 1965 had to be reorganized,
some as many as three times. As the project intends
to transfer from boneh to individual family plots in
the new fields when practicable, the boneh approach
can be considered an Iranian adaptation of the administered farm stage of development before parcella-
tion to family farms.

There is a high degree of centralization in
project organizations and activities. The village
cooperatives have representation in the supply and
marketing company. Yet it and the other service
organizations are direct instruments of project headquarters. The project authorities would like to use
the village cooperatives to perform project functions
at the village level. This may not be practicable.
These cooperatives often are not democratically
operated for the welfare of the farmers to further
the objectives of land reform. In addition, they are

under the jurisdiction of another government agency.
This would make reform and administrative control of
the village cooperative difficult. This situation
serves to differentiate the project organizations
and activities from the national land-reform organizations and activities. What to use and/or substitute as a precooperative at the village level as of
1968 still has to be resolved.

Critical Success Factors

Despite the greater difficulty in the application of moshav principles in Iran as compared to
Venezuela, adaptations have been made. Even though
the institutional framework is in the process of development, an evaluation of the Ghazvin Project in
terms of the critical success factors is in order.

1. Quality of leadership. At present the
project depends primarily on the leadership of the
Israeli consultants. Two types of national professionals are needed: administrators to take over
when the Israelis leave, and technicians, including
extension men and foremen, who must work directly
with the farmers. It is the opinion of the Israeli
consultants that both types can be trained.

2. Quality of supporting institutions. The
project operates almost independently of the institutions in the land-reform program. While this imposes
an additional administrative burden on the project,
implementation through organizations over which it
has control could be a facilitating factor.

3. Nationalist ideology. A strong nationalist
ideology has not yet been developed among Iranian
peasants. They are strongly suspicious of national
efforts to improve their welfare.

4. Government. The State is committed to
fundamental reform in the overhauling of the feudal
agricultural structure and the transformation of
illiterate peasantry to independent farmers. How effective its land-reform program can be in actual practice is conjectural. The Ghazvin Project can, howeve

be important in the implementation of land reform.
Despite all its efforts, the peasants have not as
yet identified with the State in its efforts to improve their conditions. The State itself is reasonably secure.

5. <u>Cooperative agricultural sector</u>. There is
no cooperative sector in Iranian agriculture. The
village cooperatives founded by the CORC to implement
the land-reform program have not been functioning effectively. If the Ghazvin Project could evolve functioning cooperative institutions it would meet with
government and public approval.

6. <u>Specialized role of peasant agriculture</u>.
Almost all the farming in the country is peasant agriculture. Only about 5 per cent of the value of output is produced on modern commercial farms. If
successful, the Ghazvin Project can transform the
agriculture of a large area into a modern, intensive,
commercial type with substantive increases in incomes
to thousands of farmers who have no alternative economic opportunities.

7. <u>Financial support</u>. Financing the project
presents no problems. Its development budget has
been based on advances by the Plan Organization. The
project has requested development loans from the World
Bank.

8. <u>Agricultural planning</u>. The land-reform
program has invalidated the operational aspects of
the national agricultural plan prepared earlier by
the Plan Organization. The Ghazvin Project, however,
can be an important tool in achieving its main objectives of increases in production and farm incomes.

9. <u>General economic conditions</u>. Despite increases in the national GNP the pace of industrialization allows but limited economic outlets in the
cities for the preponderantly rural population. The
income goals at Ghazvin, though relatively modest,
would represent a very substantive achievement in the
Iranian environment.

10. <u>Land tenure</u>. The Ghazvin Project is based
on the use of formerly fallow communal lands. This
reduces the former peasant holdings, whether privately owned or operated on a long-term lease, to a secondary role. Tenure does not represent a problem on
the new development fields.

11. <u>Support of moshav</u>. The Iranian adaptation
of the moshav is not favored over other agricultural
structures. The Ghazvin Project has been in the form
of a pilot regional project for the implementation of
the national land-reform program.

12. Size of country. As in Venezuela, the
large size of the country limits the application of
moshav principles to a regional scale. The Ghazvin
area is very large, and if the waters of the Taleghan
River are diverted to it, the area may be enlarged.
If the project is successful it would have an important national impact.

As for the size of the market, the output goals
of the Ghazvin Project have been made based on market
surveys and projections of consumer demand. The additional production can be profitably marketed.

<u>Endogenous factors</u>. Because of the higher rate
of illiteracy and the lack of representation in the
political power structure at either local or national
levels, obtaining the confidence of the project participants has been more difficult in Iran than in
Venezuela or Israel. The project has represented a
complete reorganization of the economic life of illiterate peasants from a highly traditional society.
They have been confused and uneasy about the rapidity
of the change and did not completely understand it.
After all these centuries, why has the Shah suddenly
become interested in their welfare, and why should
foreign non-Moslem experts be in charge of the program of change? The foreigners, of course, have ap-
proached the peasants through national civil servants
who are also suspect. The Israeli consultants are
cognizant of this difficulty and have been trying to
overcome the credibility gap.

The Israeli advisors have not adopted a doc-
trinaire attitude on the application of the moshav
principles in the Iranian environment. While pro-
gressing quickly on production planning and the agro-
technical phases, they have proceeded with caution
in the establishment of supporting institutions. The
marketing organization was not established for the
1965 operations. The villages that were to cooperate
in the new development fields were chosen in the fall
of 1964, and it was explained to them that for 1965
only the yield was to be divided on a 50 per cent
basis until the cost of development operations could
be calculated, when, as it seemed probable, a refund
would be coming to the farmers. Thus in the first
year of operations the project acted as a landlord,
and the farmers did not believe they would be given
half of the yield. Actually operations went according to plan, and by 1966 the land cultivation and
supply-marketing organizations were established.

Concentration on a one large regional project
in Iran as compared to the multi-project approach in
Venezuela has limited administrative flexibility and
experimentation. In addition, faults in its organizational structure, the delay in approval of the
Ghazvin Development Authority as an autonomous organization, has also been a restraining factor in the
application of moshav principles.

The rationalization of small family farms in
Iran is consistent with the economic and social ideologies prevalent in the country. Its consistency with
political ideology is less clear. The official ideology of the land-reform program is to break the power
of the landlords and to create an independent peasantry. No substantive changes have been made in the
political structure to reflect the new position of
the peasant. As far as the Ghazvin Project is concerned, the welfare of the individual farm family in
the context of the village as a whole is the aim of
all planning and implementation activity. Working
with the boneh work group, as already indicated,
represents a transitional phase.

As in Israel and Venezuela, the application of moshav principles in Iran is a method of integrating individualism in an accepted cooperative community pattern. Despite all the difficulties in communication with the peasants and the lack of adequate village cooperatives and regional centers, production in the difficult initial years was according to plan. This initial progress in itself can be helpful in developing better institutions and improved cooperation.

A sociological investigation made in late 1965 based on a sample of four villages concluded that the villages had not yet really identified themselves with the project.[11] They still regarded it as an objective to which they had to adapt, whether it was good or bad. Actually this same condition prevailed in the early years of the moshav olim in Israel, especially with the immigrants from Moslem countries. The report concluded that the farmers be given more information and an opportunity to express their opinions through a consultive public body for the development area.

The Project Administrator and key staff were aware of these problems and how they were dealt with in Israel. Steps have been taken for their solution at Ghazvin. Much more attention has been given to dissemination of information to farmers to explain basic policy decisions. For example, provisions for the establishment of the market supply company included an educational program for explaining its operation and for discussion of problems with the farmers. A consultive public body for the development area would be practical once approval of independent authority status for the project is given. This would be a forward step in the adaptation of project policy and institutions to the social complexity of the village.

The choice of the area was dictated by the earthquake. By strictly economic criteria, it would have been wiser to concentrate agricultural development planning in more fertile agricultural areas of the country in accordance with recommendations of the

national economic plan. The Central Iranian Plateau
will probably remain, however, an agricultural area
for some time to come, and the Ghazvin Project can
be important as a pilot project for its development.

The experiences of the early years and the
change in project organization making it an autonomous regional authority, even though the organization
will not include all project activities, should help
operations in coming years. Improving the relation
of project personnel with farmers to modify authoritarian and patronizing attitudes, an improved two-way
communication system with farmers, and their increased
participation in project activities are part of the
current program. If the dynamism of physical development is matched by improvement in implemental organizations and services, the project can be a success
in fulfilling its goal as a guided pilot program for
agricultural development and modernization.

NOTES

1. The statistical information, from a variety
of sources, has been checked with the Plan Organization, the national agency responsible for the planning
and coordination of economic development.

2. Donald N. Wilbur, <u>Contemporary Iran</u> (New
York: Praeger, 1963), p. 46.

3. Nikki R. Kedie, "Historical Obstacles to
Agrarian Change in Iran," Claremont University Asian
Studies No. 8, 1960.

4. Unless otherwise indicated the statistics
in this section were obtained from the Plan Organization, the Land Reform Organization, and the Central
Organization for Rural Cooperatives.

5. An additional 17,582 villages had been added
by December, 1968, according to the <u>New York Times</u>,
December 9, 1968, p. 72.

6. <u>New York Times</u>, December 9, 1968, p. 72.

7.   Bjorn Olsen and Norregaard Rasmussen, "Planning and Development in Iran," 1962.   (Mimeographed.)

8.   Benno Sternberg, Traditional Society and Development in the Ghazvin Plain Villages (Teheran: Institute of Social Study and Research, University of Teheran, 1966), p. 10.

9.   "Rural Economic Problems of Khuzistan," Quarterly Journal, Institute of Economic Research (University of Teheran, August, 1965), pp. 153-222.

10.   All data obtained from visit and files of Ghazvin Area Development Project.

11.   Sternberg, op. cit.

CHAPTER **12** TRANSFERABILITY
OF MOSHAV FOR
AGRICULTURAL
DEVELOPMENT

RELEVANCE OF VENEZUELAN AND IRANIAN CASES

Venezuela and Iran represent but two specific
cases of the application of moshav principles to particular conditions. Yet these country examples have
much to offer for the analysis of the general applicability of moshav principles for agricultural development in other countries. In the first place, they
include a wide variety of different types of projects,
from a simplified pattern of dry farming in a single
village to a large area project with all its basic
infrastructure, including a complex irrigation system. Second, the activities of the foreign consultants range from few experts in Venezuela, concerned
with training and advising national officials, to a
much larger group in Iran who, in addition, work out
the long-term and current plans and policies, arrange
for outside financing, and bear the operational responsibility for implementation of a very large regional project. Third, the work in Venezuela is
concerned principally with resettlement projects in
the framework of the national land-reform program.
That in Iran, on the other hand, concerns modernizing
the agriculture of a region and working with illiterate peasants who had been living in the villages and
farming for centuries.

Two features are common to both countries. The
first is the availability of considerable national
revenues for agricultural development from petroleum
royalties. Second, the agricultural sector represents a relatively closed economy. It does not have

to depend on agricultural exports for its development.
These two features do not make these two countries
unique as far as the application of moshav principles
for development is concerned. They are important facilitating factors on the financing of development.
Agricultural development projects in both countries,
however, include substantial grants, loans, and technical assistance from outside sources. Additional
sources of foreign financial assistance will be needed for the continuation of the application of moshav
principles in these countries.

A number of generalizations can be made based
on the relatively brief experience in the application
of moshav principles in Venezuela and Iran.

First, there is considerable flexibility in the
application of moshav principles to meet different
project goals, varying sizes and types of projects,
and different environments, that is, to meet the development needs of farmers from varied cultural backgrounds and countries in different levels of economic
development. The goals vary from relatively quick,
large increases in farm incomes in Venezuela to more
modest, somewhat slower increases in Iran. As to the
development environment, Iran and Venezuela represent
the two extremes of category, two in Galbraithian
growth classification: Iran, the bottom, and Venezuela, the top.

Second, while it is early to make final judg-
ment on the success of individual projects in the
two countries, the supervised credit program in Venezuela has had excellent results. It does not follow, however, that application of moshav principles
in the form of supervised credit programs can, therefore be applied willy-nilly to other countries. An
analysis of the reasons for good performance is
needed.

The basic reason for early success in Venezuela
was that most of the elements of the development package were present: inputs including credit, guaranteed
prices, marketing outlets, and a village council. In
addition, physical planning of the village and farm

plots had been completed. All that was lacking was
a village farm plan and administrative know-how to
implement the plan in using existing facilities. The
Israeli advisors acted as catalytic agents in training and helping national officials prepare plans and
implement them. The village supervised credit program represents the easiest example of the application of moshav principles. Where the basic conditions
for success obtain, this type of project seems practical for export to other countries.

Third, the application of moshav principles is
much easier when the role of foreign experts is limited to a training and advisory capacity. In this
respect the application of moshav principles was facilitated in Venezuela. Because of the scope of the
project and the lack of trained national professionals, the Israeli consultants in Iran had to assume
implementation responsibility under somewhat less
than ideal conditions. Transfer of authority to local
staff may be a problem.

Fourth, the application of moshav principles is
easier in resettlement projects than modernization
in situ, that is, working with farmers who had lived
in the area for some time. Resettlement projects,
however, still have considerable difficulties. But
dealing with settlers who have voluntarily moved to
a new area lessens many institutional problems.

Fifth, size is an important factor in regional
agricultural development projects. The larger the
project, the more important the demand on relatively
scarce administrative resources, which, in turn, enhances the role of organizational structures in meeting the greater need for administrative efficiency.
This may seem to be contrary to the economic rationalization of moshav principles with the organizational
superstructure for planning-implementation under cost-
benefit types of analyses. If the regional project
requires heavy capital investment, special irrigation
facilities, for example, the guided moshav approach
may be justified on the basis of performance, the
value of the resultant increase in output. With
heavy fixed expenses a larger project with more output
would seem more economic than a smaller.

The most rational organizational structure for a large regional project is an autonomous regional organization that would have the most effective control of its personnel. It may be impossible to achieve this organization in practice. It could not be obtained in Venezuela, and in Iran the organization does not include all project activities. Size is a definite factor in the better performance of the smaller Cojedes regional project in Venezuela as compared to Majagues, even though many other factors were also important, particularly better soils and better settlers.

Sixth, application of moshav principles will concentrate more on agricultural and economic goals than in Israel, at least in the early years. This does not mean that social and political goals are completely overlooked. The regional projects in Venezuela will definitely have rural centers that will provide social amenities, and the Iran project may have them. Nevertheless, the moshav package in both cases is likely to include fewer social and political services than in Israel.

This does not mean that social considerations are less important to the projects in these two countries than in Israel. Peasant motivation and identification with his project are basic wherever moshav principles are applied, particularly because of the emphasis on guidance for modernization. This makes the role of an adequate two-way communications system a basic ingredient for success.

In this respect also Venezuela has been easier for the application of moshav principles than Iran. There is no or very little social stratification in the new reform villages. The village council serves as an instrument for free expression. It is also able with available guidance to perform local services such as conducting a village store and credit union. Social services including housing and sanitation facilities are much more effectively supplied by public agencies in Venezuela as compared to Iran. In both countries there is a substantial literacy program. More has been done in the provision of schools in Venezuela, and the literacy level and the adaptive qualities of village leaders is higher.

As indicated, rural centers are included in the regional projects in both countries. It is likely that economic-service activities, such as processing and supply facilities, will have high priority in the centers. Schools and recreational facilities, however, will be provided in the regional centers in Venezuela. No great administrative difficulties are foreseen in supplying social services if settlement proceeds according to plan.

CONCLUSIONS

Referring again to the Galbraithian development classification, the role for the application of moshav principles, as already noted, is limited in category 1 and category 3 countries. In category 1 countries administration is the limiting factor, although there are also market limitations because of the low level of demand. In category 3 countries, such as India and Pakistan, the limiting factor is the size of holdings. A somewhat looser and possibly less costly arrangement for the provision of basic inputs and services, such as the Ford Foundation package program, may be more relevant as an alternative approach to development through small family-sized farms.

Even where applicable, as in category 2 countries, the moshav, representing a form of organization for family-sized farms, is but one of a number of possible organizational structures for agricultural development. Other possible forms for development are large centrally managed farms, either collectives or quasi-collectives, where the land is owned by the government agency, or some form of State farm where the farmers are reduced to the role of laborers. Another possible alternative is the large commercial farm. These may represent family farms, or farms operated by nonresident landlords, business men, or business corporations.

In the latifundia-minifundia syndrome in Latin American countries the governments face a policy decision whether to promote a more efficient commercial agriculture on large private holdings or to organize and improve peasant farming on small holdings. This is primarily a political decision. Land reform has usually been a political instrument to placate the peasants, often without effective implementation to improve their economic lot. Land reform in Venezuela has been more effective than in most other countries in the region. The commercial sector, nevertheless, has accounted for a large share of the increase in production in recent years, primarily in response to government policies.

The pressure for land reform in some countries has led to resettlement projects in new areas. Private commercial development activities are not forthcoming in new areas without basic infrastructure. Where the new development is made on a regional basis with large capital investment, in connection with a large irrigation project, for example, and where it is desired to settle as many peasants as possible, the moshav approach of guided, small, intensive family farms may well be the most applicable. Thus, for example, the development area to be serviced by the Aswan Dam in Egypt may be practical for the application of moshav principles.

There are both positive and negative reasons for the rationalization of large regional development projects. The positive reasons are that heavy capital investments including complex irrigation schemes necessitate careful development planning, the integration of planning and implementation, and guidance of peasant operations. The negative reason is that without integrated planning and implementation and the provision to farmers of the details of the developmental-package project investments will be wasted. There are numerous examples of such waste in many countries throughout the world.

The rationalization for the application of moshav principles in regional, agricultural, in situ projects such as Ghazvin in Iran is similar to the

regional resettlement projects. Here too the need
for integrated planning and implementation and the
guided development of agricultural operations makes
the moshav approach applicable.

The time dimension also represents an important
factor in the applicability of the moshav approach.
Where fast development is desired for economic, political, and/or social reasons there may be a strong
case for the moshav way of guided development. Governments frequently talk of quick development in response to economic, political, and social pressures,
but the methods of implementation leave much to be
desired. Israel wanted quick development to integrate
the new Oriental immigrant farmers in the economic
mainstream of the country. It seems to have achieved
this goal with the moshav in a period of about fifteen years. Venezuela wanted quick development to
implement land reform effectively and thus halt the
threat of peasant support of Communism. The moshav
may be an instrument to achieve these goals.

Is the moshav approach to large-scale regional
projects too complicated administratively for the
development milieu? Should the Majaguas project in
Venezuela prove a failure it may be that the bad initial planning by the Venezuelan authorities in choosing the site and in laying out the irrigation network
may be more responsible than the administrative difficulties, although there certainly are such difficulties. Here the moshav approach not only bears the
responsibility for the development of a large area but
has had to overcome earlier mistakes made in the location and planning of the irrigation project. It
may well be that combination of smaller regional
projects or individual projects in a regional context
can achieve better results than large regional projects.

The promotion of peasant farming under land reform may compete with a well organized private commercial sector, as in many countries in Latin America.
Services organized for the commercial sector can be
used for the peasant sector. Venezuela is an example
where the experience in public policy for the

protection and promotion of national agriculture has
helped the application of moshav principles. Despite
conflicts of interests, supporting services in extension, credit, price policies, and marketing have been
offered for such implementation. The same pattern
could prevail in other countries with such supporting
services.

Existing institutions may not be effectively
organized or used for the implementation of land reform or agricultural development. Under such conditions a simplified application of moshav principles,
such as the village credit program, can be effective,
and the moshav approach can compete on an economic
basis with alternative approaches for the support
and modernization of peasant farming.

The moshav approach under the village-supervised
credit program is both cheaper and more effective than
the single farm supervised credit programs supported
by AID. The benefits, both economic and social, are
considerably greater since they are based on the village as a unit. There is little added expense, if
any, over and above the usual implementation costs of
the land-reform program.

In addition, combining village projects in a
region allows more economic and effective administration and the introduction of regional operations in
the supply of inputs and the marketing and processing
of outputs. This is a way of extending village projects to a regional basis. This method of expansion
is succeeding in Venezuela.

The mix of different types of village and regional projects in Venezuela is being followed with
considerable interest by Latin American countries.
A number, including Chile, Peru, and Colombia, have
contracted for Israeli technical-assistance experts.
It is quite possible that integrated micro planning
on a village basis, and village-supervised credit
programs would be applicable in the Chilean land-
reform program. Work along these lines has already
been started. The application of moshav principles
for agricultural development may be promising in many

countries in Latin America for the implementation of
land-reform and agricultural-development programs.
The critical success factors vary considerably from
one country to another, and the circumstances for
possible success would have to be carefully examined
in each.

The first of the moshav principles, comprehensive, coordinated, and integrated planning, rests on
the package approach to development. Complementary
as opposed to activity concentration has been ques-
tioned in planning agricultural-development strategy.
It seems that those who are directly concerned with
the implementation of development favor the complementary approach while some, primarily concerned with
economic research, are more critical. The package,
complementary approach, however, has gained wider
acceptance in recent years.

The evidence indicates that the moshav approach,
under certain circumstances, can provide an effective
developmental package integrating planning and implementation, particularly in category 2 countries and
inthe framework of national land-reform and agricultural-development programs. It can be most effective
where there is an urgent desire for agricultural development in a relatively short period of time. The
application of moshav principles can be a factor in
increasing food supplies, modernizing peasant agriculture, raising rural incomes, and improving the
amenities of rural life.

Cooperatives represent an important part of the
moshav structure that can be used for agricultural
development. The cooperatives, whether village or regional, in the developing environment are not based
on the Western European/North American model. They
will need a considerable amount of guidance by the
State or some public agency similar to the moshav
olim in Israel.

BIBLIOGRAPHY

PUBLIC DOCUMENTS

Food and Agriculture Organization of the United Nations. <u>The State of Food and Agriculture</u>.
1965-68.

Food and Agriculture Organization of the United Nations. <u>Third World Food Survey</u>. Freedom from
Hunger Campaign Basic Study, No. 11. 1963.

Iran. Plan Organization. <u>Third Plan Frame for Agri-
culture</u>. June, 1961.

Israel. Agriculture and Settlement-Planning and
Development Center. <u>Agricultural Plan 1965/66</u>.
March, 1965. (In Hebrew.)

Israel. Agriculture and Settlement-Planning and
Development Center. <u>The Balance of Land and
Water</u>. 1955. (In Hebrew.)

Israel. Agriculture and Settlement-Planning and
Development Center. <u>Five Year Plan for
Israel's Agriculture 1964/65-1968/69</u>. April,
1965.

Israel. Bank of Israel. <u>Annual Reports</u>. 1964-66.

Israel. Central Bureau of Statistics. <u>National Income Originating in Israel's Agriculture,
1952-63</u>. 1964.

Israel. Central Bureau of Statistics. <u>The Settlements of Israel,</u> Part I. Population and
Housing Census 1961, Publication No. 10. 1963.

Israel. Central Bureau of Statistics. <u>Statistical
Abstract of Israel</u>. 1964-68.

U.S. Department of Agriculture. Agricultural Poli-
    cies of Foreign Governments. Agricultural
    Handbook No. 132. March, 1964.

U.S. Department of Agriculture. Notes on the Agri-
    cultural Economies of the 20 Latin American
    Republics. Economic Research Service. July,
    1961.

Venezuela. Agricultural and Livestock Bank. Annual
    Report. 1964. (In Spanish.)

Venezuela. Agricultural and Livestock Bank. Agri-
    cultural Credit in Venezuela. February, 1965.
    (In Spanish.)

Venezuela. Center for Training and Applied Research
    in Land Reform. Annual Reports. 1965-67.
    (In Spanish.)

Venezuela. Central Office of Coordination and Plan-
    ning. National Plan 1965-68, Agricultural
    Program. October, 1965. (In Spanish.)

Venezuela. Land Reform Law. Official Gazette 611,
    March 19, 1960. (In Spanish.)

Venezuela. Ministry of Public Works. The Majaguas
    Plan. August, 1965. (In Spanish.)

Venezuela. National Agrarian Institute. Annual Re-
    ports. 1964-67. (In Spanish.)

Venezuela. National Agrarian Institute. Operational
    Plan of Supervised Credit 1968. (In Spanish.)

Venezuela. National Agrarian Institute. Land Reform
    1959-63. November, 1964. (In Spanish.)

BOOKS

Akzin, Benjamin and Dror, Yehezkial. Israel: High-
    Pressure Planning. Syracuse: Syracuse Uni-
    versity Press, 1966.

Alminana, M. et al. Long-Term Forecasts of the
      Supply and Demand of Agricultural and Livestock
      Products in Venezuela. Jerusalem: Israel
      Program for Scientific Translations, 1965.

Asaaf, A. The Moshav Ovdim in Israel. Tel-Aviv:
      Moshav Movement Publications, 1953. (In
      Hebrew.)

Ben-David, Joseph, ed. Agricultural Planning and
      Village Community in Israel. Paris: UNESCO,
      1964.

Chorin, Yehuda. Agricultural Labor Movement in
      Israel. Tel-Aviv: Agricultural Workers'
      Organization in Israel, 1961.

Darin-Drabkin, Haim. Patterns of Cooperative Agri-
      culture in Israel. Tel-Aviv: Israel Ministry
      of Foreign Affairs, 1962.

Dayan, Shmuel. Moshav Ovdim. Tel-Aviv: Youth
      Department of World Zionist Organization, 1947.

Digby, Margaret. Cooperative Land Use. Oxford:
      Basil Blackwell, 1963.

Emelianoff, Ivan V. Economic Theory of Cooperation.
      Washington, D.C.: Ivan V. Emelianoff, 1942.

Gaitskill, Arthur. Gezira, A Story of Development
      in the Sudan. London: Faber and Faber, 1959.

Gittinger, J. Price. Planning for Agricultural De-
      velopment: The Iranian Experience. Washing-
      ton, D.C.: National Planning Association, 1965.

Granot, Avraham. Agrarian Reform and the Record of
      Israel. London: Eyre and Spottiswoode, 1956.

_____ . The Land System in Palestine.
      London: Eyre and Spottiswoode, 1952.

Halperin, Haim. Agrindus. London: Routledge and
      Kegan, 1963.

_____. Changing Patterns in Israel Agricul-
ture. London: Routledge and Kegan, 1957.

_____, and Yaron, Dov. Moshvei Olim: Survey
of Immigrant Villages in Israel. Rehovot:
Hebrew University, 1957. (In Hebrew.)

Jacoby, Erich H. Evaluation of Agrarian Structures
and Agrarian Reform Programs. Rome: FAO, 1966.

Kanovsky, Eliyahu. The Economy of the Israeli
Kibbutz. Cambridge: Harvard University Press,
1966.

Korn, Itzhak. Cooperative Farming in Israel. Tel-
Aviv: Histadrut, 1952.

Kreinen, Mordecai E. Israel and Africa: A Study
in Technical Cooperation. New York: Praeger,
1964.

Labes, Emanual. Handbook of the Moshav. Jerusalem:
Youth Department of the World Zionist Organization, 1962.

Malkosh, Noah. Cooperation in Israel. Tel-Aviv:
Histadrut, 1963.

Mellor, John W. Economics of Agricultural Development. Ithaca, New York: Cornell University
Press, 1966.

Millikan, Max F. and Hapgood, David. No Easy Harvest.
Boston: Little, Brown, and Co., 1967.

Mosher, Arthur T. Getting Agriculture Moving. New
York: Praeger, 1966.

Mundlak, Yair. An Economic Analysis of Established
Family Farms in Israel, 1953-58. Jerusalem:
Falk Project for Economic Research in Israel,
1964.

_____. Long-Term Projections of Supply and
Demand for Agricultural Products in Israel:

General View and Summary. Jerusalem: Falk
Project for Economic Research in Israel, 1964.

Orni, Efraim. Forms of Settlement. Jerusalem: Youth
Department of World Zionist Organization, 1963.

Patinkin, Don. The Israel Economy: The First Decade.
Jerusalem: Falk Project for Economic Research
in Israel, 1960.

Pinto Cohen, Gustav. Agriculture and Development:
The Case of Venezuela. Caracas: Center of
Development Studies, 1966. (In Spanish.)

Roy, Paul Ewell. Cooperatives: Today and Tomorrow.
Danville, Illinois: Interstate Printers and
Publishers, 1964.

Safran, Nadav. Israel Today: A Profile. New York:
Foreign Policy Association, 1965.

_____ . The United States and Israel. Cambridge: Harvard University Press, 1963.

Schickele, Rainer. Agrarian Revolution and Economic
Progress. New York: Praeger, 1968.

Seligman, I. G. Leadership in a New Nation: Political
Development in Israel. New York: Alberton
Press, 1964.

Shatil, I. The Economy of the Communal Settlements
in Israel. Tel-Aviv: Sifriat Po'alim, 1953.
(In Hebrew.)

Southworth, Herman M. and Johnston, Bruce F., eds.
Agricultural Development and Economic Growth.
Ithaca, New York: Cornell University Press,
1967.

The Economic Development of Venezuela. International
Bank for Reconstruction and Development. Bal-
timore: Johns Hopkins Press, 1961.

Weingrod, Alex. Reluctant Pioneers: Village Devel-
    opment in Israel. Ithaca, New York: Cornell
    University Press, 1966.

Weitz, Ranaan and Rokach, Avshalom. Agricultural
    Development: Planning and Implementation.
    New York: Praeger, 1968.

Weitz, Ranaan. Agricultural and Rural Development
    in Israel: Projection and Planning. Rehovot:
    University, 1963.

Wilbur, D. N. Contemporary Iran. New York: Praeger,
    1963.

                    ARTICLES AND PERIODICALS

Aizsilnieks, Arnolds P. "Farmer Cooperatives and
    Economic Welfare--A Reply," Journal of Farm
    Economics, XXXIV (August, 1952), 400-03.

_____ . "A Final Word on Coopera-
    tives," Journal of Farm Economics, XXXIV
    (November, 1952), 563-66.

Aresvik, Oddvar. "Comments on 'Economic Nature of
    the Cooperative Association'," Journal of
    Farm Economics, XXXVII (February, 1955),
    140-44.

Barter, P. G. H. "The Implementation of Agricultural
    Plans." In FAO Agricultural Planning Studies
    No. 3, Lectures on Agricultural Planning De-
    livered at the FAO Near East Regional Training
    Center on Agricultural Development Planning.
    Rome: FAO, 1963, 172-80.

Clark, Eugene. "Farmer Cooperatives and Economic
    Welfare," Journal of Farm Economics, XXXIV
    (February, 1952), 35-51.

_____ . "Farmer Cooperatives and Economic
    Welfare--Rejoinder," Journal of Farm Economics,
    XXXIV (August, 1952), 404-07.

"Cooperation in Israel 1964," Monthly Review of the
    Ministry of Labor, Israel, August, 1965, 255-67.
    (In Hebrew.)

Don, Yehuda.   "Adaptation of Cooperatives to Economic
    Changes," Journal of Farm Economics, XLIX
    (February, 1967), 119-30.

Dovring, Folke.   "The Share of Agriculture in a
    Growing Population," FAO Monthly Bulletin of
    Agricultural Economics and Statistics, VIII
    (August-September, 1959), 1-11.

Drayton, Leslie E.   "Cooperatives and Economic Welfare,"
    Journal of Farm Economics, XXXIV (November,
    1952), 555-57.

Falcon, Walter P.   "Farmers' Response to Price in a
    Subsistence Economy: The Case of West Pakistan,"
    American Economic Review, LIV (May, 1964), 580-
    91.

Feder, Ernest.   "Land Reform Under the Alliance for
    Progress," Journal of Farm Economics, XLVII
    (August, 1965), 652-58.

Gevirtz, Y.   "Rural Local Government in Israel,"
    The Settler, VII (Winter-Spring, 1964-65).

Giselson, Conrad.   "Cooperatives and Resource Allo-
    cation," Journal of Farm Economics, XXXIV
    (November, 1952), 558-63.

Helmberger, Peter G.   "Cooperative Enterprise as a
    Structural Dimension of Farm Markets," Journal
    of Farm Economics, XLVI (August, 1964), 603-17.

_____ , and Hoos, Sydney.   "Cooperative
    Enterprise and Organization Theory," Journal
    of Farm Economics, XLIV (May, 1962), 275-90.

Jerusalem Post. Weekly Overseas Edition, June 10,
    1966, and June 17, 1966.

Johnson, Sherman E.   "Combining Knowledge, Incentive,
        and Means to Accelerate Agricultural Develop-
        ment," 209-23.   In Economic Development of
        Agriculture. Ames, Iowa: Iowa State University
        Press. 1965.

Johnston, Bruce F. and Mellor, John W.   "The Role
        of Agriculture in Economic Development,"
        American Economic Review, LI (September, 1961),
        566-93.

Kanel, D.   "Size of Farm and Economic Development,"
        Land Tenure Center Reprint 31, Madison: Uni-
        versity of Wisconsin, 1967.

Keddie, Nikki R.   "Historical Obstacles to Agrarian
        Change in Iran," Claremont Asian Studies, No.
        8.   Claremont, Cal.:   Society for Oriental
        Studies, 1960.

Landau, Yehuda H.   "Rural Regional Development in
        Israel," Agriculture and Settlement-Planning
        and Development Center, Tel-Aviv, 1965.

Long, Ervin J.   "The Economic Basis of Land Reform
        in Underdeveloped Countries," Land Economics,
        XXXVII (May, 1961), 113-23.

Lowe, Yehuda.   "Economic Analysis of Established
        Family Farms in 1959/60," Israel Ministry of
        Agriculture.   April, 1962.

_____.   "Kibbutz and Moshav in Israel: An
        Economic Study."   In International Explorations
        of Agricultural Economics, Dixey, R. N., ed.
        Ames, Iowa: Iowa State University Press, 1964.

_____, and Remer, Y.   "Profitability of Estab-
        Moshavim in 1958/59 Compared to Former Years,"
        Israel Ministry of Agriculture, 1960.

Mehdevi, A. S.   "Iran Celebrates a 2,500th Birthday,"
        New York Times Magazine, November 31, 1965.

Mellor, John W.   "Production Problems and Issues in
     Agricultural Development," Journal of Farm
     Economics, XLVIII (December, 1966), 1195-1209.

Myrdal, Gunnar.   "The United Nations, Agriculture,
     and the World Economic Revolution," Journal
     of Farm Economics, XLVII (November, 1965),
     889-99.

New York Times, December 9, 1968, p. 71.

Osorio, A. M.   "Venezuelan Agriculture and the Eco-
     nomic Development of the Country and Land
     Reform," Politics, IV (August-September, 1965),
     35-46.   (In Spanish.)

Parsons, Kenneth H.   "The Transformation of Tradition-
     al Agriculture," Land Economics, XLII (February,
     1966), 112-117.

Phillips, Richard.   "Economic Nature of the Coopera-
     tive Association," Journal of Farm Economics,
     XXXV (February, 1953), 74-87.

Powell, John O.   "The Role of the Federación Campesina
     in the Venezuelan Agrarian Reform Process,"
     Research Paper 26, Land Tenure Center, Univer-
     sity of Wisconsin, December, 1967.

Robotka, Frank.   "A Theory of Cooperation," Journal
     of Farm Economics, XXIX (February, 1947), 94-
     114.

"Rural Economic Problems of Khuzistan," Tahqiqat
     Eqtesadi, Quarterly Journal of Economic Research,
     III (August, 1963), 153-222.

Ruttan, Vernon W.   "Equity and Productivity Objectives
     in Agrarian Reform Legislation: Perspectives
     on the New Philippine Land Reform Code," Indian
     Journal of Agricultural Economics, XIX, 114-30.

Sadan, Ezra.   "Cooperative Settlements in Israel:
     Problems of Resource Allocation," Journal of
     Farm Economics, XLV (August, 1963), 547-62.

Savage, Job K. "Comment on 'Economic Nature of the
     Cooperative Association'," Journal of Farm
     Economics, XXXVI (August, 1954), 529-534.

Schickele, Rainer. "Land Economics Research for
     World Agricultural Development." In Land
     Economic Research, Ackerman, J. et al., eds.
     Baltimore: Johns Hopkins Press, 1961.

_____ . "Resettlement Problems and Poli-
     cies." Netherlands Journal of Agricultural
     Science, V (November, 1957), 239-54.

Shine, J. "Regional Councils," The Settler, V
     (Spring-Summer, 1964).

Verlinsky, N. "Tnuva, the Cooperative Marketing
     Society for Agricultural Produce," Afro-Asian
     Institute for Labor Studies and Cooperation,
     Tel-Aviv. Undated.

Weingrod, Alec. "Administered Communities: Some
     Characteristics of New Immigrant Villages in
     Israel," Economic Development and Cultural
     Change, XI (October, 1962), 69-84.

_____ . "Reciprocal Change: A Case Study
     of a Moroccan Immigrant Village in Israel,"
     American Anthropologist, LXIV (February, 1962),
     115-31.

Weintraub, Dov. "A Study of New Farmers in Israel,"
     Sociologia Ruralis, IV (1964), 1-51.

Weitz, Raanan. "Economic, Organizational, and Social
     Problems of Family Farms," National and Univer-
     sity Institute of Agriculture, Rehovot, 1961.

_____ . "Family Farms vs. Large-Scale Farms
     in Rural Development," Artha Vijnana, V
     (September, 1963), 225-40.

_____ . "Rural Development Through Regional
     Planning in Israel," Journal of Farm Economics,
     XLVII (August, 1965), 634-51.

Wells, Jerome C.   "The Israeli Moshav in Nigeria,"
     Journal of Farm Economics, XLVIII (May, 1966),
     279-94.

Willner, Dorothy. "Politics and Change in Israel:
     The Case of Land Settlement," Human Organiza-
     tion, XXIV (Spring, 1965), 65-72.

                         REPORTS

Adeyemo, D. D., Ezem, R. S., Fanimokun, D. O., and
     Olaniran, O. Organization and Management of
     Farm Settlements in Israel. Report to Foreign
     Training Department, Agricultural Extension
     Service, Ministry of Agriculture, Israel, 1964.

Barkai, Haim. The Public, Histadrut, and Private
     Sectors in the Israeli Economy. Sixth Report
     by the Falk Project for Economic Research in
     Israel. Jerusalem: Falk Project for Economic
     Research in Israel, 1964.

Central Office of Coordination and Planning, Venezuela.
     Report on Project for the Integral Development
     of Majaguas. Caracas, 1962. (In Spanish.)

Committee for Joint Agricultural Planning, Israel.
     The Settlement of the Land. Report of the
     Committee for Joint Agricultural Planning.
     Rehovot, 1960. (In Hebrew.)

Eisenstadt, S. N., Lissak, M., and Weintraub, D.
     Comparative Analysis of Processes of Agricul-
     tural Development and Modernization. Jerusa-
     lem: Hebrew University, 1966. (Mimeographed.)

Gil, Benjamin. Settlement of New Immigrants in
     Israel, 1948-1953. Joint Report of Falk
     Project for Economic Research in Israel and
     Central Bureau of Statistics. Jerusalem:
     Central Bureau of Statistics, 1957. (In
     Hebrew.)

Hamashbir Hamerkazi, Ltd. Report of the Israel
    Cooperative Wholesale Society, 1964. Tel-
    Aviv, 1965.

Fritzle, Charles. Planning Agricultural Development
    in Tropical Zones with Special Reference to
    Introduction of New Crops. FAO Report to
    Government of Venezuela. Rome: Food and Agri-
    culture Organization of the United Nations,
    1965.

Jewish Agency. The Agricultural Settlement Depart-
    ment. Reprint from Reports for the period
    April, 1960-March, 1964, submitted to Twenty-
    Sixth Zionist Congress. Jerusalem: Jewish
    Agency, November, 1964.

Ministry of Labor, Registrar of Cooperative Societies.
    Report on Cooperative Movement in Israel, 1963.
    Tel-Aviv, Afro-Asian Institute, 1964.

Nahalal, Its Formation, Way, Work. Report prepared
    by Moshav Nahalal on its Twenty-fifth Anniver-
    sary. Tel-Aviv: Am Oved Ltd., 1946. (In
    Hebrew.)

Plan Organization, Iran. Ghazvin Area Development
    Project Reconnaisance Report. Tel-Aviv:
    Tahal Ltd., August, 1963.

_____. Ghazvin Area Development
    Project Reports. Tel-Aviv: Tahal Ltd.,
    1965-68.

_____. Ghazvin Area Development
    Project Feasibility Report. Tel-Aviv: Tahal
    Ltd., August, 1966.

_____. Ghazvin Area Development
    Project Marketing Report for Year 1345.
    Ghazvin: Tahal Ltd., June, 1967.

Powell, John D. Preliminary Report on the Federación
    Campesina de Venezuela: Origins, Organization,

Leadership, and Role in the Agrarian Reform
Program. Research Paper of Land Tenure Center,
University of Wisconsin, September, 1964.

Settlement Study Centre. Regional Cooperation in
    Israel. First Report of Settlement Study
    Centre. Jerusalem: Sivan Press, 1965.

Sternberg, Benno. Traditional Society and Develop-
    ment in the Ghazvin Plain Villages. Report to
    University of Teheran, Institute of Social
    Study and Research. Teheran, March, 1966.
    (Mimeographed.)

Weitz, Ranaan. The Next Stage in Agricultural
    Settlement. Report to the Twenty-Sixth Zion-
    ist Congress. Jerusalem: Jewish Agency,
    December, 1964.

Yalan, E. Private and Cooperative Agricultural
    Settlement: Physical Planning. Report to
    International Seminar on Rural Planning.
    Jerusalem: Ministry of Foreign Affairs, 1962.

                    UNPUBLISHED MATERIAL

Buechler, Hans C., Erasmus, Charles J., and Heath,
    Dwight B. "Land Reform and Social Revolution
    in Bolivia." Land Tenure Center, University
    of Wisconsin. Undated. (Dittoed.)

Center of Integral Planning of Farm Settlements.
    "Projects for the Integral Development of
    Bocono," Caracas, 1963. (Mimeographed.)
    (In Spanish.)

_____.

    "Project for the Integral Development of
    El Cortijo." Caracas, 1964. (Mimeographed.)
    (In Spanish.)

Colmenares, Jesus Humberto. "Analysis of Agricul-
    tural Production in the Department of the
    Valley." Unpublished Senior Thesis, University

of the Valley, Cali, Colombia, 1964.   (In
Spanish.)

Course for Agricultural Planning and Regional De-
        velopment.   "Composite Rural Structure."
        Course held in cooperation with OECD.   Herzlia,
        Israel, May-August, 1963.

Enzer, Meier.   "The Moshav Movement."   Unpublished
        manuscript.   (Typewritten.)

Galbraith, John Kenneth.   "Underdevelopment: An
        Approach to Classification."   Paper presented
        to Rehovot Conference on Fiscal and Monetary
        Problems in Developing States.   Jerusalem,
        August, 1965.

Ghazvin Area Development Project.   "The Establishment
        of a Supply and Marketing Company."   Memorandum,
        June, 1966.   (Mimeographed.)

Halperin, Haim.   "Agricultural Activities."   Extract
        from Case of Histadrut before Anglo-American
        Inquiry Committee.   March, 1946.   (Mimeographed.

Helmberger, Peter G.   "Cooperative Bargaining in
        Agriculture."   Unpublished Ph.D. dissertation,
        University of California. Berkeley, 1961.

International Symposium on Role of Cooperative Or-
        ganization in Rural Development.   Sponsored by
        Government of Israel in cooperation with Food
        and Agriculture Organization of the United
        Nations.   Tel-Aviv, March, 1965.   Following
        mimeographed papers used:

        Benjamini, Hagai.   "The Cooperative Settlement
          as a Means of Strengthening Family Farms."
        Darin-Drabkin, Haim.   "Structure of Agricul-
          tural Cooperative Movement.
                              .   "Main Aspects of Agri-
          cultural Planning in Israel."
                              .   "Cooperative Coordinating
          Factor of National Planning and Local Initia-
          tive."

_____. "Aspects of Agricultural
Planning in Western European Countries and
the USSR."

Don, Yehuda. "Finance and Economic Management
of Cooperative Agriculture."

Kaddar, Gershon. "Influence of Cooperative
Setup of Agricultural Settlement on Agricultural Credit System in Israel."

Khan, N. A. "Adaptation of Cooperative
Structures to Community Traditions in Developing Countries."

Korn, Itzhak. "Planning of New Moshavim."

Lowe, Yehuda. "Variability of Income of Family
Farms in Cooperative Villages in Israel."

Olunwasanmi, H. A. "Adaptation of Modern Cooperative Structures to the Development of
Nigerian Agriculture."

Schweitzer, A. "Cooperative Settlements in
Israel under New Cooperative Bill."

Pinner, L. "Cooperation in the Private Sector
of Agriculture."

Siegens, George. "Opening Address."

Smith, Louis P. F. "Cooperative Organization
of Family Farms as a Factor in the Introduction of Modern Technology in Traditional
Villages."

Sternberg, E. "Cooperative Society's Services
in the Moshav and the Evaluation of their
Economic Efficiency."

Stipetic, V. "Cooperative Organization of
Agriculture as a Factor Facilitating the
Introduction of Modern Technology in Tra-
ditional Villages."

Interregional Technical Meeting on Rural Resettlement. Sponsored by Government of Israel in
cooperation with International Labor Office.
Ashkelon, Israel, April-May, 1965. Following
mimeographed papers used.

Enzer, Meier. "The Moshav."
International Labor Office. "Final Report."
Kaplan, B. and Rokach, A. "Rural Resettlement
in Israel."
Olivares, B. Manuel. "Rural Resettlement in
Venezuela."

Johnson, V. Webster and Kristjanson, B. H. "Observations on Land Distribution Program in Iran." Teheran, 1959. (Mimeographed.)

Kanovsky, Eliyahu. "The Economy of the Israeli Kibbutz." Unpublished Ph.D. dissertation, Columbia University, 1961.

Land Reform Organization. "Implementation of Land Reform Program in Iran." September, 1965. (Mimeographed.)

National and University Institute of Agriculture. Rehovot, Israel. Unpublished lectures and studies, all undated and mimeographed:

Berguer, Yakov. "Agricultural Production and Marketing Boards.
_____ . "Production and Marketing Boards for Agricultural Branches."
Bernstein, F. and Weintraub, D. "Social Structure, Political Organization, and Economic Development."
Deshen, Schlomo. "Case of Breakdown of Modernization in an Israeli Immigrant Community."
_____ . "Structure of Social Life in Israeli Rural Society."
Eres, A. "Evaluating Three Different Planning Methods in A Farm Management Praxis."
Levinger, A., Regev, V., and Yaron, D. "Application of Linear Programming to the Planning of a Kibbutz Farm." (In Hebrew.)
Lowe, Yehuda. "Economic Analysis of Family Farms in a Moshav."
_____ . "Economic Structure and Functions of the Village Cooperative in Moshavim."
_____ . "Factors Determining the Profitability of the Dairy-Fodder Branch on Family Farms in Israel."
Nevo, Naomi. "Shkuma, A Moshav in the Western Negev."
_____ . "The Human Factor in Farming: The Family Unit in the Moshav."
Shapiro, Ovadiah. "The Task of Rural Leadership in Development Processes."

Sprinzak, A. "Land Settlement Department of
  Jewish Agency."
Vayness, Itzhak. "Law of Cooperative Farming."
Weingrod, Alec. "Administered Communities."
_____. "Social Factors in Village
  Planning."
Weintraub, D. and Lissak, M. "Social Aspects
  of Agricultural Settlement in Israel."
Zussman, Pinhas. "Agriculture in Israel."

OECD Seminar on Regional Development. "Regional
  Development of Israel." Paper submitted by
  Israeli delegation. November, 1964.

Olsen, P. B., and Rasmussen, P. N. "Development and
  Planning in Iran." Unpublished manuscript,
  1962. (Mimeographed.)

Parviz, Amir. "Report of Activities in 1343 and
  Programs for 1344." Speech by Managing Director of Central Organization for Rural Cooperatives, Seminar of Ministry of Agriculture,
  Teheran, February, 1965. (Typewritten.)

_____. Speech delivered at Farmers' Day Cele-
  bration, Teheran, September, 1965. (Typewritten.)

Powell, John D. "A Brief Political History of Agricultural Reform in Venezuela." Abstract of
  M. A. thesis, University of Wisconsin, 1964.

Rehovot Conference on Comprehensive Planning of
  Agriculture in Developing Countries. Jerusalem:
  Jewish Agency, 1963. Following papers used:

  Admoni, Y. "The Adaptation of Extension Methods
    to Different Social Patterns in Israel."
  Arnon, I. "Adaptation of Agricultural Research
    Results to Field Practice."

Sadan, Ezra. "Agricultural Settlements in Israel:
  A Study in Resource Allocation." Unpublished
  Ph.D. dissertation, University of Chicago, 1962.

Seligman, A. "Regional Settlement in Israel."
    Jerusalem, Jewish Agency. Undated. (Mimeo-
    graphed.)

Seminar on Adapting Agricultural Cooperatives and
    Quasi-Cooperatives to the Market Structures
    and Conditions of Undeveloped Areas sponsored
    by the Agricultural Development Council.
    Lexington, Kentucky, April, 1967. Following
    mimeographed papers used:

    Behrman, Jere. "Notes on Theoretical Con-
        siderations in which Agricultural Coopera-
        tives Might Aid Economic Development."
    Hardie, Ian W. "Cooperative Theory and
        Market Implications: A Selected Review."
    Spaeth, David H. "Quasi Cooperative
        Arrangements--Japan and Taiwan Experience."
    Eicher, Carl. "Israeli Innovations."

Study Group on Problems of Individual and Group Set-
    tlement. Sponsored by Government of Israel
    in cooperation with Food and Agriculture Or-
    ganization of the United Nations. Tel-Aviv,
    April-May, 1956. Following mimeographed
    papers used:

    Aloni, Moshe and Kessler, Zvi. "Private
        Farming in Israel."
    Assaf, A. "Social Elements in the Workers'
        Smallholder Settlement."
    Bar-Elan, H. "Agricultural Training in the
        New Settlements and Problems of Extension."
    Bonne, A. "Nationalization of Land in Israel:
        A Successful Approach to Land Tenure in a
        New Society."
    Doudai, A. "Regional Planning in Israel."
    Kaddar, Gershon. "Family Farms in Cooperative
        Villages."
    Kaplan, Benjamin. "Lakhish Settlement Project."

Weitz, Raanan. "Administration of the Moshav in the
    Future." Statement of Head, Settlement Depart-
    ment, Jewish Agency to Agricultural Center,
    1965. (In Hebrew.)

_____. "Development Rate of New Settlements
According to Ethnic Origins." Unpublished
manuscript. (Typewritten.)

_____ . "The Economies of Water Supply in
the National Economy: A Case Study of Israel."
Settlement Study Centre, National and University Institute of Agriculture, November, 1964.

World Land Reform Conference. Sponsored by Food and
Agriculture Organization of the United Nations.
Rome, June-July, 1966. Following mimeographed
papers used:

Barraclough, Solon. "Land Tenure Conditions
and Socio-economic Development of the Agri-
cultural Sector in Seven Latin-American
Countries."
Landau, Y. N., Marton, S. T., and Weitz, R.
"Some Development Problems of Family Farms."
United Nations. "The Role of Peasant Organi-
zations in Land Reform and Related Community
Development Programs with Special Reference
to Latin-American Countries."

ABOUT THE AUTHOR

Maxwell I. Klayman is Professor of Economics at the State University College of New York at New Paltz, where he is in charge of the Latin America Area Studies Program and is also engaged in teaching and research in economic development and land problems in developing countries. He holds graduate degrees from Harvard and Iowa State University.

Dr. Klayman was an economist in the Food and Agriculture Organization of the United Nations for 17 years. Although he was stationed in Rome for most of this period, he has traveled extensively, particularly in the Near East, Latin America, Europe, and the Far East. He has been an agricultural economics consultant to government and private industry in Israel, Colombia, Turkey, Yugoslavia, India, and Thailand. He has also been a consultant to the Inter-American Development Bank. He has contributed several articles to books and journals.

Dr. Klayman has also been a member of the staff of the Economics Faculty, Universidad de Valle, Cali, Colombia; the Graduate School of Public and International Affairs, University of Pittsburgh; and the Department of Agricultural Economics, University of Maryland.